'As one of his target audience, I found that his account works on both levels as a compelling narrative-cum-guidebook'

Margaret Driscoll, *Sunday Times*

'As a writer McCrum is almost able to make us feel what it is like to have a stroke. His advice to those who have a stroke is not to despair or surrender, and he is an outstanding example . . . The book is upsetting in parts, but very well written. It is essential that we learn to understand experiences of this kind which affect so many people'

Lewis Wolpert, Professor of Biology as applied to Medicine, University College London, *Mail on Sunday*

'By telling the story of his own relatively privileged experience with such simple humanity, honesty and generosity of spirit, Robert McCrum has provided a little patch of common ground on which other victims of what he prefers to call "brain attack" can gather and take some comfort'

Sheila Hale, *Times Literary Supplement*

'Moving and exquisite . . . excellent'

Simon Winchester, *Evening Standard*

'A tremendously useful book for anyone who has ever been close to a stroke victim. By turns moving, witty, angry and profound, *My Year Off* is a worthy companion to *The Diving Bell and the Butterfly*'

Ian Pearson, *Ottawa Citizen*

'Strikingly honest . . . Robert McCrum seems like the patient you are sharing a room with who has already been through all of that and who gets on your nerves with all his patient's wisdom. And yet you're happy that he's there and that you can still listen to him'

Michael Allmaier, *Frankfurter Allgemeine*

'Also the story of a great love'

Claudia Ehrenstein, *Die Welt*

MY YEAR OFF

Robert McCrum is the author of six highly acclaimed novels and co-author of a non-fiction bestseller, *The Story of English*. He lives in London with his wife and daughters, and is currently literary editor of the *Observer*.

ROBERT McCRUM

MY YEAR OFF

PICADOR

First published 1998 by Picador

This edition published 1999 by Picador
an imprint of Macmillan Publishers Ltd
25 Eccleston Place, London SW1W 9NF
and Basingstoke and Oxford
Associated companies throughout the world
www.macmillan.co.uk
Published by arrangement with Alfred A. Knopf Canada,
a division of Random House of Canada Limited, Toronto, Canada.

ISBN 0 330 35240 7

5 7 9 8 6 4

A CIP catalogue record for this book is available from
the British Library.

Typeset by SetSystems Ltd, Saffron Walden, Essex
Printed and bound in Great Britain by
Mackays of Chatham plc, Chatham, Kent

TO SARAH

Contents

MY YEAR OFF

A Severe Insult to the Brain

Wo aber Gefahr, wacht das Rettende auch.
(*Where danger waits, salvation also lies.*)

Friedrich Hölderlin

When I was just forty-two I suffered a severe stroke. Paralysed on my left side and unable to walk, I was confined to hospital for three months, then spent about a year recovering, slowly getting myself back into the world.

When I was seriously ill in hospital, I longed to read a book that would tell me what I might expect in convalescence and also give me something to think about. There are many books about stroke in old age, but I was young and had been vigorous and there was nothing that spoke to me in my distress.

I have written this book to help those who have suffered as I did, and indeed for anyone recovering from what doctors call 'an insult to the brain'. I've also written it for families and loved ones who, sucked into the vortex of catastrophic illness, find themselves searching for words of encouragement and explanation. People express every kind of sympathy for stroke-sufferers, but the carers are often the forgotten ones. To all concerned, this book is meant to send a ghostly signal across the dark universe of ill-health that says, 'You are not alone.' It's also intended to show those of us who are well what it can be like when our bodies let us down in the midst of the lives we take for granted. Some will say that it's a *memento mori*, and that's undeniable, but I hope that it will also be heartening, especially to those who have given up all hope of recovery. I don't mean to offer false or cheap optimism, but I am saying that, if my example is to be trusted, the brain seems to be an astonishingly resilient organ, and one capable, in certain circumstances, of remarkable recovery.

The other audience for this book is, of course, myself. The consequences of my stroke were simply too colossal to be ignored or shut away in some mental pigeon-hole. Writing the book has been a way to make sense of an extraordinary personal upheaval, whose consequences will be with me until I die. Besides, I am a writer. Communicating experience is what I do, and quite soon after I realized that I was going to survive the initial crisis I also realized that I had been given a story that made most of what I'd written previously pale and uninteresting by comparison.

Whatever you, the reader, take away from it, there's no escaping that it is a personal book, my version of an event that changed my life. The philosopher Wittgenstein writes, 'How small a thought it takes to make a life.' Throughout my period of recovery I was often alone with my thoughts. When, finally, I came to record these, this book became the mirror of an enforced season of solitude in the midst of a crowded life. I've called it *My Year Off* because, despite the overall grimness of the experience, there were, at every stage, moments of acute irony and, even, of the purest comedy to brighten the prevailing gloom and chase away the clouds of melancholy. P. G. Wodehouse, one of my favourite writers, once said that 'There are two ways of writing . . . [One is . . .] a sort of musical comedy without music and ignoring real life altogether; the other is going right deep down into life and not caring a damn.' There is, I'm afraid, not much 'musical comedy' about having a stroke.

At times, my year off was one of all-pervading slowness, of weeks lived one day, even one hour, at a time, and of life circumscribed by exasperating new restrictions and limitations. The poet Coleridge observed that it is the convalescent who sees the world in its true colours, and, as a convalescent, I have been forced into a renewed acquaintanceship with my body and into the painful realization that I am, like it or not, imprisoned in it. I have learned, in short, that I am not immortal (the fantasy of youth) and yet, strangely, in the process I have been renewed in my understanding of family and, finally, of the only thing that really matters: love.

[1]

One Fine Day

29 July 1995

Things do not change; we change.

Henry Thoreau

My year off began with a headache, a glass of champagne – and a question. As it happens, the first two were not connected and the truth is that no one will ever know exactly what happened inside my head on the night of 28/29 July 1995, but probably it went something like this. First, for reasons that are still mysterious, a surreptitious clot began to form in one of my cerebral arteries, cutting off the blood supply to part of the one organ in the body that, next to the heart, is most greedy for blood. Eventually, perhaps some hours later, like a breaking dam, the clot burst into the right side of my brain, causing an uncontrolled 'bleed' that would result in irreversible destruction of the brain tissue deep inside my head.

I was oblivious to this cerebral drama; all I knew was that I had a raging headache, and then, the next morning, that I could hardly move. Overnight, I had suffered what the specialist would call a 'right hemisphere

4

infarct', and what the world knows as 'a stroke', a word whose Old English origin connotes 'a blow' and 'a calamity'.

Actually, it's a calamity that will befall some 450,000 individuals in North America (including Canada), and 150,000 in Britain each year, but when it happened I was completely ignorant of the affliction that Sherwin B. Nuland, author of *How We Die*, calls the third most common cause of death in the developed countries of the world.

It was just another bright summer Saturday morning, and here I was in bed, unable to get up – alone at home, a four-storey town house in Islington, North London. My wife, Sarah Lyall, a journalist with the *New York Times*, was away in San Francisco. We had been married scarcely two months, and it was odd to be on my own again. It was odder still to be so helpless, but I was in no pain, and, in retrospect, I realize that I was barely conscious. Downstairs, the grandfather clock was chiming the hour: eight o'clock. I could see that beyond the heavy maroon curtains it was a lovely day. Through the open window, the sounds of the street filtered in, sharp and echoey in the stillness of the weekend.

I was supposed to drive to Cambridge that morning to visit my parents. So, time to get up. But there it was – I could not move. More accurately, I could not move my left side. Overnight, my body had become a dead weight of nearly fifteen stone. I thrashed about in bed trying, and failing, to sit upright, and wishing Sarah were with me. For some unknown reason, I experienced no anxiety about my condition, just irritation and puzzlement. Why should I, who had recently sailed through a full medical examination, be unable to do as I pleased?

It was my dentist, Mr Glynn, who, a year earlier, had

first questioned my immortality. 'Teeth,' he observed, studying the X-rays of root-canal work to my upper-right quadrant, 'were not designed to last more than forty years.' He snapped off the light. 'And, frankly, nor were we.'

I was forty-one then, and whenever I was reminded of Mr Glynn's wisdom by some ache or twinge, I would wonder when some other body part would follow the example set by my teeth and protest, 'Enough!'

As my forty-second birthday approached, Sarah, a New York doctor's daughter, was anxious for independent verification that she was not marrying a crock. She'd witnessed enough of my candle-at-both-ends lifestyle to believe that this was a desirable prenuptial precaution. My assurances that McCrums lived for ever (all my grandparents died in their eighties) cut no ice. So, at her insistence, I made an appointment with Dr Guy O'Keeffe, who has a pretty little surgery near Eaton Place. From Dr O'Keeffe's examination room, the world seems secure, a place for healthy young women to bring up big bouncy babies: the air is flavoured with Johnson's baby powder, and highbrow Muzak tinkles in the background.

Dr O'Keeffe himself – sandy-haired, trim and boyish – seemed a promising recipient for intimate disclosures. Good health, his manner says, is our birthright; everything can be diagnosed, treated and cured. So he poked and prodded and pricked. He took blood and urine. He weighed and measured. He eavesdropped on the secret colloquy of my vital organs. In half an hour or so, he was asking me to put my clothes on again. The tests would be sent for analysis but, according to all the visible signs, I was fit. 'For a tall guy you're okay, but keep an eye on your cholesterol,' he said. It was good that I didn't smoke, but I'd be wise to watch the drink.

Of course. We chatted about 'units': I am a lifelong subscriber to the British media maxim that 'White wine is not a drink'. Dr O'Keeffe nodded competently and made another little note. A daily half-bottle of wine was okay with him.

I returned to the street, ready for anything. Jungle warfare? I could hack it. Cross-country skiing? I blessed my hardy, long-lived ancestors. No question, mine were a better class of gene.

That was in June. In the meantime, Sarah and I had come back to London from our wedding, in Philadelphia, to begin our new life together. Our honeymoon seemed to segue into a month of dinner parties at which my new American wife was introduced to some part of my circle for the first time. Clearly, we were going to live for ever and then happily ever after.

In July, Sarah flew to San Francisco to interview the novelist Amy Tan about her new book *The Hundred Secret Senses*. We were to be apart for eight days. I remember taking her to the airport and praying, as I watched her in the rear-view mirror – a small blonde figure with an oversize red suitcase waving goodbye on the pavement – that no harm should befall her.

Now here I was, a week later, unable to get out of bed. I have relived this moment a thousand times in a fruitless quest for some explanation – the moment my life divided into 'old' and 'new'.

Strangely, I had felt ready for a change, though I could not say what kind. At that time, I earned my living as the editor-in-chief of the publishers Faber and Faber, working with a variety of writers from Kazuo Ishiguro and Peter Carey to Paul Auster and Milan Kundera. I also wrote fiction and had, for several years, combined this with occasional freelance journalism in troubled parts of the world: Peru during Mario Vargas Llosa's presidential campaign, Cambodia during the UNTAC (UN Transitional Authority in Cambodia) election, and, most recently, East Timor. Like many of my generation, I'd envied those, like my parents, who have lived through wars and revolutions. Consciously or not, I'd always hoped my trips would yield a frisson – a moment of danger from which none the less I'd emerge unscathed. Mentally, I wore a flak jacket and jeans under my yuppie suit and I liked to think I was more at home on the road than in the chic, heartless salons of Thatcher's London, though in truth I had begun confiding to Sarah a vague dissatisfaction with my working life.

Indeed, on the very evening of my collapse, I'd done something I now think of as typical of my 'old' life. I'd gone out for dinner at the Ivy restaurant in Covent Garden with my friend the literary agent Kathy Robbins, specifically to discuss Life (mine and hers). Before taking the taxi to the West End, I'd swallowed a couple of Nurofen tablets for the headache that had been troubling me all day, and at the Ivy I ordered a glass of champagne while I waited for Kathy to arrive. In that life, a glass of champagne would dispel most troubles. How often, as editor-in-chief, had I downed champagne with Faber authors in the Ivy's upstairs dining room. So I gave no thought to the headache: I'd had this problem, on and off, for years. Indeed, there had been a time in my twenties when I was sufficiently worried to seek medical advice, after which the complaint had vanished as miraculously as it had first appeared.

By the time Kathy and I were sitting with our coffee,

kvetching about the world in the restaurant's restful half-light, I was conscious that my headache was still nagging. I remember yawning with unaccountable weariness, wondering why, after only two glasses of champagne, my speech was so muddy and indistinct. My American Express receipt shows that I paid for our meal at 22.38. My signature is steady. Then we rose from the table and made our way to the street. But something was not quite right. My legs felt spongy, as though I was walking through treacle, every step effortful and uncertain. But I said nothing. I believed in my body. Whatever it was would pass.

Opposite the Ivy, in the St Martin's Theatre, *The Mousetrap* was playing – 'the world's longest-ever run', now in its forty-third year. I had occasionally observed that Agatha Christie's thriller and I had aged well together, but tonight I was ready to call in the understudies. We reached St Martin's Lane, a walk of perhaps a hundred yards, during which every step had become more difficult for me. Here, I said goodnight to Kathy and, desperate to be home, hailed a taxi, articulating the address with some effort. The driver repeated it contemptuously, as if picking up a drunk. I climbed heavily on board and sank into the back seat.

When we reached Islington, my legs felt like lead and I was walking like a deep-sea diver, but I made the front door without falling over and let myself in. I was plainly unwell, but my symptoms were unfamiliar. So I turned to that sovereign English remedy: I decided to make myself a cup of tea.

Downstairs in the kitchen, I listened to a cheery message from Sarah on our answering machine. It included a San Francisco hotel number to call but, feeling quite extraordinarily tired, and calculating that the time difference was not in my favour, I decided to wait until morning. Then, clutching my comforting mug of herb tea, I went upstairs to bed. I remember resolving, as I drifted off to sleep, to rise early to beat the weekend traffic on the Cambridge road.

When a stroke occurs and the brain suffers 'a haemorrhagic infarct', the body experiences a colossal disturbance of its innate sensory equilibrium. Literally overnight, I was changed from being someone who could order an expensive meal in a fashionable restaurant to being an incontinent carcass, quite unable to make any sense of his body. I was conscious and alert (I thought) but my limbs were not responding.

My recollection of the first phase of the morning is disconnected and hallucinatory. Perhaps I passed out, or fell asleep, because the next thing I remember is the clock in the hall chiming ten. Ten o'clock! I would never get to Cambridge! Time to get going! I rolled with difficulty to the edge of our big brass bed.

Then I was falling heavily to the floor, dragged over the edge of the bed by the dead weight of my left side. I was shocked and dismayed, and my first thought was to telephone for help. There was a phone on the bedside table, but of course it was now out of reach and anyway I'd left Sarah's hotel number downstairs in the kitchen. So there I was: cut off. In extremis, the body is merciful. My feelings were ones of mild frustration, 'Oh no!' rather than 'Jesus Christ!' At worst, I felt like Alice under the glass table trying to reach the key that would open the door to the magic garden. I tried in vain to remember the name of Sarah's hotel. Wentworth? Grand Western? Nothing came. Even if I could reach the phone what help would it be?

A new anxiety was distracting me. I was desperate to

pee. Suddenly there was a hot cascade of urine on my chest (I was lying on my back, naked). Afterwards, I suppose I became unconscious because when I came to again it was much later. The street was noisier and busier and I sensed from the light on the ceiling that the sun was high. When the telephone rang briefly, maddeningly, and stopped, I knew that downstairs in the kitchen the answering-machine would be clicking into action. Up here in the bedroom it was out of earshot.

Time blurred. When the clock chimed again, it was three. If this was a nightmare, it was time to get back to the waking world. But it was not a nightmare, and the fact that I could neither sit nor stand was all too real. As the afternoon wore on, the bedside phone rang briefly several times. We had set the machine to respond after two rings and in that other life that now seems so distant I had often, to Sarah's amusement, hurled myself across our bed to pick up and answer before the machine clicked on. Today, the scoreline was: British Telecom 7; McCrum 0.

What did I think about, lying there on the floor? Oddly enough, it was my missed rendezvous with my parents that became my obsession and I entertained all sorts of explanations to the conundrum of my immobility. Perhaps, like Stephen Hawking, I was suffering from motor-neurone disease. Perhaps I had a brain tumour. My cousin Jane had died of a brain tumour. At times, bizarrely persuaded by the remaining strength in my right side, I imagined hobbling across the street to my car, somehow driving with one arm. I was like a rat on a wheel, revolving desperate escape plans. I had no inkling of how ruthlessly I had been disconnected from the world of appointments and obligations, or how long it would be before I returned to it. Suffer a stroke and you find that the complex wiring we call 'the individual in society' is peremptorily ripped from the fusebox of everyday life. I had blown a connection in Nerve Central and all my circuits were down.

Then the phone rang again, and stopped, as before. I felt I had to do something decisive. I knew there was a phone on the floor in the living room downstairs. Somehow I had to get there. With what I now see must have been an extraordinary effort, I dragged myself under the frame of our big brass bedstead with my 'good' right arm, noticing with interest the little flergs of dust and the strange debris that collects in such places – forgotten paperbacks, discarded Kleenex, a pair of Sarah's tights – and then squirmed, commando-style, over the carpet to the head of the stairs.

Here, reaching out to the banister, which fortunately was on my right side, I pulled myself over the top step. Again my dead weight took control, and I found I was sliding helplessly and painfully head first down the stair-carpet to the mezzanine landing where I had a borrower's-eye view of my library of modern first editions: Kazuo Ishiguro's *A Pale View of Hills*; *The Rachel Papers* by Martin Amis; *A Good Man In Africa* by William Boyd; and Raymond Carver's *Will You Please Be Quiet Please?*

I vividly remember – indeed, I will never forget – this part of the day on the landing at the angle of the stairs. For some hours, I lay on my back staring up at a framed brown-green school map of French colonial Indo-China, a souvenir of that trip to Phnom Penh in 1993. Then I had been looking for an adventure. Now I seemed to be caught up in one. I had crossed by night from what Susan Sontag (in *Illness As Metaphor*) calls 'the kingdom of the well' to 'the kingdom of the sick' and, though I still had no name for this new country I was in, it was dawning on me that I was no longer the person I'd been twenty-four hours ago.

I was puzzled and curious. It was almost as though I was not in my body, the body that seemed to have let me down so badly. (I still wonder if the 'I' who is typing this with my 'good' right hand, is the same as the 'I' who used to peck away, two-handed, at 50 w.p.m.) From time to time my thoughts, such as they were, would be interrupted by the phone. Two brief rings, then silence. In the stillness of the afternoon, and from my position on the stairs, I thought I could detect, faintly and faraway in the kitchen downstairs, the whir and click of the machine and then Sarah's voice. But I was too far off to distinguish her message and, anyway, what could I do to answer? I was terribly frustrated. I wanted to call out: 'Darling, I'm here, please come and help me.'

But could I do this? To test speech and memory, I began, weirdly, to recite 'Jabberwocky' out loud, forming the words with difficulty.

> ''Twas brillig, and the slithy toves
> Did gyre and gimble in the wabe;
> All mimsy were the borogoves,
> And the mome raths outgrabe . . .'

As evening drew on I manoeuvred myself on the mezzanine landing for the descent down the final flight of stairs to the living room. I did not want a repetition of that painful and undignified slide. I did not want carpet-burns. Controlling my weight with my right hand on the banister, I inched head first down to the hallway. It was gloomy here, and pleasantly cool. The massive family portrait of my bearded Victorian great-great-grandfather, also named Robert McCrum, glowed in the shadows. The clock, whose chimes had punctuated my day, was ticking steadily nearby. More squirming and then I was in the spacious living room and there, across the carpet on the floor, was the downstairs phone. I felt like a pioneer who, in crossing the Rockies, finally arrives in California.

British Telecom records show that I called my parents – it never occurred to me to call Emergency – at 19.53 and that the call lasted two minutes. My mother, who was by now thoroughly alarmed at my failure to appear in Cambridge, picked up. Apparently I told her I could not move. She tried to keep me on the line but I had already rung off.

I felt incredibly happy.

Now things began to happen fast. When the phone rang again, it was my younger brother Stephen. He and his fiancée, Emily (who, awkwardly, had chosen that very day to announce their engagement), were on their way from Camden Town; they had already phoned the police. I heard a siren outside in the street, the heavy boots of authority clomping up to my front door, and then a voice through the letterbox. I replied with the utmost difficulty, 'No, I can't open the door.'

Weeks later I discovered the reason for the rare, almost unprecedented, alacrity of the force: my house had formerly belonged to Salman Rushdie, and the officers, unshakably convinced that I was the victim of a botched assassination attempt on the writer's life – poisoned, perhaps, or sprayed with nerve gas – detected a vista of spectacular career advancement in this sudden and unexpected drama. Alas, my brother, after some comical misunderstandings, put them straight on this.

Another siren; the sound of splitting wood. The police

had climbed into the garden and were coming through the back door. I remember worrying that I was naked, but exhaustion was stronger than modesty. After my long day, it felt good to have people – there seemed to be rather a lot of them – taking an interest in my situation. Paramedics in green overalls were towering over me with the cheery bonhomie of furniture removers, rattling out questions to establish the state of my consciousness. 'Who are you? What's your name? What's your date of birth, Robert? What's your address?'

Quite a crowd had gathered outside the house, No. 41, St Peter's Street – curious neighbours alerted by the arrival of the paramedics and the police. Perhaps they hoped for a murder. Noel Road, where the playwright Joe Orton was bludgeoned to death in 1968, is just around the corner. Soon, I was propped up in the ambulance. I took Emily's hand and felt her answering squeeze. The doors closed; the siren began to wail and we were on our way. I was so happy. I was with my family. I was going to hospital. I had survived. Through the window I could see the weekend world going on outside: shoppers crowding; cars manoeuvring through traffic; people with pints standing outside pubs. This world now seemed remote and unimportant. I had become a prisoner of ill-health, but I had yet to discover the terms and length of my sentence.

One moment I was in the sea-green light of the ambulance on the way to Casualty; the next I was lying on a gurney listening to two young doctors discuss my case in an undertone. From time to time a young medic with garlic on his breath would shine a flashlight into my eyes, a standard test for brain function. Stroke victims are very likely to suffer swelling of the brain, which is often what kills them. When I heard that a specialist had

15

been reached on the telephone, I became afraid that before my parents arrived from Cambridge this surgeon would trundle me into his operating theatre and slice the top off my head like a watermelon. A phone conference ensued. I lay there expecting the worst. But the specialist never appeared and I was eventually wheeled into Intensive Care for the night. By then, all I wanted to do was sleep. Huge, yawning waves of tiredness carried me down into a new dreamless darkness. Occasionally, I would be woken by the nurse's flashlight in my eyes, checking for vital signs. Sarah tells me that my life was in the balance at this time, but all I felt was a rather blissful detachment and serenity. I did not panic. There was no bright light at the end of a long tunnel. I did not see my past whizz before me. Actually – I remember thinking this – if I was going to die, this was not such a bad way to go.

Quite soon after this first night of my 'new' life, someone used that phrase, 'an insult to the brain' – a commonplace of stroke care – and, as I digested the implications of what I'd just suffered, I could not prevent myself imagining rogue neurons viciously hissing, 'Your mother is a water buffalo,' to my sensitive cortex. Slander, calumny, or insult – call it what you will – I knew at once that I had survived an extraordinarily close call, what friends and acquaintances, visitors to my bedside, would later sometimes like to refer to, with slightly ghoulish fascination, as 'your brush with death'.

[2]

An Awfully Big Adventure

29 July – 1 August

> For a man to die of no apparent cause, for a man to die
> simply because he is a man, brings us so close to the
> invisible boundary between life and death that we no
> longer know which side we are on.
>
> Paul Auster, *The Invention of Solitude*

The moment when J. M. Barrie's Peter Pan describes
dying as 'an awfully big adventure' is a mawkish and
embarrassing moment in an often mawkish and embarrassing play. Nevertheless, it's an observation that
contains a kernel of truth. When I analyse it now, I find
that my own experience provides some intriguing, and
probably misleading, answers to the enduring conundrum of our mortality.

In England, death is shrouded in Victorian euphemism. People do not 'die', they 'pass away'; they are not
'buried' but 'laid to rest', and not with 'flowers' but
'floral tributes'. For some, the only alternative response
to this scary subject is the kind of flippancy, for ever
associated in my mind with the works of P. G. Wodehouse, in which so-and-so 'handed in his dinner pail' or

'fell off his perch' and was now, as John Cleese puts it in that famous *Monty Python* sketch, 'pushing up the daisies', in a speech I cannot resist quoting:

> This parrot is no more! It has ceased to be! It's expired and gone to meet its maker! This is a late parrot! It's a stiff! Bereft of life it rests in peace – if you hadn't nailed it to the perch it would be pushing up the daisies. It's rung down the curtain and joined the choir invisible! This is an *Ex-Parrot!*

Just as grief is the half-sister to rage, so laughter is grief's twin brother. There can be something strangely uplifting about a funeral, a moment of catharsis in which we can also celebrate our continuing survival.

So I confess that my first reaction, as I came round in University College Hospital, but still drifting in and out of consciousness, was a kind of weird exhilaration. *Yes!* I had survived. I was not yet an ex-parrot. Lying naked under a pink blanket in the intensive care unit, wired up to the monitors, I was aware of being in the antechamber to the grave and even now, months later, I can still recall the eerie fascination of this experience and of having, by the greatest good fortune, returned to tell the tale. A sober assessment of my situation in the grim aftermath of what I was learning to call 'my stroke' soon tempered this mad euphoria. If I had known then what I soon came to discover about what the doctors were now referring to as 'your stroke', my relief might have been mixed with terror as well as gratitude.

Next to cardiac disease and cancer, stroke is the most common cause of death in the Western world and, oddly, a word that in medical circles is rarely attached to either a definite or an indefinite article. This fell noun is also a term so commonly misapplied that, for very many people, it lacks a lethal connotation. Of those who survive the initial 'insult', about half will be left with permanent severe disability. The physical consequence of stroke is a horrifying catalogue of damage that includes personality changes, impaired sensation, paralysis, incontinence, visual or language problems, deafness, blindness, seizures, and even swallowing difficulties, the distressing manifestations of what the textbooks describe as 'neurological deficits'. Approximately one third of those who suffer a stroke will die, often from a second or third subsequent assault on the neurological system.

I did not die, of course – and I was never in any pain – but, physically speaking, I'd been poleaxed. My left leg was immobilized and my left arm hung from its socket like a dead rabbit; the left side of my face, which drooped badly for about a week, felt frozen, as if Mr Glynn had just given it a massive Novocaine injection. I could not stand upright; my speech was slurred; to cope with my incontinence, my penis was attached to a Convene, a condom-like device that drained my urine into a plastic bag; every few hours a team of three nurses would turn me over in bed, as if I was a slow-cooking roast. In place of pain, there was an hallucinatory sense of detachment, and I was also oppressed with an overwhelming fatigue. The smallest thing left me wanting to lie down and go to sleep; the muscles on my left side were so weak that to sit in a chair – which I wasn't able to do, even with three nurses to help me, for some days – was exhausting. I was, besides, terribly confused about what had happened, confused and stunned, though unimpaired, intellectually: my memory seemed to be functioning just fine and I had no difficulty in recognizing people who

19

came to see me, though I noticed that it sometimes took me a few moments to recall their names. On the other hand, I still have no recollection of where University College Hospital actually is, or how I got there, though I can recall the room and the cramped, sultry high summer atmosphere.

Of all the people who were so kind to me in those first hours, there was one nurse I came to think of as my guardian angel, a graduate trainee – I think – from Cambridge with beautiful corn-coloured hair, a lovely smile and the most gentle manner of any nurse I'd experienced then or subsequently. 'What's your name?' I mumbled through my frozen jaw, as she bent over my bed. 'Whicker,' replied the angel. Curious, I asked how she spelled that, and was told that 'Wicce' was a traditional Anglo-Saxon name, a tiny spark of English history which amid the bleeps and wires of twentieth-century medicine I found strangely comforting. After I was moved from University College Hospital I never saw Wicce St Clair Hawkins again, but for her sweetness towards me in those first few dreadful hours of consciousness in hospital, with the dawning recognition of profound physical catastrophe, I shall always feel intensely grateful.

Sarah arrived from San Francisco, white and hollow-faced with worry and loss of sleep. For the first week, she slept on a camp bed in the corner of my room, jumping up in alarm whenever I stirred in sleep, though I do not remember this. She had endured her own terrible drama en route. 'Robert isn't feeling very well,' my mother had said, and her ominous telephone manner had led Sarah to believe, she told me later, that I was likely to die at any moment. In a daze she had got a flight to London, and had spent the eleven-hour trip huddled under a blanket, drinking shots of whisky. She says she had never felt so alone as she did that night, in the darkened plane surrounded by people. At one point she turned in desperation to her neighbour. 'Do you mind if I talk to you a moment?' she said. 'My husband's just had a stroke.' The woman looked at her. 'I don't know anything about strokes,' she said, and went back to *Cosmopolitan*.

Sometimes, it seems that no one knows anything about stroke. The word itself sounds so inoffensive. As a verb, it's a synonym for brush or sweep or caress. You 'stroke' a baby or a lover, and of course it's also associated with idleness, as in 'he never does a stroke of work'. And then again it's linked, more accurately now, with old age, though even here it's seen as a survivable affliction. History reminds us that both Woodrow Wilson and Winston Churchill functioned as, respectively, President and Prime Minister, after suffering mild strokes in old age. (Wilson's, of course, was serious; he never really recovered from it and the United States government was effectively run, during the last years of his presidency, by his fierce wife, Edith.) Such behaviour would be unthinkable today – the media would not permit it – though until one of the world's leaders suffers a serious stroke in office it's likely that the public will remain, like the woman on the plane, ill-informed and largely indifferent. In Britain, the fact that Prime Minister Tony Blair's father, Leo, suffered a severe stroke at the age of forty has helped to raise the public profile of an affliction that is either taken for granted or misunderstood. Perhaps if Sarah had confided to the woman what she most feared – that I would be dead by the time she landed at Heathrow – she might have elicited a more sympathetic response.

In the life of twentieth-century man and woman there

are not many mysteries, but Death remains. In an age when more and more is explained, when even the brain is slowly beginning to yield up its secrets, the Grim Reaper shows no sign of losing his ancient power to fascinate and terrify. And those who contrive, however briefly, to meet him and yet survive also exert a special hold on our imaginations. As my convalescence unfolded, I discovered a substantial and fascinating literature on the subject of death, of which the most notable is the poet John Donne's *Devotions*.

Donne, a near-contemporary of William Shakespeare, was a friend of Robert Harvey, the pioneer of cardiac 'circulation', and had what we would think of as a distinctly twentieth-century appreciation of the body and its limitations as the vessel of our humanity. Like many writers of his time, Donne addressed Death as a familiar, and we know him for his oft-quoted sonnet, 'Death be not proud'. What his less well-known *Devotions upon Emergent Occasions* reveals is a mind acutely tuned, in a rather modern way, to the psycho-drama of sudden illness. 'A sick bed is a grave;' Donne writes, 'and all that the patient says there, is but a varying of his own Epitaph.'

By a strange coincidence, a few days after my stroke a media acquaintance and fellow forty-something, Michael Vermeulen, the London editor of *Esquire*, died of a heart-attack brought on, apparently, by years of hard living. I read his obituaries in hospital with guilty fascination, remembered our last, and quite recent, conversation in the foyer of the Groucho Club, and brooded sadly on the vagaries of chance. As Donne puts it, '. . . never send to know for whom the bell tolls; It tolls for thee.'

Meanwhile, in my immobilized state all I could do was lie in my sickbed, stare obsessively at the cracks in the ceiling, or out of the window at the 'little patch of blue that prisoners call the sky', and think. My brain, which had just let me down so badly, was perhaps never so active. The paramedics' question – for ever linked in my mind with that headache and the Ivy's glass of champagne – was a fundamental one. Who are you? Yes indeed. Who am I?

[3]

In the Blood

1–2 August

I am the family face;
Flesh perishes, I live on,
Projecting trait and trace,
Through time to times anon,
And leaping from place to place
Over oblivion.

Thomas Hardy, *Heredity*

Who am I? is, of course, the ultimate question, a question that every one of us would be wise to face up to at some moment in our lives. In fact, I had begun to approach the issue in an oblique way some years before, in 1987, when I wrote and presented a BBC documentary film about my McCrum forebears, an exploration of the Scots–Irish settlement of Northern Ireland entitled *In the Blood*, a phrase that eerily fore-shadowed, as it turned out, my stroke. During those helpless moments in the hallway of my Islington house, I had looked up at the portrait of my great-great-grand-father, Robert McCrum, an Ulster linen millionaire whose hard-earned fortune was squandered by his only son, on the wall above me and wondered what on earth he, for whom adversity was as natural as the remorseless northern weather, would have made of my bizarre predicament. Later, as I lay in the hospital, I began to wonder what, if anything, my family history could say to me in these new, and dramatically changed, circumstances.

Whatever way you look at it, McCrum is a peculiar name. That's what I discovered when I was five years old, at Newnham Croft primary school in Cambridge. McCrum-Crumbo-Crumble-Crummy was the usual declension. At least my classmates did not know that the authentic Scots derivation means 'son of the bent one' (which begins to make some sense when you inspect the bizarre fantasies of my namesake, the great American cartoonist R. Crumb).

When my family looked for a past, they found it in the romantic Highlands. As children, my sister Elizabeth and I were often told that McCrum was a corruption of McCrimmon and that we were descended from 'the pipers to the lords of Skye'. But on the one occasion I actually went to Skye I found the appealing McCrimmon connection to be utterly fanciful. If my unusual name was a corruption of anything, it was MacIlchrum (alternative spellings: MacGilliechrum, Cromb, Crum, McCrumb, MacCrum) and belonged to lowly peons of the Clan MacDonald, scattered through the Western Isles and across the rough green pastures of Northern Ireland. These McCrums were the 'sons of the bent one', with clear implications of bastardy. The Ulster Scots' ancestry is full of blood, mystery and confusion. In short, I'm from a people who do not know exactly who they are or where they come from, a scarecrow lineage, patched together from the flotsam and jetsam of planter history. I confess I have come to identify with this ragamuffin ancestral collage.

I was born at home on 7 July 1953, in Cambridge, at 8 King's Parade, opposite the King's College Chapel, in a little white room that now sits above an antique shop. The world I came into was quite severely academic, professional, meritocratic and, on the face of it, as fortunate and privileged as you could wish for. It was also a world recovering from the traumas of the Second World War – hunger, separation and loss – a world in which the frank acknowledgement and discussion of emotion was seen as needlessly self-indulgent. My mother, Christine, is the daughter of the headmaster of Rugby School, an institution immortalized in *Tom Brown's Schooldays*; my father, Michael, was the senior tutor of Corpus Christi College; as newlyweds, they were living in college lodgings. Later, we would move nearer the fens and the River Cam to Ashton House, a fine old eighteenth-century turnpike lodging house with a bumpy flagstone vestibule, overlooking Newnham Road.

For a child, Cambridge is a kind of airy green paradise, and my memories of those early years before I went to prep school at the age of nine are filled with play, sunshine and laughter, and the high wide skies of the fens. After primary school, I went briefly to the celebrated King's Choir School, known throughout the world for its choral tradition and the Christmas Eve service of Nine Lessons and Carols, though I was not a chorister and cannot sing. Now my own life began to follow a pattern set down by my father, literally at birth. I was entered for the English upper-middle-class handicap, a well-worn human steeplechase that involved negotiating a series of academic jumps. So, after a year of King's, I was sent to Horris Hill, a remote boys' prep school housed in a mock-Tudor monstrosity in the Berkshire countryside not far from the Greenham Common air base that would dominate British newspaper headlines in the mid-eighties during the row over the deployment of Cruise missiles.

Boys: in the McCrum family, wherever you looked there were boys. The women seemed to produce nothing else; I have two brothers; my father would later become Head Master of Eton, the most famous boys' school in the world, and I know that the world I've begun to describe here is a 'boy's world'. When I married Sarah my secret prayer was that, if we should have children, they should include a girl.

At Horris Hill (often known to its inmates, predictably enough, as 'Horrid Hill') I wrote my first novel in a Lyon Brand exercise book, a story of some one hundred pages in the Daphne du Maurier tradition about a gang of smugglers who came, as far as I can remember, to a sticky end at the Plymouth assizes. It was at this prep school that I had my first, and until my stroke my only, experience of hospital. In the autumn of 1964, when I was just eleven, I developed septicaemia in the forefinger of my right hand and was routinely treated with penicillin. The septicaemia spread rapidly and settled in the the ankle of my right leg, which became as painful and swollen as if I had suffered a sprained ankle. That, however, was not half the problem. The penicillin failed; the septicaemia raced through my body; I became seriously ill.

I was rushed to hospital in nearby Reading. The failure of the penicillin treatment meant that the ankle had to be 'aspirated' (i.e. drained) under general anaesthetic while the doctors found an antibiotic that was effective against the infection. Night after night I was wheeled into the operating theatre, and once the danger was over I remained hospitalized for several weeks with my leg encased in plaster. Not until the plaster was removed would I know whether I was to be crippled for life with a 'game leg'. As it turned out, I made a complete recovery, but I can still recall the shadow of potential disability looming as I rested at home (listening to Flanders and Swann on the family gramophone) while my parents tried bravely to prepare me for a life of physical restriction.

At thirteen, fully recovered, I cleared another academic hurdle and went to Sherborne School, in the midst of Thomas Hardy's Wessex. The English boy's education at prep and public school is a rite of passage that's been described many times. I can add no thrilling detail to the shame, the cruelty and the indignity that has not already been told by others, except to observe that those horror-stories are all true, in my experience. By the age of sixteen I had galloped doggedly over these fences and got my scholarship in history to Corpus Christi College, Cambridge. Before I went to up to university, I spent eighteen months odd-jobbing (in England), drifting and travelling (in Europe), and ended up teaching English at Geelong Grammar School, in Victoria, Australia, where I learned more in one year than in the previous ten put together. After that I settled down for a while to three happy years at university, where I directed plays (including an adaptation of Flann O'Brien's *At Swim-Two-Birds*, cheekily billed as a World Première) at the Edinburgh Fringe, wrote an unpublishable novel (moving from du Maurier to Beckett with none of the usual intervening stages either of wit or wisdom), achieved my degree, and secured a postgraduate Thouron scholarship to the University of

Pennsylvania in Philadelphia. My American year gave me an unconscious appetite for the United States that I was at pains subsequently to satisfy, and with happy consequences I could never have predicted.

Eventually, having recognized that I was not cut out for the groves of academe, or even the high tables of Oxbridge, I came home, and by some kind of fortune got a job, first as publicity assistant and then as in-house reader with the then independent publishers Chatto and Windus. I had been proud of my decision to look for postgraduate work in the United States, but in truth I was hardly deviating from a well-trodden academic racetrack. Even in London, the habits of school and university died hard. I sat in the library in my lunch hours and toiled away on another work of fiction, a perfectly dreadful comic novel, now happily lost, about a young man slaving away in a public library during his lunch hours. When I think of it today, I recall Dr Johnson's famous put-down: 'Your work is both good and original. Unfortunately, the part that's good is not original, and the part that's original is not good.'

Like almost everyone of my background and upbringing, the only unresolved questions of my twenties were: when, and to whom, would I get married? and what job would I get? These questions were both answered in April 1979, when I became engaged to my university girlfriend and was taken on as a senior commissioning editor with the publishers Faber & Faber. Thus, in the space of a few weeks, my course was set. After a number of false starts, I now published several works of fiction – from *In The Secret State* (1980) and *The Fabulous Englishman* (1984) to *Mainland* (1992), *Jubilee* (1994) and *Suspicion* (1996) – and also, from 1982 to 1986 collaborated with the renowned broadcaster Robert MacNeil on a television history of our language, *The Story of English*.

Apart from my insignificant private struggle as a young writer in Westminster Public Library, mine was a quintessentially English upbringing of extreme security and considerable privilege. After one night in a hot, noisy, chaotic National Health Service ward of University College Hospital, I realized how much I'd come to take this sort of special treatment for granted. In the next hospital to which I would be transferred, I had a private room, the reward for twenty years of Faber-sponsored BUPA (British United Provident Association) private healthcare subscriptions. Later, as the days stretched to weeks, I discovered the limitations on BUPA's healthcare package: the final weeks of my illness were devoted to a daily renegotiation of my right to health care as the hospital managers haggled over the cost of my room with chilly BUPA administrators, a quite different breed from the smiling and nurturing Florence Nightingales offered to the public in the television advertisements. (In the end, after some argy-bargy, BUPA came to honour their commitments.)

As I read over what I've just written, I'm struck by the way in which so much of my early life seems to point in some odd way towards the moment of my stroke. Of course, I know this is nonsense, that our fortune is tied up with fragility and contingency, and yet, there it is: my profound and inescapable sense of Fate, reinforced, I suppose, by surviving my stroke.

Fate, a concept familiar to the pre-modern mind, is no longer part of our everyday vocabulary and yet, even as I write this book, I cannot escape flirting with the idea that my stroke was an event that was somehow coming to me, that it was, in some inexplicable way, my destiny.

The irresistible allure of the grandiose explanation reminds me that, for all the astonishing technical advances of the twentieth century, we still possess an unquenchable instinct to make ourselves part of a story. It's this that makes us human. Yet talk to any doctor in this vein and they will pooh-pooh such suggestions. Large or small, a stroke, they will say, is no more than the smallest physical malfunction, a wonky configuration of blood in a cerebral artery. This is the 'insult' to the miraculous and fascinating organ we call 'the brain'.

[4]

Brain Attack

3–5 August

> When a man dies he undergoes a mutation in his brain
> we know nothing about but which will be very clear
> someday if scientists get on the ball.
>
> Jack Kerouac, *On The Road*

After the first, immediate crisis, with which the National
Health Service had coped superbly, I was moved, courtesy of BUPA, to a private room in the Nuffield Wing of
the National Hospital for Neurology and Neurosurgery,
Queen Square. The irony of my condition as a neurological patient was that I'd often watched the results of
brain surgery from my office. The Queen Square headquarters of Faber & Faber overlook this world-famous
hospital. For nearly twenty years, I'd stared out of my
window at shaved and hideously scarred shuffling figures
in pyjamas, like concentration-camp survivors, and
wondered about their fate. For so long, I had faced this
imposing red-brick façade across the square. It was
strangely intriguing finally to be wheeled into its shabby,
cavernous Victorian interior, as cool as a vintage wine
cellar, though the unmistakable mixture of hospital

smells – hoovered carpet, disinfectant, wood polish and urine – is evocative only of disease, sickness and physical catastrophe. Now I was in the care of neurological experts for whom stroke was just the most common of the many possible illnesses of the brain.

So what is stroke? Strokes can be divided into two broad categories according to the type of pathological process involved: infarction related and haemorrhagic. The former, which accounts for about three-quarters of all strokes, involves processes similar to those underlying many heart-attacks. The other major cause of stroke is haemorrhage, which accounts for about 20 per cent of acute cerebrovascular events. Typically, an artery in the brain will burst. This will lead to a blood clot, which in turn may cut off the blood supply to part of the brain. In either case, one crucial question is: on which side of the brain did the event occur, left or right?

The two halves of the brain have different functions, and control different sides of the body. The right brain controls the movement on the left side, and is more specialised for creative functions such as visual–spatial analysis, some aspects of emotional processing and handling certain negative emotions, and musical perception. The left side, which holds sway over the right side of the body, is specialised for reading, writing, numeracy and language. In my case, the stroke occurred on the right side, thus affecting the left side of the body. The 'insult' was probably located in the basal ganglia, a motor part of the brain that is also closely associated with the frontal lobes which are themselves responsible for planning and reasoning and decision-making. The basal ganglia's function is as a facilitator, a co-ordinator (Tourette's syndrome in which actions occur without volition is a disorder of the basal ganglia). Much of this, of course, is speculative: when it comes to the brain, the best doctors will admit that it is medicine's dark side of the moon.

It's the brain, or more accurately the central nervous system, that is threatened by stroke. In Britain, and in North America, the traditional term 'stroke' is slowly being replaced by 'brain attack', in the hope that new language will change our attitude towards the illness, and perhaps help modify our behaviour towards it (making us less complacent about it, and helping to improve survival rates). But even the new term 'brain attack' does not convey the whole story. A stroke is all to do with blood, or the absence of it. In medicine, 'stroke' is the description of an acute disturbance of the brain due to an interruption of the flow of the blood supply.

There are many different kinds of stroke, ranging from the most minor neurological episode – the transient ischemic attack (TIA), which can be so slight and quick that the sufferer is unaware of having had it, to the stroke which leaves the victim utterly unconscious. It's worth making the point that a TIA can presage a larger stroke, and that if someone who suffers a TIA can see a doctor immediately, there are preventive measures that can dramatically reduce the risk of a subsequent and more severe assault on the brain. (In America, especially, some doctors are experimenting with the use of the drug tissue plasminogen activator, TPA; in Britain the only drugs used in TIA are aspirin, warfarin and persantin, and of these aspirin is by far the commonest.)

If you suffer a TIA you are thirteen times more likely to suffer a stroke in the following year. The signs of a TIA might include a mild slurring of speech or an unexplained transient weakness in an arm or leg. In such cases, the doctor's attention will be focused on three essential fields: first, the potential narrowing of arteries in the neck, from which bits of blood clot might break off and travel up to the brain; second, the possibility of clots in the heart; and third, the presence or absence of high blood pressure. Once these areas have been examined, the search will move to the the quality of the patient's blood and the cell biology of the patient's blood vessels. I was given the same three tests to determine what had happened to me. In my case, having passed them with flying colours, I was subjected to a closer and closer scrutiny of my blood. In the end, however, I was advised that, so far as could be determined after the fact, there was no treatment that would have prevented my stroke, and no certain explanation for why it had happened. Like most such episodes, it came out of the blue. I am occasionally asked if I am troubled by this, but the answer is, I'm not! (Life is too short.)

So, throughout my convalescence, I regularly gave blood, a procedure I came to dislike intensely. Once the doctors had ruled out the most common cause of stroke (smoking and high blood pressure), they began searching for more subtle causes. In recent years the scientific analysis of blood has become markedly more sophisticated. Perhaps I was suffering from Leiden Factor V? Was Lupus Anticoagulant to blame? I gave blood samples to, among others, a Dr Thomas, a Dr Cohen, a Dr Abraham, and finally to Professor Sam Machin, a no-nonsense haematologist of world renown. One of the many fears I encountered in the aftermath of my stroke was the anxiety that if Sarah and I were to have children I might somehow pass on the weakness in my brain. (Each of these excellent doctors assured me that this is quite impossible.)

During my year off I have turned repeatedly to

speculation about the genetic programming in my head that led up to that moment on 29 July. Was this simply a catastrophic version of a weakness that had already manifested itself in the lives of my ancestors? Did old Robert McCrum – who died in 1915 – die of stroke? I have, of course, no sure way of knowing (his death certificate refers simply to 'respiratory failure'), and the experts scorn the notion that one can inherit such weakness. It is, perhaps, some comfort to know that he died old.

Stroke is seen as an old person's illness for the obvious reason that, statistically speaking, the propensity to stroke increases with age. If, for example, you take a random group of a thousand Britons or Americans over the age of seventy-five, you will find that between twenty and thirty will suffer a stroke each year. (In the general population at large, the ratio is about 0.5–1.0 stroke per thousand population per annum.) Among old people many strokes are so small, and so few are the significant symptoms, that it can be almost impossible to determine what has taken place. When a series of very small strokes accumulates in this way, a general deterioration becomes evident over time: steps more hesitant, memory less reliable, handwriting less legible, movement less vigorous – the physical decline we associate with old age. In the end, an elderly person who has suffered in this way may well be simply carried off by a larger, and finally fatal, stroke. (Men and women beyond the age of seventy-five suffer ten times the incidence of strokes as those between fifty-five and fifty-nine.)

In my case, after the immediate crisis was over, I was prescribed a modest daily 75-mg dose of aspirin to thin the blood and then, after some months, a very mild dose of Pravastatin to reduce my (slightly elevated) cholesterol level. Actually, the relationship of cholesterol to stroke is unclear. Many doctors will say that modest elevations in cholesterol are probably not as important as they can be in heart disease. None the less, cholesterol is associated with the degeneration of the blood vessel wall in the disease known as atherosclerosis (hardening of the arteries) in which cholesterol plaques in the blood vessel wall tend to clot, thus blocking off the blood vessel. Cholesterol is only one of many potential causes of stroke, but in a subject in which there are so many imponderables, it has the advantage that it can be both measured and treated. It's for this reason that, in an illness that has so many mysteries, it attracts rather more than its fair share of attention.

Whatever the cause of stroke, almost any preventive measure is worth taking. The plain fact is that, in Britain and North America, someone will have a stroke approximately every five minutes. The onset of stroke is usually sudden and it is this suddenness that is one of its chief characteristics, as the word itself implies. The most common symptom of stroke is a weakness or paralysis of the arm or leg on one side of the body. This is known as 'hemiplegia'. My hemiplegia affected my entire left side, from my left cheek and tongue to my left hand to my left foot, while internally my left lung was also weakened, so that I was often short of the breath required for sustaining speech.

'Cerebral haemorrhages', about 15 per cent of all strokes, as I came to learn, are usually the direct result of the rupture of one of the tiny arteries deep inside the brain, an organ patterned in all directions by a network of tiny blood vessels as fine and feathery as the skeleton of a leaf. If, as I did later in my convalescence, you visit the Royal College of Surgeons in Lincoln's Inn Fields, you can study the beautifully intricate network, a filigree tracery, of arteries that supply the brain, in any number of fascinating three-dimensional models on display there.

The brain, detached from its sheltering skull and stored in formaldehyde, looks a bit like a peeled walnut. In a living body exposed brain tissue has the appearance of cold porridge, the 'grey matter' of English slang. It's this rather unpromising material that contains the core of who we are. As Stephen Pinker puts it in *How The Mind Works*, 'The brain's special status comes from a special thing that the brain does, which makes us see, think, feel, choose and act.' When the brain is damaged, for example, in its visual areas, the patient is unable to recognize the world in which he or she finds himself. For such people, their world, as Pinker puts it, 'is like handwriting they cannot decipher. They copy a bird faithfully but identify it as a tree stump. A cigarette lighter is a mystery until it is lit.'

The remaining 85 per cent of strokes are caused by the partial or complete blockage of an artery, either by the local narrowing and eventual blockage of an artery caused by clotting, or by the sudden arrival of a clot from elsewhere in the body (i.e. from an artery in the neck, or from a chamber in the heart) and thereby resulting in the cutting off of the blood supply – and the death of brain cells – to an organ as dependent on the blood supply as the heart and lungs are on oxygen. The main cause of arterial blockage is the deposit of fatty substances in the wall of the blood vessel. This results in stenosis (narrowing); occlusion (blockage); or embolism (the formation of a blood clot on the damaged arterial wall). This 'cerebrovascular disease' is often linked to the degeneration of arteries elsewhere in the body, especially the heart. The main causes of arterial wall damage leading to narrowing and blockage are, first, high blood pressure and second, the accumulation of fat in the vessel wall. Of these, high blood pressure is far more important. This goes some way to explaining why, as a patient during these months, I found virtually every member of the medical profession I met for the first time wanting to take my blood pressure.

If the causes of my stroke were obscure, the effects were clear enough, and occupied a great deal of my attention. In the months after my stroke, I became fascinated by the workings of the brain and used to meet regularly with a subtle and delightful Irish neuro scientist, Professor Ray Dolan of the Wellcome Department of Cognitive Neurology, at the Institute for Neurology in Queen Square, who gave me a series of informal seminars in the mechanics of the brain, so far as they are known today. Within the field of neuroscience, the Institute is a state-of-the-art organization researching a subject that is still very much in infancy. Waiting one day in the high-tech minimalist foyer of the Wellcome building, I was amused to note a beguilingly frank advertisement for a forthcoming seminar: 'The functional organization of working memory processes within the lateral frontal cortex – do we know anything yet?'

Dolan explained that the brain consumes 25 per cent of the energy production of the body. 'It is as if the body is a slave to the brain,' he told me. 'The extraordinary thing about the brain is that while the body has obviously adapted to our physical environment, the brain has adapted to a psychological or social environment that has been, we assume, a major shaper of the brain and of how it is structured.'

This is an allusion to one of the big debates within

the field of contemporary neurology: to what extent has the brain evolved and developed according to Darwinian theory? The most famous protagonist of Darwinian theory as applied to psychological development (opposed by the science writer Stephen Jay Gould) is Stephen Pinker. In an interview Professor Pinker told me: 'After having argued that language was some kind of distinct part of the human mind, the natural question was: so what are the other parts?' The central idea of *How The Mind Works* can be stated in a sentence: 'The mind,' says Pinker, 'is a system of organs of computation, designed by natural selection to solve the kinds of problems our ancestors faced in their foraging way of life, in particular, understanding and outmanoeuvring objects, animals, plants and other people.' In other words, 'the mind is what the brain does'. Or, as he says, 'To put it crudely, the brain is like a computer that evolved.'

One of the most important recent developments in neurology is the recognition that the brain is rather more plastic (i.e. adaptable) in its functions than was once thought. The Victorian images of the brain that we've inherited were derived from railway systems, or the telephone switchboard, and suggested a rigid framework. Nowadays, the emphasis is on the adaptability of the brain to meet particular needs. Damage in one area will result, neurologists believe, in compensatory activity elsewhere. According to one Nobel prizewinning neuroscientist, Gerald Maurice Edelman, 'The brain is a selective system, more like evolution than computation.' Despite the extraordinary efforts now being devoted to neurological investigation, as the medical historian Roy Porter puts it, 'Neurological conditions remain amongst the most intractable.' Which brings us back to the brain's place in our bodies.

A great deal of the body's energy is devoted to the brain (and vice versa). Most of that energy comes from the breaking down of glucose into carbon dioxide and water, a biochemical process that requires a high level of oxygen. Unlike the body's muscles, the brain is unable to store glucose in reserve; it depends instead on a constant supply from arterial blood, and the same is true of the necessary oxygen. When the brain is deprived by a stroke of oxygen or glucose, it begins to suffocate almost immediately. Irreversible brain damage will occur within fifteen to thirty minutes of the initial deprivation, unless blood flow resumes.

The brain is the miracle of the human frame, and aptly its biggest mystery. In recent years, neurological inquiry has become, with the study of genetics, the leading edge of medical research. The use of radioactive or fluorescent tracers and newly developed techniques of micro-electrode neurophysiology have brought the study of the brain centre-stage in the theatre of medicine. For the first time, researchers like Ray Dolan are making new discoveries about the organization of language and memory, and the way in which emotions interact with cognition, and how cognitive functions are composed of innumerable sub-processes.

When I asked Dolan how easy it would be to replace the brain with a computer, he replied: 'You would need an awful lot of chips. There are twenty billion neurons in the brain and each of those neurons makes on average ten thousand connections.' He went on to describe 'the extraordinary computational power of the living brain to represent so much, to be able to remember so much and its almost limitless memory capacity'. To put it another way, if you were somehow able to link up all the laptop computers of a city like London, you would be

41

only just beginning to equal the capacity of one ordinary brain.

I also met with Dolan's vivacious colleague at the Institute, Richard Frackowiak, who crisply described the brain as 'an organ in a box with a hole at the bottom where the brain stem is situated'. A cerebral haemorrhage, he said, 'squashes the brain. The pressure rises because the skull is absolutely rigid. In the worst possible case, the brain is actually squeezed out – that's called "coning". The pressure pushes it down through the hole at the bottom. But that is exremely rare and happens only in the more severe kind of stroke. You can get everything from fifteen minutes' paralysis of the hand to a profound coma, from triviality to something fatal.' Most people, in fact, die from other complications, notably cardio-respiratory difficulties. So how, I asked him, does a stroke kill you?

'Well,' Frackowiak replied, 'it squashes the parts of the brain that deal with your heart rate and your breathing. It's the same as being hanged, really. You die because your heart stops and you stop breathing.' He went on, 'There are many other ways you can die with a stroke. Lying in bed, you can get a raging pneumonia and die simply because your lungs fill up with fluid and you can't breathe, can't get oxygen in. And then there are many potential medical complications that can occur.'

We talked about the brain's resilience to stroke. 'The brain,' said Frackowiak, 'is uniquely adaptable, but it's not like the liver. You can cut out seven-eighths of the liver and it'll regenerate. So it's not as resilient as the heart or the liver, and that's why it's stuck in a rigid box [the skull] and covered with fluid to absorb shock. It is beautifully designed. It is extraordinary. It weighs only

1.4 kilograms and yet it defines our whole personality, and our interaction with the world.'

The brain and the spinal cord, or central nervous system, is located at the core of our very being; this is the epicentre of the earthquake in the life of a man or a woman that is constituted by a stroke.

In the West, about three-quarters of acute stroke cases occur, as we have seen, in people aged sixty-five or more. But this means that 25 per cent of all strokes will occur in people under that age; another estimate says that a fifth of all strokes occur in people under the age of forty. So, while stroke is *perceived* as an old person's illness, the statistical reality is that large numbers of younger people today are having to come to terms with a sudden and devastating affliction of which they know little or nothing. In Britain, about two hundred young, 'socio-economically active people' (as the jargon has it) are affected by stroke *every week*. The general public is almost completely unaware of this staggering statistic.

The remoteness of the affliction perhaps explains our general ignorance of it, except, perhaps as the mysteriously devastating illness that fells our elderly relatives. I suppose the first time I must have become conscious of 'stroke' was when, as a child, I read *Treasure Island*. The opening chapters of Robert Louis Stevenson's masterpiece are among the most compellingly urgent ever written, and the moment when the mysterious sea captain ('the brown old seaman, with the sabre cut') fights Black Dog and collapses on the floor of the Admiral Benbow always seemed to me especially gripping:

I heard a loud fall in the parlour and, running in, beheld the captain lying full length upon the floor. At the same instant my mother . . . came running downstairs to help me. Between us we raised his head. He was breathing very loud and hard; but his eyes were closed, and his face was a horrible colour . . . It was a happy relief for us when the door opened as Doctor Livesey came in.

'Oh doctor,' we cried, 'what shall we do? Where is he wounded?'

'Wounded? A fiddle-stick's end!' said the doctor. 'No more wounded than you or I. The man has had a stroke, as I warned him . . . I must do my best to save this fellow's trebly worthless life; and Jim here will get me a basin.'

A great deal of blood was taken before the captain opened his eyes and looked mistily about him.

Such was the treatment for stroke in the fiction of my childhood, and I suspect that memories of this passage, and others like it, formed the bulk of my adult knowledge of stroke, too.

Regardless of age, the physical and psychological damage is the same. The cost to society in economic terms is staggering: in the USA and Britain, respectively, $30 billion and £2. 8 billion each year. About one third of those afflicted by stroke between the ages of thirty-five and sixty-five are disqualified from work by disability. The majority of stroke-survivors will have a paralysed arm, and many will be unable to walk normally. Between 50 and 75 per cent will have some form of permanent disability.

The heartbreaking nature of such disability is vividly evoked by Sheila Hale who, writing in the *London Review of Books* in March 1998, poignantly evoked the post-stroke experience of her brilliant historian husband John: 'The sociable stranger with the donnish manner would like to know who you are and what interests you. He will listen attentively and respond enthusiastically. Whether you speak English, Italian, French or German, you will have no doubt that he follows your meaning. The trouble is that however hard you try you will not be able to understand a single word he is saying . . . It is more than five years since my husband, a Renaissance historian, lost his language following a stroke.'

Lying in the National Hospital, of course, I was ignorant of these statistics and these kinds of affliction, but I could not escape the wholly unscientific sensation that while some irrepressible quirk in my bloodline had dumped me in this predicament, at the same time some peculiar longevity-gene had saved me from its direst outcome.

[5]

My New Life

1–5 August

We defy augury. There is a special providence in the fall
of a sparrow. If it be now, 'tis not to come; if it be not to
come, it will be now; if it be not now, yet it will come.
The readiness is all. Since no man of aught he leaves,
knows aught, what is't to leave betimes? Let be.

William Shakespeare, *Hamlet*, Act V, scene ii

Of all my conscious moments at the National Hospital,
the nights were the worst. Night is when the patient
imagines dying. It was at these moments that I was most
acutely conscious of the stark truth that everyone faces
in hospital: no amount of loving care and attention (and
I was greatly blessed in this) can disguise the fact that a
dramatic illness emphasizes our solitude and isolation.
We came into the world alone and, no matter what
prudent provision we make for the future, we shall leave
it alone. As Pozzo says in *Waiting For Godot*, 'They give
birth astride of a grave, the light gleams an instant, then
it's night once more.' If I had a headache at night – like
the harbinger of the stroke itself – my first thought was:
I'll be dead in the morning; I'll never see Sarah again.

In fact, she would appear at my bedside, with unfailing good humour and a cheery, clarion 'Good morning!' at about eight o'clock, immediately after the hospital breakfast (coffee, a choice of sausage or bacon, juice, and cold toast, accompanied inevitably by a tiny plastic cup of Lactulose, a sickly sweet laxative), bringing fresh clothes, the day's post and the British newspapers, her addiction. Then I would be wheeled off by one of the nurses to have a bath. This was a laborious and exhausting process during which I tried to forget that the nurses were literally manhandling me, moving me in and out of a wheelchair specially designed for use in the bathroom, levering me into the bath and then washing me all over. There's no place for privacy in hospital.

Sarah's presence, and her optimism, soon chased away the demons of the night, and we quickly evolved a visiting routine in which her role was to control the flow of visitors and quiz the doctors about my progress and my likely recovery. As an American, Sarah was used to a level of information and medical advice that British doctors, who seem to cherish the mystery of their profession, still find slightly unnerving.

My doctor, Andrew Lees, an elegant, soft-spoken neurologist of great natural warmth and wisdom, advised me to think of the bleed in my head as a kind of bruise; over time the scavenging macrophage cells would literally eat up the damage to the cerebral tissue, leaving that part of my brain permanently disabled. I could see for myself what he was talking about. An early MRI scan located the bleed, a menacing black blot, deep in the brain at what the medical report said was 'the proximal right middle cerebral artery at its trifurcation'. Over time, the sinister stain would shrink and fade, but, despite this brilliant pictorial representation, I am, even now, two years later, no nearer an absolutely reliable explanation of why that bleed occurred in the first place.

It is the special peculiarity of the affliction called 'stroke' that its dynamics remain mysterious. The absence of an explanation for such a thunderbolt enhances the sense the stroke-sufferer has of being a victim of a malign fate. While about 40 per cent of all strokes are unexplained, the same uncertainty accompanies the process of recovery. I believe this is unnerving for patients and doctors alike. In medicine, the contract between the doctor and the patient is based on trust and a supposition of expertise, of knowledge. When my rehabilitation specialist, Dr Richard Greenwood, a tousled, academic-style neurologist, widely acknowledged to be the head of his profession, sheepishly confessed to me that doctors are actually quite ignorant about the brain, it was oddly comforting. At least we were somehow all in this together.

None of this uncertainty discouraged the Queen Square doctors from returning obsessively to the scene of the crime. Had a clot originated in the chambers of the heart? I was sent off for a trans-oesophageal echo cardiogram. Was the thyroid to blame? I gave yet another sample of blood for analysis. The secrets of the body in question will not stop modern medicine from asking myriad questions. Despite these investigations, which occupied much of my attention during that first month in hospital, no one was able to advise how long I would be incapacitated. This made things maddeningly difficult, at times even frightening. Would I ever walk again? When I first fell ill, one doctor told Sarah that I'd spend the rest of my life in a wheelchair, and for several weeks every doctor she spoke to gave the vaguest of answers to this simple, and most fundamental, question.

In the absence of reliable data the experts took refuge in a frustrating reticence, a studied vagueness; 'probably' I'd be fit in 'about a year'. After six months, it would be 'fairly clear' how much movement would return to my left side; then 'perhaps' my arm would become 'useful'. Meanwhile, I was still profoundly restricted, anxiously watching for evidence of brain-repair; on the rare days that my left side began to respond it was as though I had discovered a sixth dimension.

Such moments of joy were rare; I cried a lot in hospital. Sometimes the tears were slow and weepy; at others, uncontrolled and desperate. I could cry for any reason and none; I was told that this is characteristic of stroke victims. Dr Lees also assured me that those parts of my brain which control memory, thought and personality were unaffected; but Sarah was naturally concerned that I might have suffered a change of personality. I have since learned that this fear is exceptionally common among the carers of stroke-sufferers. In turn, the terrific psychological pressures arising from stroke can lead to the irretrievable breakdown of many relationships. Sadly, 'stroke' and 'divorce' seem often to be closely linked.

I became aware of Sarah's anxieties when I noticed, with some amusement, that she was surreptitiously leafing through the pages of the notebook in which I'd begun to keep a record of my experiences. I feigned sleep and watched her checking the latest entries, presumably looking for tell-tale gibberish. I resisted the temptation to fill a folio or two with 'all work and no play makes Jack a dull boy', like the deranged Jack Nicholson character in *The Shining*.

I did not pray. Several visitors later asked if, having 'looked into the abyss', I'd experienced any religious emotions, to which I can honestly reply, I did not. What

I did find was that the world seemed almost unbearably precious. Shut away in my room, with the finest English summer in memory scorching outside, I had a craving for sky, earth and sea, which I satisfied in the oddest way by watching sport and nature programmes on television.

In the hours of reflection that followed the end of *Channel Four Racing*, I would brood on the paper-thin gap between health and sickness. As adults we forget that we live in our bodies. The unexpected failure of the body is a shocking catastrophe that threatens the flimsy edifice that we call the 'self', especially when one is reduced to the condition of a baby. In *Hannah and Her Sisters*, Micky Sachs, a grand-prix hypochondriac, decides he has a brain tumour. 'Do you realize,' he moans, 'what a thread we're all hanging by?'

The irony is that this kind of drama was precisely what I'd been looking for. Now that I come to write about it, I find I cannot explain my former addiction to physical risk except to say that I think of myself as a coward who wishes he were not. It seems to me that my need to search out the dangerous parts of the world comes from my fascination with history. For me, history is made up of hazardous turning points and dangerous corners – encounters, skirmishes, battles, insurrections – in which the individual is tested against the cold steel of the historical process. There is also the thrill of visiting a terrain that is utterly unfamiliar and physically punishing. And then there's the unavoidable competition with my father, who had served on HMS *Victorious* in the Pacific as a junior navigating officer in the Royal Navy during the Second World War and had known the thing that those of us born after 1945 will never know. I suspect this unconscious competition is common to quite a few men of my generation.

Somewhere I had acquired a taste for the intoxicating smell of jet-fuel and rotting vegetation: I had to see new places, experience new things. In the spring of 1993 – some months before my final flirtation with adventure, the journalistic trip to that Indonesian hell-hole, the island of East Timor – I had gone with the photographer Tim Page to Cambodia during the UN-supervised election.

When I was lying in hospital, unable to move, it was this South-East Asian journey that came to haunt my consciousness, as I faced up to the possibility that I would never travel again. Just as I had spent that first day of my year off lying at the corner of the stairs under a brown-green map of Cambodia, so I spent the subsequent weeks winding in my imagination through the sub-tropical jungles of Indo-China, reliving those lost moments of danger. As the American writer, William Maxwell, puts it so memorably, 'I have liked remembering almost as much as I have liked living.'

Imagine a country whose people have been killing each other without mercy for twenty years or more, a country whose fields have been seeded with millions of lethal anti-personnel mines, and whose main political parties also deploy private armies. Imagine a land of violent, despotic traditions, rife with malaria and malnutrition, a land virtually without laws, clinics, metalled roads, safe water or telephones. And then imagine deciding to hold a democratic, Western-style election here. Neither a surreal joke, nor a nightmare fantasy, this was Cambodia, 1993. The UN presence (UNTAC) was, quite simply, a fantastic invasion by one of the strangest armies ever to march into Indo-China: multinational troops from countries as far apart as Algeria, Poland and the Philippines; big-bottomed civilians, pallid spooks, bright-eyed do-gooders, yuppie careerists, and a cluster of foreign correspondents, conflict-junkies who would not have seemed out of place in films like *Apocalypse Now* or *The Killing Fields*. Among the American ex-pats in Phnom Penh at that time was the journalist Nate Thayer, who would later track down and film Pol Pot as he faced denunciation by his people in a jungle on the Thai–Cambodia border in the months before his death.

Tim Page and I were invited to join one of the daily UN fact-finding trips into Khmer Rouge territory, a journey that would traverse the world-famous Angkor temples, then still off-limits to civilians. We found two UNTAC officers who gave our driver the information that a mine had exploded the night before, injuring five people, one seriously – the planting of mines was often a clue to imminent military activity – and we drove deeper into no man's land. No one seemed to know anything about the mine. The road had become strangely empty. Suddenly there was a radio-squawk, our call sign. We listened. Word had come through that the road ahead had been mined by the Khmer Rouge. For the first time that day, everything seemed dangerous. There were discoloured patches of sand further down the road. Were these mines? Who could say? We were not inclined to risk finding out. At the nearby Bangladeshi base, the battalion commander, an impressive young officer in charge of about forty troops, told us that the day before, at midnight, a young man had been brought in, horribly mutilated by the mine blast we had been told about earlier. The captain, at considerable personal risk, had driven through the darkness to get the victim to the provincial hospital. 'Every day we get a mine injury,' he told me. '*Inshallah*, he will live.'

After we had returned to Siem Reap, Tim and I made our way to the provincial hospital. Between three hundred and seven hundred people a month are maimed by mine blasts in Cambodia. In Siem Reap, local casualties filled an entire wing of the hospital. As we approached, we passed the families of the injured, cooking meals and washing clothes in the courtyard. Inside, a crushing heat and the stench of sickness; it was like stepping into another age. There was no air-conditioning, not even a fan. There were beds in every corridor, with men and boys of all ages recovering from amputations. The look of utter hopelessness on the face of a Cambodian amputee was hard to bear, and harder to forget. Eventually we found our casualty. He was lying, tended by his mother, near the doorway, weak from blood loss but alive. His right hand and both legs below the knee had been blown away. The stumps were heavily bandaged and covered in a *krama* (the traditional Khmer check scarf) to keep off the flies. His name was Liu Loeun. He was twenty-one. If he was lucky, he would receive prosthetic treatment; if he was not, he would end up begging for dollars from tourists in the ruins of Angkor. When I think of him now, I consider my disabilities trifling in comparison, and so they are – I have all my limbs – but I know from my own experience some of the mental anguish he will have gone through. I recall the tenderness with which his mother, at his bedside, soothed his brow, a stark reminder that at such moments perhaps only our mothers can supply the love we need.

During that first surreal day at home in Islington, I had called my parents instinctively, and not merely because theirs was a telephone number I knew by heart. The longer I stayed helpless in hospital, the more I came to understand why it is our blood relations who will respond, instinctively and without question, to the claims of family. Since my divorce from my first wife, I had lived in a world seemingly outside family, but there were moments during those first hospital days when it seemed that family was the only world that mattered. At the time, I could hardly express the thought, but I found it intensely moving to see my father in his London suit nobly and indefatigably appearing each day at my bedside, while my mother moved about among the nurses in the background. And at the centre of this new world was the tirelessly supportive, uncrushable, smiling figure of my wife of two months, my beloved Sarah. If I were now to reduce my experience in hospital to two key words they would be 'family' and 'love'.

To while away the long hours of August, Sarah began to read aloud to me. Together we returned to *Alice in Wonderland*, while Sarah also introduced me to her own childhood favourite, E. B. White's *Charlotte's Web*. We both felt there was something profoundly consoling about these old friends. I found my own thoughts spinning back to infancy (the rooks caw-cawing in the beech trees of Ashton House), and then forwards through the years. It was a self-examination enforced by the visitors to my bedside. A novice to hospital, I discovered that the patient must submit to a parade of relatives, friends, ex-lovers, co-workers, parents, siblings, each one presenting a tiny fragment of lost time for renewal. The patient is the star of the show, but the audience varies: lame-duck specialists; ghouls; true friends; compassion junkies; hypochondriacs; and people who welcome the chance to address a captive audience. (It intrigued me to see the relief on my friends' faces when, as one put it, they discovered that 'you are not a drooling vegetable'.) Each post brought new letters: letters of sympathy, letters of encouragement, letters from people I hadn't spoken to, or heard from, in years. And when I wasn't bombarded by the past, I found I was alone with a rather interesting person, someone I had never spent much time alone with: myself.

In this way, I became my own Cambodia, with the enforced leisure and opportunity to explore myself, to analyse what made me tick, and to discover what mattered to me. Alone in my room, with only my right arm functioning properly (my right leg, though intact, was of no real use to me in this state), and with the demons of physical exhaustion constantly at hand, I began to keep a diary. This was Sarah's idea, and I later discovered that she was writing one, too. I think the diaries helped preserve sanity for both of us. I have reproduced here the diaries we kept during August and September 1995. I can think of no more faithful account of our emotions at this time, and of what we both went through, separately and together. If, as Sarah says, I sometimes find it difficult to express my emotions in conversation, at least in my diary (which is printed just as I wrote it, with a few inevitable omissions) I found myself expressing my feelings quite freely.

My first, barely legible, scribble starts on 1 August (three days after I fell ill):

. . . one thing I can say about what's happened – it's not boring. I don't remember much about last night, but I do remember being afraid of surgery. After a lot of discussion among the doctors, I was finally wheeled into a ward. I felt very tired and kept falling asleep. It was very hot and I found myself revolving telephone numbers in my mind to keep awake. In the ward (which was noisy and suffocating) I tossed and turned all night. From time to time a nurse would shine a flashlight in my eyes and ask my date of birth. Finally, towards dawn, I managed to signal to a nurse who brought a cold towel and wiped my face which had become very dry with the heat.

Sarah's diary takes up the story with this entry on Wednesday 2 August:

Robert continues to make progress. His speech is clearer, the movement in his right side is stronger [*actually, it was largely unaffected*] and according to the doctors he is showing small signs of improvement in his left side. His spirits go up and down and he is unable to express them – I try to do it for him, to anticipate what he might be thinking and verbally beat it out of him – and then I end up feeling wretched and so bossy and peremptory. I am so afraid he won't improve, that he will never be able to walk, even though I know that is very likely not the case. I am so scared. I alternate between being very optimistic and completely despairing. I lay on our bed at home today screaming to all hell. The neighbours must have thought I was being murdered. Then I called Kathy Lette [*a friend; the author of* Foetal Attraction] and sobbed and sobbed.

Flowers continue to pour in – letters and phone calls – R. has begun to start to dictate some very funny Thank You letters. His mind is perfectly intact. The doctors scare the hell out of me. Now they're saying it's a clot surrounded by a little bit of bleeding, which complicates things because if they use anti-coagulants to dissolve the clot, they will exacerbate the bleeding. We've gotten so many flowers that we have started to put them all down the hallway, using up the available space there too.

It was at about this time that plans were made for me to be moved from University College Hospital to the Nuffield Wing of the National Hospital in Queen Square. I was oblivious to the discussions that were taking place in the corridor outside my room, and continued to scribble in the big Black 'n' Red notebook that stayed at my bedside throughout these weeks.

MY DIARY: THURSDAY 3 AUGUST
Sarah is with me now. I've no idea when, or how, she got here, but it's wonderful to have her back. Her mother, Susan, is here, too, rather amazingly. Is this the ultimate mother-in-law joke: that you have a life-threatening crisis and when you come back into consciousness you find . . . Your Mother-in-Law? Presumably she's flown in from America. My parents are also ever-present, as are Mark and Stephen [my brothers].

Sarah's diary for the next night expresses what may have been the genesis of this book:

FRIDAY 4 AUGUST
R. very discouraged, and it's so hard to get him to talk. He would like to do two things: one, to talk to other people who have had this happen to them; two, to talk to Dr Lees more often. I think he feels terribly abandoned.

Home for the night, the first night by myself – feeling so exhausted and beaten up and lonely, but also very guilty because the truth is it's really nice to be able to be at home. R. fills the air and it makes me remember what normalcy would feel like. I am pathetically wearing his T-shirt and his boxer shorts.

My diary: Saturday 5 August

I have lost all track of time, but I know that today is about a week since the stroke happened. Mum and Dad came and sat next to me while I dozed. I did not feel inclined to talk to them. Later Dad very sweetly read me some favourite passages from P. G. Wodehouse, and cheered me up a lot. In the morning I read my post. I seem to have had an amazing number of letters and cards. The one I liked the best was from Jaco and Elizabeth [*Dutch publishing friends*] on Skyros to say that they've lit a candle for me in some Greek shrine 'and will burn down the whole island if necessary'. I had more of a headache today, but Sarah says I am making progress. I don't see the evidence for this, and feel endless frustration at being stuck here in the National Hospital. There are no visitors today, no doctors; I dictated a note to Roger Alton [*my friend the features editor on the* Guardian]. The world of the *Guardian* seems quite incredibly remote now and perhaps I shall never recover it. Who knows? However, I no longer feel quite so helpless. Darling Sarah has been wonderful. On the TV I watched *Europe Express* and *Jaws, the Revenge*. I find I have become quite addicted to television, perhaps because I cannot properly hold a book or newspaper to read. I feel idle and lazy and rather trapped. At least there is room for Sarah to stay the night. She sleeps on the floor in the corner and is being very, very patient. I love her so much, and feel frustration at not being able to express it.

I have no recollection of being moved to the National Hospital but once I was installed, with my cards and flowers, the room became a kind of home, and I diverted myself with the pleasures of classical music, constructing imaginary lists of *Desert Island Discs*, of which my favourite went as follows (I've always longed for the chance to publish this, though perhaps not in these circumstances):

1. J. S. Bach: Suites for Unaccompanied Cello 1–6
2. Mozart: Concerto for Violin and Orchestra No. 5
3. Schubert: Erlkönig, D 328
4. Mahler: Das Liede von der Erde
5. Brahms: A German Requiem
6. Britten: Serenade for Tenor, Horn and Strings
7. Beethoven: Sonata No. 17, op. 31 No. 2
8. Richard Strauss: Four Last Songs (Vier Letzte Lieder)

It was during these long days, listening weepily to 'Four Last Songs' on my Discman, that it began to dawn on me exactly what kind of person she was I'd married, even though at that moment I wasn't fit to be married to anyone, either physically or emotionally. As I wrote in my diary on 5 August, 'The truth is: I feel oddly detached from the outside world. My image of myself during these days has been of a beetle or cockroach without a leg, flailing helplessly and covered in dirt, on the brink of extinction.'

[6]

Sarah

10 October 1993 – 5 August 1995

> But wherefore say not I that I am old?
> O, love's best habit is in seeming trust,
> And age in love loves not to have years told.
>
> William Shakespeare, Sonnet 138

Lying in the National Hospital in the long aftermath of my stroke, with the question 'Why me?' reverberating through my thoughts, I found myself engulfed in the love of my family and especially of my wife. In my more melancholy moments I felt that the lesson in love I was getting perhaps justified the appalling physical cost.

As I revolved my life history, searching for clues, sometimes wondering why I had been singled out for this malign punishment (a reaction common to all young stroke-sufferers), I became fascinated by Fate, and her cousin Chance. Of course, there's good luck and there's bad luck. When I considered my good fortune I always returned to the inspiring, ironical figure of Sarah. Nothing had been more fortuitous than our first encounter in October 1993, but once that meeting had happened, it seemed an irrevocable, immutable moment in both our personal histories.

In October 1993, in my capacity as editor-in-chief of Faber & Faber, I was due to go to the annual Book Fair in Frankfurt. To me, this had become a regular autumnal chore and it was the measure of my disaffection with my life at this time that, when I secured a commission from the *Guardian* to write an article about the business of the fair, I launched into a ferocious attack on the whole institution.

The Book Fair runs from Wednesday to Sunday, often in a tawny, Indian-summer week at the beginning of October. I remember sitting alone in my hotel room chuckling over my copy, a sustained anti-Frankfurt rant. I was due to file in time for the Saturday edition; in practice, this meant arriving at my conclusions by midday on Thursday, before the Fair was properly under way. So my piece was based less on actual reportage than on an accumulation of frustration in which I described an important bookselling institution as 'the *Jurassic Park* of the international literary scene – a glossy, highly organized but empty racket whose chief beneficiaries are the hoteliers, restaurateurs and taxi-drivers of the city'. Shortly after completing this breezy polemic on Wednesday afternoon, I plunged back into the business of the Fair.

My friend Morgan Entrekin, the publisher of the Grove Atlantic Press, a true Southern gentleman and one of the world's great party animals, had invited me to join him and 'some friends' for dinner. To tell the truth, though I love Morgan dearly, I was not eager to go. From experience, I knew that these 'friends' would be gloriously blonde and probably none too bright but, more to the point, so tremendously keen on Morgan that there'd be little room for anyone else. I was not anxious to make up the numbers at the court of King Morgan. On the other hand, I had had no better offer that night, and we were to meet at the bar of the Park Hotel. I did not at this time have much in the way of a permanent relationship. I had been married in my twenties, a marriage that had collapsed in 1984, shortly after my thirtieth birthday. (Its failure, I'm afraid, was largely my fault.) Although it was nearly ten years since my first wife and I had separated, my life remained unsettled. I was still, metaphorically, in trouble.

For ten years and more the Faber & Faber office had provided me with a kind of alternative family: its authors as my friends and dependants, its staff as my intimates and surrogate siblings, and its chairman, my friend Matthew Evans, as an older and quasi-paternal figure. Now, belatedly, I had reached the point at which I was recognizing the limitations of such an institution, and of such relationships. After a decade of personal irresponsibility I was looking for a change. But that realization did not stop me from relishing one more throw of the dice in the casino of singlehood.

That night in Frankfurt, I arrived late at the rendezvous. Morgan was already in place, enjoying his role as Mein Host; clearly unattached, he was already attended by two or three very attractive blonde women from the Calvinist parts of northern Europe. I was wondering if I should make my excuses and leave when he took me aside and explained that he'd also invited a journalist from the *New York Times*, who was covering the book fair for her newspaper, one Sarah Lyall. He suggested vaguely that it might do me some good, as a writer, to have a friend on the *Times*. Well, I'd met a few American journalists in my time, and I remember thinking, Some chance. Anyway, I decided to stay. A moment or two later, this slight blonde figure came shyly into the bar, and we were introduced. I don't remember much about our first conversation (Sarah claims now that I simply bragged about having filed my copy with the *Guardian*) but I do remember feeling tremendously excited and stimulated by her presence, her company, her conversation . . . Unlike some Americans of my acquaintance, she seemed to have a highly developed sense of humour (I still remember the thrill of finding someone with whom to share a joke about that staple of British journalistic practice, 'the fact too good to check'), an acute appreciation of irony and a way with words that was, to me, perfectly delightful. We fell into a conversation that seemed to go on all evening, first at dinner and then, because we were all going back to the Frankfurterhof Hotel for post-prandial drinks, during what would have been otherwise an interminable walk through the rainy, confusing streets of Frankfurt. It was then that I asked her why she'd become a journalist and she replied, very frankly, and rather to my surprise, that it was probably fear. (At that moment, she seemed to me the least fearful person I'd met in ages.) When she'd graduated from college, she told me, she'd felt strangely nervous about looking for a job; nervous about dealing with people in authority; nervous about finding her way around the world. So her decision to become a reporter was counter-intuitive, as she put it, 'like an arachnophobe choosing a career handling spiders'. I liked the fact that Sarah looked to journalism to up-end cosy assumptions (as the Chicago night-editor's dictum has it, 'If your mother says she loves you – check it out'). It was during this perambulation through the freezing night that she asked me how old I was. I'd already cunningly established that she was twenty-nine, going on thirty, though in truth she looked barely twenty-one. It was then that I caught myself lying about my age. How old was I? 'Thirty-nine,' I snapped – supposing that forty would have seemed impossibly antique. I heard the lie with a flutter of surprise. I must be interested.

I was more than interested. I was in love; indeed, we both were. When I try to recall that time now, after the dramas of my year off, what sticks in my mind is the moment when Sarah said that, no, she was not free for dinner on Sunday night, but that she probably could manage Monday, or Tuesday, or Wednesday, or Thursday . . . or Friday.

The next few weeks flashed by. London. New York. London again. And then I was preparing to go away once more. Here my old nomadic life was in conflict with my new relationship, though it seemed that I'd met someone who was almost equally peripatetic. Indeed, it was not until I found myself *in extremis* that I discovered the extraordinary reserves of courage and resilience in Sarah's nature.

Although I was excited about the possibilities that Sarah seemed to offer, I was committed to a potentially dangerous journalistic trip to the Far East, to East Timor. My friend the photographer Julio Etchart and I had already made plans. The rainy season was approaching. We could not delay a moment longer. Early in December 1993, we took off for the sad city of Dili.

Flying via Bali, we arrived in East Timor shortly before Christmas. All my thoughts were with Sarah, who hadn't wanted me to go, but I was exhilarated to be on the road again. No question that this was the fabled East Indies. Blink, and you could almost mistake the palm trees and corrugated roofing for the Caribbean. Almost, but not quite. As we passed through Customs I was conscious, among the taxi drivers pushing for work, of searching eyes – uniformed officials and soldiers with guns.

We rode into the capital in a beaten-up blue taxi with door handles made of coathanger-wire and a garish photograph of Pope John Paul II on the dashboard. It was very hot, the streets were almost deserted, and beyond the broken promenade, small boys dived and splashed in the bitter sea. A hog rootled among the mangroves on the shore. Further on, there was a piazza, a statue of the Blessed Virgin Mary, and on the corner a street vendor was selling noodles in the shade of a mahogany tree.

When we arrived at our hotel, we were aware that many people hanging about the dark lobby were noting our arrival with interest. My visa said I was a tourist, but a one-legged Australian swinging on crutches like Long John Silver, swigging from a can of local beer, asked if we were selling guns. After dark, troops in crash helmets rode shotgun in open trucks. Within hours, I was conscious only of the oppression and the fear. *Timor conturbat me* . . . What I'd been told was true: East Timor was an occupied territory, a police state, an infernal paradise, one of the saddest places in the world. Some time during my first twenty-four hours here that famous line from *Doctor Faustus* popped into my head: 'Why, this is Hell, nor am I out of it.'

Such are the paradoxes of global communication that it was not difficult to find a telephone from which to call through to Sarah in New York on the far side of the world, and thus we spoke, night after night, while the police spies hung around the gloomy, air-conditioned hotel lobby, watching my every move but unable, I judged, to understand what I was saying. In answer to her questions, I explained to Sarah that there was, along the mean, dusty streets of Dili, a kind of desolate normality to everyday existence. 'It's so *boring* here,' whispered one of the hotel maids. Outside, especially to the south and east, there was the conflict between the army and the guerrillas, a story that had gone comparatively unreported. I persuaded Julio that it was time for us to take the bus into the interior.

Eventually, we reached our destination, a Roman Catholic mission on the edge of a forest. Father Fernando De Souza, the local priest, was forty years old. His mission and its church were at once a school, a surgery, a place of recreation, a refuge, a social centre and a source of inspiration. Beyond the walls of the mission there were spies, policemen, informers – the Indonesian army of occupation. Inside, there was teaching, prayer and song – at almost every hour of the day there seemed to be groups of nuns and schoolchildren rehearsing anthems and Christmas carols. (I thought of Sarah in the frosty air of New York at Christmas, and felt terribly far from home.) Father De Souza said he would arrange for us to make contact with 'the armed struggle'. He said it might take some time. So we settled down to wait. I passed the time with a copy of *The Woman in White*. The day slowly faded. The hours ticked by. Night fell. We sat on the verandah of the mission, waiting. I remember looking up at the stars of the southern hemisphere wheeling overhead and wishing that I had more such times in my life for reflection. When such a moment came, with a vengeance, eighteen months later, alone in the National Hospital, I remembered Father De Souza's mission and found myself weeping inconsolably.

After waiting for hours in the tropical darkness, I finally met a guerrilla I'll call Joaquim Guterres, who described the activities of the freedom-fighters. Some time after midnight he handed over messages for fellow resistance workers who had somehow managed to flee abroad, and then he disappeared silently into the dark.

Next day, we bade farewell to Father De Souza and took the bus back to Dili. We were tailed and spied on to the last. At Dili airport, officers of military intelligence were on hand to arrest and then interrogate us with futile, and quite alarming, belligerence, but for some reason that still baffles me, neither my notes nor Julio's film were confiscated. Within hours, we were back in a world that remains largely indifferent to the terrible plight of East Timor. I filed my copy, and took the first plane to New York. It was nearly Christmas time and the city seemed more than usually magical. It was then one evening, over dinner, that Sarah and I began to speak – in a hypothetical way, I insisted, and with the immature person's fear of commitment – about getting married. Looking back, I suppose I was vaguely conscious of being no longer a very young man, and of knowing that Sarah was the person with whom I wanted to spend the rest of my life, in the state of matrimony – a state any amount as risky as Indonesia.

After East Timor I needed no encouragement to devote my time to her. Her conversation was always so delightfully whimsical, variously flippant, ironical and charming. Our first year, from Christmas 1993 to Christmas 1994, was much about looking forward to the time we'd spend together. We made a point of visiting each other, either in London or New York, at least once a month, and the year flashed by in a whirl of bargain-basement transatlantic flights. Less than twelve months after we'd first met we were engaged to be married and the date for the wedding set: 13 May 1995. I was, in the words of romantic fiction, 'the happiest man alive'.

I used to save up books to read on my red-eye trips from New York to London. One of these, devoured in a single flight, was Sherwin Nuland's compulsive bestseller *How We Die*. I returned to it when I began to write this book, and found the following passage marked in the margin: 'In previous centuries, men believed in the concept of *ars moriendi*, the art of dying.'

On All Saints Day, 1 November 1994, Sarah came to live in London. I decided that this was a momentous transition for me and I decided to attempt a diary (soon discarded, however). My first entry ran: 'Our first day together passed like a dream. S. slept all day, and five enormous suitcase now fill the downstairs living room. This, apparently, is just the hors d'oeuvre to the main course. Watching Channel Four News, we discussed the difference between "yob" and "hooligan".' Sarah now says that I had also to explain to her the meaning of 'toff'.

We were married outside Philadelphia on a glorious day in spring. In my speech I said that, like the defeated British troops at Yorktown, I'd had my world turned upside-down by an American. I'd certainly never expected to return to Pennsylvania in such idyllic circumstances. Sarah was, I said, 'my American Revolution, my Declaration of Independence, my first and only Amendment, my Supreme Court and my Boston Tea Party', deeply felt sentiments that were greeted with drunken whoops of joyous acclaim by family and friends. Our honeymoon was spent in Morocco. When we came back to London, Sarah found an assignment waiting for her from *Vanity Fair*. Would she go to San Francisco to interview the novelist Amy Tan? So at lunchtime on Saturday 22 July I took her to Heathrow for the flight. As I accelerated the car away from the unloading bay, I remember watching her diminutive figure on the kerb in the rearview mirror . . .

[7]

'Robert McCrum Is Dead'

6–12 August

The report of my death was an exaggeration.

Mark Twain, 1897

One morning at the National Hospital the bedside phone rang at nine thirty. 'The Holloway Police here. We have to identify a dead body. Where is Queen Square?' Me: 'I'm not dead; I'm just a patient.' Cop: 'I'm sorry, sir, but we have orders to identify this body and I was given this extension. Where's Queen Square?' Me: 'I'm not a corpse, thank you very much. Don't you have a map?' Cop: 'I was hoping for a bit of co-operation and politeness.' Me (suddenly furious): 'The kind of politeness, I suppose, for which the Metropolitan Police are renowned.' I slammed the phone down.

Sometimes I wondered when I was going to open the newspaper and read my own obituary. I discovered that, in the outside world, my stroke had caused something of a stir among the small world of media-dwellers, writers, journalists and editors, who had lived as I once had. It was as though the Grim Reaper had coughed, or tapped us all on the shoulder. The chairman of Faber & Faber,

Matthew Evans, joked that he was becoming so fed up with answering questions about my state of health that he wanted to sport a lapel button: 'Robert McCrum is dead.'

So the year faded and summer turned to autumn, while I eagerly monitored the tiny external changes that constitute convalescence after a stroke. At first, my left leg had been totally paralysed and wholly unresponsive to the commands of movement. Miraculously, it seemed, within a few days, I was beginning to be able to move it, very slightly, as it lay at rest on the mattress. The left side of my face, which had seemed so numb and lifeless, was beginning to recover sensation, and my speech was slowly becoming more intelligible.

My confidence, however, remained shot to pieces, and I had the greatest difficulty in finding any motivation to participate in the physical therapy offered by the National Hospital's rehab experts. I would be wheeled through the hospital's labyrinthine corridors to the gym, and would lie on the chilly plastic exercise bench, barely able to move, and longing to be left alone to sleep. At this stage, the exercises were absolutely basic, essentially an attempt to remind my brain that I still had a left leg (and arm) by simple attempts to get me to move the affected limbs and to try to stand upright, a seemingly impossible feat at that time. Sarah had to battle hard to get me to respond and used to refer, ironically, to what she called 'tough love'. I had no inkling what kind of inner battle she herself was going through at this time.

SARAH'S DIARY: SUNDAY 6 AUGUST
I feel so very sad and scared. R. making progress but he is so depressed and so unable to try – the smallest thing tires him out – it's as if he doesn't care. I worry, I worry,

that this has changed him, that he is not the same man. We went into the Square, him in a wheelchair, today, and my heart just about broke. What are we going to do? I don't know who he is, who I am, what we've gotten ourselves into. I feel that I have no one in the world to lean on, no one to help me. What if it never gets any better? What will I do then? If I keep his spirits up, I wonder, will I actually be able to do something for him, or is it just hopeless? I feel bone tired and not up to it, and so very, very frightened. It is as if the trap-door opened and we all fell through, and we're just continuing to fall and fall and fall.

7 AUGUST, MONDAY MORNING

R. seems cheerier and more motivated this morning, a little less tired. I gave him a huge lecture last night – and then started to cry. I feel like I am floundering, not knowing how to go about this. Everyone says that if he has the will to do it he really will come right back to normal. It's just going to take time.

It's amazing what your mind goes through, the stages of shock I suppose. My first thought was that he would be dead before I got back to London. Then I thought, his reason will be gone, his mind shot. Then I thought he would spend the rest of his life totally paralysed. Now I have other worries: that he'll be in a wheelchair for ever (the worst case there is), or that he will be somehow changed, not the same man I married – dependent and depressed – his joy all gone, the light gone from his eyes. Those seem like small things compared to a death or a life, but right now they feel all-encompassing. I don't remember what normalcy is any more. I don't remember if that in fact is the goal. I suppose that what we are all striving for is to get him up and walking and working

72

again, but I am wondering if I should ratchet down my expectations in anticipation of the possibility that they might be dashed again. I think of my expectations before all this: success at work, laughs and love and understanding at home, knowing that when I made a fuss during the film *Jefferson in Paris* R. would understand and would indulge my desire to leave in the middle and would take me home to dinner. Now what are my expectations? That he will be able to work, that we will able to live together again. That he will find his work as rewarding now as he did before. That when we have children, he will be able to take care of me some too. That one day I'll be able to lie in bed in the morning and R. will bring me a cup of tea and give me a kiss on my forehead and tell me that he loves me, and that everything will be alright.

I believe that at this time Sarah's biggest struggle was with my obstinacy; and one of the battlegrounds between us was speech therapy. I found it humiliating to have to accept that, though my thought processes seemed unimpaired, my utterances needed help from a speech therapist. The failure of articulation seemed such a fundamental failure, and one that went to the core of my self-esteem. My therapist, Dr Renata Whurr, a mild-mannered, friendly woman and an acknowledged expert in her field, gave me a set of exercises, which I loathed. ('Press lips together, then release: three times. Push lips forwards, then release: three times. Stretch lips sideways, then release: three times. Repeat *Ban – Bee – Boo*: three times. Repeat *Dan – dee – doo*.' Etc., etc. *ad nauseam*.) I had always spoken quickly; now it seemed that even the words I was uttering had become scrambled, although in fact, compared to many stroke-sufferers, I was extremely fortunate and never experienced the confusion of, for example, saying 'elephant' for 'pillow' or 'banana' for 'knife', or 'Pass the dinosaur' for 'Pass the milk, please.' Many people lose language altogether – aphasia: in the worst cases, left-side stroke-victims will have to relearn what words mean, and how to use them. (One woman I spoke to during convalescence, Annie Bristowe, a vigorous forty-two-year-old, discovered after her stroke that her accent, which had been 'somewhere between Cheltenham and Chelsea', had become perfectly Scottish, 'like Janet out of *Dr Finlay's Casebook*'.) Another famous case is the stroke suffered by the playwright, and author of *A Man For All Seasons*, Robert Bolt. Like me, Bolt was treated at the National Hospital but, as his secretary puts it, 'It was very difficult to understand exactly what he was thinking because his speech was so impaired. He was tailoring his thoughts to what he thought he could say, so what came out was very simple. He found "yes" difficult, so he'd say "of course" which has overtones to it. You had to keep thinking, he doesn't really mean that. He kept saying to a doctor that he had to tell Phil Hurricane something. No one knew who Phil Hurricane was.' It turned out that 'Phil Hurricane' was Bolt's secretary, Gill Harrison.

I, at least, still had my voice, but it sounded peculiar to me, and I was finding it hard to enunciate properly. When I slowed down, my speech was fine but tremendously effortful. I became terribly angry about this disability, and Sarah noted that I showed flashes of anger when practising to pronounce strings of swear words, an exercise Dr Whurr had suggested. In the absence of firm direction from the neurologists, Sarah and I tended to quiz Dr Whurr for independent corroboration about my chances of recovery. In her diary, Sarah wrote that,

'She [Renata] seems to feel he'll be all right, but maybe he'll walk with a limp which sounds fine – except that there is such a wide variation in "limp". It just seems like such a small thing to me at the moment, a limp, given everything else – but I know that even that can be devastating.'

In the week following the stroke I had been unable to look in a mirror, and I was beginning to worry about my appearance. On Monday 7 August I noted in my diary,

I shave sitting in the bath, looking at my reflection in the bath taps. I have not seen my face in a mirror since I fell ill, and I'm frightened at what I might find. (In fact, apart from a slightly drooping left side to my face and an expression of great sadness, I find that I am not a freak.) Afterwards I clean my teeth one-handed with considerable difficulty [*it's suprisingly hard to unscrew a tube of toothpaste one-handed*] and get given fresh clothes. Then I am wheeled back to my room. Now I am sitting in a chair with my headache and Sarah is on the phone. Sarah seems to have understood my condition very well, and is tremendously organized. She is being quite amazing. At 12.15 Dr Whurr comes in. She arrives half an hour after Dr Lees who has pronounced my progress to be 'very encouraging'.

This morning Sarah read to me from *Alice in Wonderland* once again and we laughed together over Bill the Lizard. It occurs to me that as a patient I am regressing to a state of childhood in some ways, surrounded by parents, waited on hand and foot. I feel like a child, and helpless like a child too.

When I read my notes now I'm reminded that I became at times quite irritated by the intrusions of the medical profession, and wanted to be left alone with my fatigue, which was still overwhelming: 'All these professionals feel they have the right to ask impertinent questions – Q: "Are you depressed?" A: "Yes, but it's none of your business." Q: "How does your speech sound to you?" Answer: "Blurred." It turns out that I am reading too quickly. To top it all, yesterday, I bit my tongue as I was eating. It is still very painful.' Half my tongue was still paralysed: I could not feel or control its movement inside my mouth.

I feel shattered. It's been hell – and with each day, a fresh round of horror to deal with. Robert's stroke is really quite severe – nine days into it, he still can't move his left arm and his left leg, and his speech is quite thick and stuttery, because he's numb on the left side of his face. His mind isn't affected, but he's so very depressed and so very exhausted that it's torture spending time with him. I'm so relieved he's not dead. I'm so scared he'll have to be in a wheelchair. I'm so scared that what we've had together – the wonderful flushes of first love, but hardly years of time built up together to cushion blows like this – will all evaporate now, and that our life together will never be good again. I'm scared that what we've had will evaporate for him, that he'll remember it as some distant flash of memory, that what we'll have to do is get to know each other again, in a new way, filled with this bitterness (and my bewilderment, and anger, and fear) that this has happened to us. I think – I think – I worry – that I'm just not strong enough to bear it.

I keep thinking: If he's okay in three months, in six months, in a year – he'll be okay. But what if he comes home, and he can't walk properly? How will he handle it? How will I? I can't be strong enough for both of us, and R. has such a hard time expressing his feelings – such a hard time, it was just starting to change, things were just starting to get so wonderful, he was being so sweet and so cuddly and such a good husband – and I worry that it'll all go back to some horrible situation, where he hates me and where our life together doesn't mean anything at all.

There are moments I feel that almost approximate happiness. Tiny little moments, when I forget, when the phone rings and I think it'll be him, saying, 'Hello, Mrs Wife,' and we'll be planning our evening together. Then I can disassociate myself from it, and say, 'Robert's had a stroke,' and consider it just as a fact from far away – not as an organic reality whose implications will reverberate for months and years to come.

My concerns, meanwhile, were strictly practical:

8 AUGUST
I think the worst part of being so helpless is the nurses' attention to one's inevitable 'bowel movements'. Two nurses lift me onto the 'commode', a wheelchair with a hole in the middle. Then they wheel you into the lavatory, pull your pants down and leave you to it. When you've finished you pull a kind of communication cord [*setting off a buzzer at the nurses' station*] and they come and wipe you down and wheel you back to bed. It's messy and humiliating and I dread it. How low and/or helpless can one become?

On some days, the highs and lows seemed to follow each other in a confusing procession and my mood would seesaw wildly. When I was able to show Dr Lees the movement in my left leg – my left arm, hand and foot were still paralysed – Sarah's diary reflects our excitement:

WEDNESDAY 9 AUGUST

Signs of hope. R. is speaking much more clearly and beginning to move little things – flexing his leg, from side to side, as he sits in the chair. Today he stood more or less by himself. Dr Lees said it looked very very encouraging and the physiotherapist came by and looked at him and said he would definitely walk again (how well, I suppose we don't know just yet. We don't know how much of it depends on his own will and how much on what's going on in his brain). I feel resigned to six horrific months, so long as there is hope at the end of it.

Meanwhile, the investigation into the chambers of my heart was scheduled to continue a few streets away at the Middlesex Hospital, a journey that, in my helpless state, involved being stretchered in and out by ambulance, a laborious procedure that reminded me, as I watched the workaday world hurrying past, how 'disabled' I'd become.

MY DIARY: THURSDAY 10 AUGUST

Sarah arrived like a breath of fresh air, or like a ray of sunshine, at eight-fifteen. I have had a poor night and a very early wake-up, so it's wonderful to see her. Yesterday afternoon, after the tests on my heart, as I waited at the Middlesex, helplessly, for the ambulance, I found myself reflecting grimly on what it means to be disabled, and in a wheelchair. In the waiting room there's a huge box labelled 'Human Blood'. I wonder whose?

It was during this visit to the Middlesex that I found myself confronting my incapacity in my mind and making a kind of resolution to resist it, come what may. As I put it in my diary:

> I made a kind of private vow to myself that I will not be in this state for long, if I can possibly help it. Being a patient is, as the word implies, totally passive. You are dependent upon the nurses; you are always saying thank you and falling in with the nurses' jokey routines. If you don't, you become a 'bad' patient, to be punished in all kinds of subtle but unmistakable ways. The point is to be passive and appreciative.
>
> Yesterday, I had what I think of as that *Alice in Wonderland* feeling again. Queen: 'Sentence first, verdict afterwards.' (And the fact that the words don't come out right, like Alice.) I wrote four postcards this afternoon – with instant tiredness and some difficulty, but ultimately a sense of achievement: communication achieved, despite everything!

The reality of my office was never far away during these weeks. The Faber headquarters, at No. 3 Queen Square, were, as the crow flies, barely two hundred yards away, facing the National Hospital. I was always conscious of my professional life just across the frontier of ill-health. Inevitably, with so much time on my hands, my thoughts returned to the beginning of my life in publishing. One particular evening, a celebration dinner for Peter Carey's first book, *The Fat Man In History*, lodged intransigently in my mind. The dinner was held by Matthew Evans at his home in Canonbury Place and we all drank so much wine that when Matthew woke up next morning he later said (I remembered in hospital) that he thought he'd 'had a stroke'.

A smoked salmon salad has just arrived from the River Café – at first I was a bit embarrassed by Ruth Rogers' extraordinary generosity, now I'm just incredibly grateful – and my room is full of delicious smells. Mum and Dad have just arrived, faintly scandalized by these scenes of luxury. When they are in the hospital they behave as if visiting a school on Speech Day, very gracious and grateful, with words of interest and encouragement to all concerned. Sarah returns at about six, and we watch the closing stage of the first day of the Test match on TV. She announces that her new shrink has told her to tune into her inner being, to see what is in her nature.

Horrible, fretful, fretful dreams. I dream that I was with someone who fell down a hole and no one knew. I just left him there, to die, and felt that I had murdered him (R? Probably). I think I then murdered someone else – there was a horrible scene where I set up a whole party for this person – food and drink and everything – and I pretended to wait for him to come when I knew he never would. And then there was a scene of carnage, where another woman went crazy and shot a lot of people and my own crimes were overlooked in the confusion. I let everyone think that it was she who had killed the people I had killed. Then someone came with me (someone who believed the story that I was innocent) back to the place where I had been living and helped me remove my things.

The idea was that I was leaving for Europe for a year

or so, and that I would travel on my own with just a few possessions and that it was something I felt I should have done long ago. But I was going with this enormous weight of guilt upon me.

I'm really not very hard to read, am I? I look at Robert sitting there (he is reading the newspaper, folded on a tray in front of him for convenience) and I'm filled with so much love for him, and so much fear for the future.

Evening. It's so hard to be back at work, because it reminds me of the lovely luxury of normal life. Walking around, coming and going as you please, making telephone calls – all the things R. can't do, at the moment. I feel so guilty that I can, and so angry that when the phone rings it's not him with authority in his voice saying, 'What's happening?'

As my recovery stretched into its second week my initial fears that I might suffer a second, and more severe, 'insult' began to recede. Obviously I was getting better. However, I was still terribly confused, chiefly about the passage of time.

MY DIARY: FRIDAY 11 AUGUST
I calculate that I have been ill for about ten days, though I'm not sure about this. I don't feel dangerously unwell, though paralysed of course, but I suppose I was very ill for a day or two.

Today there is a big scandal in the ward. A chap in the room at the end has refused surgery. This is unheard of, and everybody is up in arms.

Like patients the world over, I became very attached to the nurses in the Nuffield. I found them amusing, sexy, attentive and, of course, tremendously caring. How could I not? This was an intense period of my life, and they were an intimate part of it. Occasionally, as I began to get better, one or two of them would come into my room towards the end of their duty hours and sit at the foot of my bed, and we'd chat. I'd learn about the ways of the hospital, who they liked and disliked; who was well and who was sick; who was mending, who was not. There was a secret narrative to the Nuffield ward of which I was just a tiny part, and it was intriguing to find out about the neurological dramas in the adjoining rooms. There were all kinds of tiny nuances to hospital life of which I was totally unaware, and of which I gradually got the hang the longer I stayed there. When individual nurses went on holiday, I found I missed them intensely. When my favourite nurse, Julia Baretta, came back from her holiday I wrote, 'Julia is back today, thank God!' Meanwhile, the routine went on, seemingly at a snail's pace.

My diary: 11 August
It's a long hot day outside, but cool in here, and Dr Whurr is about to arrive for speech therapy. In physiotherapy this afternoon, supported by Sandy, my delightful Scots physiotherapist, I managed to shuffle a few faltering steps using only my 'good' right leg, a very odd feeling.

At about five, Mark [*my brother*] comes to visit me with some crayons, a very nice, extremely thoughtful present which cheers me up considerably. After he's gone I start to do a drawing for Anna [*my niece*] about a tree-monster in Cambridge. My thoughts turn back to childhood and I find I am crying uncontrollably and have to stop.

Then I find that I have this fixed idea that something will happen at six o'clock. What? Nothing happens. I have to learn to slow down mentally. I also discover that my sense of time is very peculiar: I often can't tell the late afternoon hours from each other – or the morning hours, for that matter. I will stare at the clock and try to figure out what hour it is – five or seven? – admit defeat and give up.

The routine of the hospital never varied. There was an inexorable rhythm to each day – meals followed by exercises – that became evocative of school. Visitors provided the only interruption to the routine, but often I was simply too tired to see them. Once the first crisis of the stroke had passed and I was left battling fatigue and depression, the days merged into each other in a weird narcoleptic blur that the regular entries in my diary hardly convey. In the evening I'd be given Dothiepin (Prothiaden). This was partly an anti-depressant and partly a sleeping pill, and it made me extremely lethargic in the morning, and contributed to the drugged atmosphere I seemed to be living in.

MY DIARY: 11 AUGUST

I am reading Marcus Aurelius' *Meditations* in the 60p Penguin edition (a perfect size and weight for one-handed reading) and today found this passage: 'In the life of a man, his time is but a moment, his being an incessant flux, his senses a dim rushlight, his body a prey of worms, his soul an unquiet eddy, his fortune dark, and his fame doubtful. In short, all that is of the body is as coursing waters, all that is of the soul as dreams and vapours; life a warfare, a brief sojourning in an alien land; and after repute, oblivion.' I read this through a veil of tears with a shock of recognition, as if spoken to across a vast abyss of time and history.

Wordsworth, famously, spoke of poetry as emotion recollected in tranquillity. In hospital, I experienced memory as emotion recollected in immobility. When I tried to attach precise months and years to the things that had happened to me I was often forced to admit that much of what had taken place seemed fuzzy and indistinct. The eighties returned to me as a brilliant kaleidoscope of work, alcohol, travel, sex and insomnia. I wouldn't have missed it for the world, and I didn't. Publishing in that decade seemed at times to be as much about extravagant hospitality as about the struggles of the unknown writer. And yet, when I went back to 1981, there was none of the euphoria or excitement people now associate with the eighties.

The mid-eighties also saw the launch of *The Story of English*, the television series I'd worked on during the previous four years. When I look at the programmes now I cannot imagine how I was able to find the time both to research and write the scripts, and also to be an effective editor at Queen Square. I seemed to have so much energy then; we all did. In the quest for explanations, some people suggested, perhaps predictably, that I'd had the stroke from overwork, but there's no medical evidence to support this. There are things you do when you're young that defy analysis. The programmes were a huge success in America, largely thanks to the popularity of our presenter, Robert MacNeil; the accompanying book spent several weeks on the *New York Times* bestseller lists; for a few months in 1986 my feet hardly touched the ground. I was thirty-three then, and thought I was immortal.

SARAH'S DIARY: 11 AUGUST

It's amazing how quickly you can move from the world of the well into the world of the sick. I, who was so worried about the indignities of pregnancy, and who have always been so faint-hearted about and repelled by the idea of hospital and sick people, am now conversant with a whole new culture. I think of all the things that could have happened, that could have been worse: R. could have had a head injury or broken his spine or had his arm mangled in a meat-rendering machine, or been blinded by a shard of flying glass, or been hit by a car and broken every bone in his body.

Small improvements each day. R's speech is improving a lot, but he is still speaking with a stutter and slurring a little, and so I hope that he will be fine soon – it'll make it so much easier for him to communicate. And it will improve his spirits too. The last week has been a real testament to anti-depressants already. I'm still so afraid.

As I began to recover, my responses to the outside world became sharper. Within two weeks of the initial 'insult' I was once again becoming conscious, as I had not been for several days, of the passage of time, and the frustrations of delay:

MY DIARY: SATURDAY 12 AUGUST

At the weekend, even the BUPA-sponsored Nuffield goes half-speed. At twelve o'clock the standby physiotherapist came, and we did basic manoeuvres for about an hour. By the end I was exhausted, and then slept like a log. I am getting more competent at basic standing, but my speech is still very slurred, I think. It's frustrating, but I am slowly getting over the first shock of the stroke. I have to find time to get my equilibrium back. Mum and Dad came to visit, Sarah went shopping and I had the regular Nuffield lunch: soup, sandwiches and fruit, none of it very appealing to eat. Taste, and the pleasure in food, has gone.

Then they took me out into Queen Square in the wheelchair. I felt sorry for my parents, having to wheel me around at their advanced age [*actually, neither was then yet 70*] and at a time when I should be looking after them, not vice versa. I think they have been stunned by the experience of my being in hospital with a stroke, though of course they will not admit it.

Back in the ward I read some more Marcus Aurelius and then slept heavily. Later on, Julio Etchart came by, and we chatted about our foreign trips together, especially East Timor, which seems very far away, very remote and, now, quite impossible.

Tonight – it is now seven o'clock – I slept three or four hours, and still feel very sleepy. I find I think about sex a lot, having sex with the nurses – silly stuff, but hard to put out of my mind, not having had sex for so long. [*One of the first things I did when I came round at University College Hospital was to check, with my good right hand, that I could still have an erection. I could.*] I am also keen to get back to my laptop word processor as soon as possible if I can. I have become obsessed by the names on the hospital furniture. I lie in bed staring at the ceiling or the wall or the television screen or the door frame . . . All the articles of furniture here seem to have been made by a company called Nesbit Evans.

To pass the time, and to test my memory, I find myself trying to remember, alphabetically, author by author, the Faber list. Does this mean I am going crazy?

It would be several months before I faced up to the fact that the half-baked wish of my 'old' life had come true, and that I could no longer function as the editor-in-chief of Faber & Faber.

[8]

'Not a Drooling Vegetable'

12–24 August

> I never travel without my diary. One should always have
> something sensational to read in the train.
>
> Oscar Wilde: *The Importance of Being Earnest*

Cyril Connolly's *Enemies of Promise* is often quoted
by English writers for its identification of the ultimate
threat to a young writer's creativity, 'the pram in
the hall'. For me, during my years at Faber & Faber,
there was another passage that used to haunt my
imagination almost as profoundly. 'As repressed sadists
are supposed to become policemen or butchers,' writes
Connolly, 'so those with an irrational fear of life become
publishers.' Perhaps Connolly's intuition is fundament-
ally accurate, but speaking for myself I found that
my life as a publisher overflowed with activity and
incident and interest, especially in retrospect. In the
National Hospital, I continued to review my nearly
twenty years at Faber & Faber. Lying on your back in
bed for two months, virtually unable to move, is a
strange experience. Immobility made even the slightest
and most trivial events from the past seem historical.

Everything, the smallest thing, assumed a heightened significance to me. I traced extraordinary imaginary journeys across the fissures and vacant spaces of the ceiling. I stared at the little square of blue that signified the outside world, and wondered about my place in it. Often I reflected on the moments of recent history I'd watched from the sidelines.

There was, for instance, that house I'd negotiated to buy in the spring of 1992. The day I arrived the place was empty, but I was still uneasy about going in. I stood on the doorstep with the key, nervously looking over my shoulder. There was a huge pile of rubbish in the area outside, and junk mail, stuffed through the letterbox, drifting glossily on the doormat within. Inside, it was gloomy, brown and dank. The hall light didn't work, but once I got the shutters open, I could see what was what. Books, clothes, an empty wine glass. The previous occupants had obviously left in a hurry. Well, I could fix that. On the top floor there was a wonderful writing room, filled with light and sunshine. A huge ink stain on the carpet indicated where the last owner had had his desk. He'd already told me he'd written his book up here. I searched up and down, but could find no other evidence of *The Satanic Verses*. The books on the shelves dated to February 1989, which was when the Iranians imposed the *fatwa*, and when Salman Rushdie had fled into hiding. Being here now was rather like visiting the *Marie Celeste*. For the first few months after I moved in I wondered anxiously about the likelihood of an assault on the house by an Iranian hit-squad, though the Special Branch had given every kind of assurance that the house was safe.

It often occurred to me in hospital that my house in St Peter's Street had witnessed more than its fair share of personal catastrophe. Occasionally, when the doctors spoke of my eventual return home – an idea that was becoming an increasingly important part of my personal, convalescent agenda – I found myself dreading the idea of going back to the place in which I might have died.

The doctors are, for the first time, making optimistic pronouncements. Dr Lees said he was very encouraged. Dr Whurr the speech therapist (R. calls her 'Dr Click') said I should stop worrying, that from now on it was all recovery; and that he will be all right. What he will be like physically at the end of this process still remains to be seen – the physiotherapist who saw him today said we could expect three months – three months! – in the rehab centre and then that he won't have a normal gait (her word) at the end of it all. I think it is probably too early to predict. It seems that a lot of it depends upon how well his brain heals on its own. But yesterday for the first time I felt something very near to happiness. I felt that this will be all right in the end. It will be a weird feeling and a massive change of life, to spend the next three months more or less apart, with me here in London at the home I consider Robert's more than mine, and him in hospital, in a hospital learning to walk again. The poor, poor thing. I look at him lying in bed asleep (the physiotherapy tires him out terribly) and wonder if he actually comprehends what he is in for. I hope the two of us can weather this. I'm convinced that if he can, I can. He's snoring the tiniest bit, lying on his back stretched out to the length of the bed in blue shorts and a green shirt, his hair is soft and shiny and falling nicely. His body is wonderful. He could be at home asleep.

It's cooler today. Dr Click [*Whurr*] came by at twelve o'clock. I am making good progress with my speech, apparently, but I must remember to practise. Apparently, some stroke survivors can't even swallow: it can take six months to get them able to do this. In the middle of the morning Ish [*Kazuo Ishiguro*] visited. It was very nice to see him. He was quite frisky and admitted he was relieved to find I was still myself. [*As a child, he'd known a relative who'd suffered a severe left-side stroke, and had bad memories of profound neurological trauma.*] The truth is that the visitor's assumption of the patient's incapacity runs deep. And not just the visitor's, either. For example, there's a Mr Kemal, one of several Arabs here, down the hall. The nurses order him around as if he was stone deaf and/or mentally retarded. 'Come on, Mr Kemal. Do you want some lunch, *lunch*? LUNCH? A bit of fish, a piece of *chicken*, CHICKEN?' Why do people become nurses, I wonder?

Even the good nurses have no idea how much they can hurt, how much hurt they can cause by wrenching my left arm, which is still totally paralysed and helpless, at the wrong moment. There's one nurse who causes pain every day. She is loud, brash and infuriating. I think she must be insecure. But the others, Colette, Julia, Linda, the Scottish lady and Mamie the West Indian, are all great, and I have become very fond of them.

Hospital food: pâté and cold toast, chicken Kiev, soggy vegetables, chips, salads, summer pudding.

I realize now when I think about it that I was last in hospital when I was (I think) about ten years old. I remember the whole experience of the anaesthetic, the surgeon counting 1, 2, 3 . . . and the fading from consciousness, and the big children's ward that I was in, all those years ago in Reading, and then being at home, lying in bed watching black-and-white TV with my leg in plaster, and the real fear that I would never walk again. And now – strange irony – I can't walk at all.

We're getting into a real routine – I come in in the morning, go to work [*at the* New York Times' *London bureau*] in the afternoon, and come back in the evening. Tonight we watched a video of our wedding for the first time together. When we got to Robert's speech, he did something I had never really seen him do before – he started to cry. I had been trying so hard to get him to talk about how he feels. But now he's starting to talk about it more, and what he says is quite astonishing and quite encouraging, that he feels philosophical and ruminative, and that he's regarding the whole next phase of his life (the learning to walk phase) as a project, a goal. I pray that he will keep feeling that way and not get discouraged or feel sorry for himself. When he cried I wondered if he was crying for the lost self he saw in the video. He said earlier that he felt sad because we had been so happy and doing so nicely together before this happened, and that's how I feel too. It seems so cruel. But then, but then. I read recently about someone who had a cerebral aneurysm and who fell into a coma and died, and then . . . Reg Gadney [*a thriller writer published by Faber*] tells us about his sister who died of a massive stroke six weeks ago. I feel I want to shout thanks to the heavens. He's alive and the worst is over and I can bear the rest.

MY DIARY: 14 AUGUST
It is now two weeks since I came here, and although it

seems an age, in another sense it's no time at all. Today a nice bunch of letters from America. I have received some extraordinary letters since I first came here, a whole sackful, in fact, with some very nice thoughts from the most unlikely people. I realize that people have been extremely shocked by what has happened to me – and more shocked than I have been in some ways – although I have perhaps not yet come to terms with what's happened.

While I continued to adjust to what had happened, my doctors were already planning to move me out of the National, where bed-space was at a premium, to a longer-term specialist rehabilitation hospital where I could concentrate on reactivating the parts of my body that were no longer functioning. I was offered a choice of two, including the Devonshire, an institution renowned among physiotherapists for the comprehensive service it offers the rehab patient. Sarah, true to her American attitude to health care, was determined to check out the facilities herself rather than take a doctor's word for them.

MY DIARY: 14 AUGUST
Sarah has just gone off with Matthew [*Evans*] to inspect the Devonshire Hospital, and I have Mahler's third symphony playing on the Walkman. I am slowly learning to accept my condition, but the point about it is that I have no real idea how ill I have been, or might be again.

At this time I still feared a recurrence of the stroke, a recurrence that would kill me, I was certain. In fact, the likelihood of such was extremely slight, and not long into my convalescence Dr Greenwood reassured me

that, statistically speaking, I was extremely unlikely ever
to suffer a stroke again.

Today I managed to sit on the commode and have a
good 'bowel movement' (the nursing euphemism) after
lunch. Amazing how much things like this come to
matter when you're a patient – I have become quite
obsessed by my digestive processes, in short by my
bowels. No nice way to say this. The nurses always refer
to it in that way. They say, 'Have we opened our bowels
today?' rather as if they were asking, 'Have we opened
our post today?' Which I find hilarious. That is their big
concern, I suppose. Besides death, constipation is the
big fear in hospitals.

My face feels still numb around the jaw, as if I have
had an injection from the dentist. It has been this way
for some days now, but seems to be wearing off slowly.
My speech, though slurred and difficult, is better than it
was. I have made a note here to look up the word
'autoclaving', a word that seems to be written on the
bottles that are given to us for urinating into.

Some of the other patients, especially the Arab diplo-
matic staff who occupy many of the other rooms here,
seem to bargain and haggle over the cost of rooms, so if
a room costs sixty pounds, they'll haggle and say 'How
about twenty-five?' One of the nurses said skittishly the
other day that they sometimes expected to be paid with
a string of goats or sheep. There are, in fact, a lot of
Arab patients here and thus a lot of Arab jokes. Mr
Haifa next door is known as 'Jaffa Cake'. His visitors
stand on my balcony and smoke cigarettes in the evening
and chat, as if they were in Beirut.

Today in the elevator I encountered my worst fear, a

twenty-something woman with a neat incision in her head, a shaved skull, and stitching like a rugby ball. She smiled at me in a glazed way, but did not speak, and we passed like ships in the night, and I found myself thinking about her all afternoon. This is what I was afraid of when they first brought me in – the fear that they would cut me open and operate on my brain. But apparently they don't do this now; they used to, but don't any more.

The thing about Queen Square is that there are all sorts and conditions of people here, often very acute cases, and you do see some extraordinary sights. In the physiotherapy ward there is an elderly, emaciated Arab gentleman who has what are known as 'antlers' on his head. This is a kind of metal brace designed to keep his head upright on his spine. It looks very peculiar, but I have got quite used to it now. There is also an AIDS victim suffering from brain damage, who drools and groans, and can't stand upright. He is very haggard-looking and very sick, with Kaposi's sarcoma all over his face.

TUESDAY 15 AUGUST

Last night I had a terrible headache which stopped me sleeping. For a while I wondered what would happen if I just conked out there and then. The nights are often the worst – the night is a time of fear, and wondering if I will survive. I feel very lonely and frightened then. I found myself going over the previous six hours and wondering what Sarah would say if she found me dead, and how she would cope. I love her so much, and she has been so wonderful while I have been here.

While we were watching our wedding video, I found myself crying uncontrollably. Partly they were tears of rage and tears of frustration, and tears of love for Sarah in her predicament, and tears of happiness that I should be married to her – to someone as wonderful as her, and perhaps tears of relief, too. One thing I really admire is the way Sarah continues to work at her journalism while visiting me in hospital.

Today I have a new physiotherapist, John, who is small and wiry and dark, and rather good. He is much less pernickety than Sandy the amusing Scot has been, and concentrates on my legs. At the moment there is no movement from the left arm, but there are a few 'flickers' (that's the word they all use) in the left leg, and I can now sort of raise it up so that my knee is bent when I am lying in bed.

It's another boiling hot day. There are standpipes in Yorkshire, on the television. Today I discover that Dr Click's husband is a publisher of educational books, which explains why she has been so keen to discuss books each day. I also discovered that Dr Lees's first name is Andy or Andrew, not Adrian, as I had thought. (He still seems to me like an Adrian, not an Andy.)

I still find I can't keep track of time. I don't know why this is.

The headache makes me feel very irritated with the inefficiency of the ward. It's still not clear when the [*illegible*] people will come, or when will I have the final transoesophagal cardiogram test at the Middlesex Hospital. I think back over the first two days after the stroke, and remember lovely Wicce St Clair Hawkins, the tawny-haired nurse who was so kind and thoughtful to me in the beginning.

This morning, en route from my bath, I meet nice Dr Lees in the hall. For some reason, I feel intensely embarrassed to encounter him out of bed and so obviously vulnerable in my wheelchair. He tells me he is still trying to track the causes of the stroke, and says he has found antibodies in my thyroid, but no clot in the chambers of the heart. I am too unsure of myself to ask what any of this means, in practice. He says, none the less, that he wants to do the transoesophagal cardiogram, an investigation of the chambers of the heart.

Susan [*Sarah's mother*] rings from Maine. She sounds to be in fighting form, and it will be nice to have her back here soon. She has been so wonderfully supportive during these difficult weeks.

I discovered today that Sarah is also writing what she calls a 'psycho-diary'. God knows what she is putting in it – probably complaints about my bad temper during these last few days. One of the things about the irritation of being in hospital is that there are so few people you can take your irritation out on. So she has become a lightning conductor for my rage. The one thing that will always calm me down, I've found, is being read to. Sarah has a fine reading voice, very pleasant and soothing and I look forward to our reading sessions. *The Lion, the Witch and the Wardrobe* brings back so many memories of childhood. We sit in a shady green part of Queen's Square, and read aloud to each other, or rather, Sarah reads aloud to me. She reads very pleasantly, and it's restful to sit in the cool of the evening, watching the winos on the benches in the distance while the gnats buzz over our heads in the twilight.

It was the measure of my loss of confidence in myself after the stroke that my biggest fear on these outings was that I'd run into someone from the Faber office across the square. At this stage, it was still my ambition to recover enough fitness to be able to resume my old life as editor-in-chief. The more my convalescence unfolded the more I came to recognize that I could not possibly cross the square back to my old job. At first, the constraint was physical; as time went on, the reservation became psychological. It seemed depressing to acknowledge that forty-odd years had been tossed casually into the dustbin of history.

> I dread seeing a colleague [*I wrote in my diary*] to whom I'll have to explain myself. We always choose a time when everyone's gone home, i.e. after seven o'clock, and on the whole we aren't disturbed. We go to the far end, behind the statue of Queen Charlotte, and sit under the trees. I have taken this square for granted for so long, have walked through it and round it, not thinking, and now here I am, an integrated part of its little eco-system, and I am quite a bit grateful for the greenery I can experience here. I do occasionally feel very sad that I can't have more of the summer to myself.

The dusty trees of Heaven and bedraggled rose-bushes of the square became all the more precious as battered, metropolitan representatives of the English countryside that I could otherwise glimpse only on television.

MY DIARY: WEDNESDAY 16 AUGUST
Today, a very cheery visit from Robert Harris [*friend, and author of* Fatherland], who arrived with some Fortnum and Mason biscuits and a bottle of Krug vintage champagne. What a good friend he is! People say the most extraordinary things in hospitals – Robert said he felt 'very envious of my experience'. I think he intended a joke, but I was not in a mood for irony and said, rather coolly, that he was welcome to it. We agreed that would

both have dinner at the Manoir au Quat' Saisons with Raymond Blanc when I get out. Apparently Raymond Blanc had a stroke some years ago, and has now made a full recovery. Well, that's some kind of role model.

I know it's going to be a long haul. But it's hard to adjust to that. I dreamed last night that I had polio [*her father had suffered polio as a child*] and couldn't walk. For a bit – but that when I started to recover Robert still had it far more seriously. I felt pathetic and weak and sorry for myself, while my side was paralysed. I keep wondering what this is like for him. I feel very alone and very scared. I look at him – I know it's not fair – and I pray that his leg and arm will start to move again – right now. The doctor has just come in and said there is no way to predict what he'll be like in 12 months' time. Robert has a raging headache again. I am so afraid that it means that something else will happen. I think I will always be afraid, for the rest of our lives. If it was bad before, my worry is a hundred times worse now. Everything seems so precarious. It's hard not to feel a real panic, a constant sense of being overwhelmed, as if you're drowning.

It's getting better, but slowly, and the people you deal with in positions of authority really are quite unable to offer much reassurance. The thing is, I think they don't know. Robert's left leg is moving a bit, and also his left shoulder, but not his arm at all. His speech is almost back to normal, except when he talks quickly – then he tends to stutter. My moods go so up and down – euphoria when he seems to be making progress, despair when he doesn't, a sense of dread all the time. The hard part is the feeling that you have to have all the optimism in the world to help the person get better, while preparing yourself for the very worst outcome. I'm not sure how to get both of those at once. People say I should take it one day at a time, but that's hard to do.

MY DIARY: THURSDAY 17 AUGUST
The Middlesex [*Hospital*] has just rung: I may not eat or drink till all the tests are done today. This is because of the anaesthetic I shall have to take for the transoesophagal operation. So the thing about being a patient is that you have to accept whatever the medical profession decides, without complaint, and if, like the guy down the hall, you refuse or disobey, there's a big crisis.

A bit later Dr Chandra – young, impressive, well dressed – comes in to describe what the next lot of tests will be like. There will be a camera down my throat, then another blood test. He says that after six weeks they can make a fairly good prediction of what sort of recovery I should have in the long term.

The operating staff, in their green gowns, float about the hospital like actors backstage. In the operating theatre they are on stage of course, and this is where the real drama is. The back of the hospital is just like a Richard Rogers building run amok – blackened air vents and wrought-iron fire escapes. The building roars like a hive of bees in the hot sun, and I sense that microbes, perhaps a hundred years old, are lurking in the rust of the metal. There is a curious intimacy in a hospital – nobody has anything to hide. Once you are here you have to expose every part of your body to the nurses. There's no privacy. As well as this, you are weak and they are strong. This can make nurses seem like sadists or authoritarians.

The truth is that [*the members of*] the medical profession hate a mystery, though actually they live with it every day of their working lives; they have to know the reasons for things, and they have to be in control. The thing then about having a stroke is that they don't know why it happened, and they are not in control. As a patient, all you can do is to lie here, and allow time to take its course, and time to heal. There is no other cure. If I was in an African village I would have no different a treatment: the fact is that I have had almost no medication since I arrived here, apart from anti-depressants, and the only future medication will probably be an aspirin a day.

Today the nice Chinese nurse Philippe (the one they all call 'Phirrip'!) gave me a mirror to shave with. I find myself with a sad, defeated expression that reflects my inner mood after nearly a month here. The good news is that at least my facial appearance is not hideously deformed, as I believe it can be.

Several months later, when I came to read *The Diving Bell and the Butterfly* I encountered, in Jean-Dominique's Bauby's description of his appearance after *his* terrible stroke, the actualization of my worst fears at this time:

Reflected in the windowpane I saw the head of a man who seemed to have emerged from a vat of formaldehyde. His mouth was twisted, his nose damaged, his hair tousled, his gaze full of fear. One eye was sewn shut, the other goggled like the doomed eye of Cain. For a moment I stared at that dilated pupil before I realized it was only mine.

In fact, many of the people who came to visit remarked on how well, and young, I looked, comments which seemed, to me, cruelly at odds with my inner feelings.

Today I had routine physiotherapy in the morning with John Marsden, then I went across to the Middlesex, and had the camera shoved down my throat. First they sprayed my throat with a kind of cocaine substitute or substance designed to freeze the throat. Then they give you a mild shot of anaesthetic to lull you, and then they stick a camera smeared with jelly down your throat, and then they film you from inside the throat, or rather, they film the back of the heart from inside the throat.

The doctors said I was a good patient, and I certainly did my best to put up with the pain and difficulty of the operation as easily as possible.

It was nice to go to the Middlesex Hospital by ambulance and see something of the outside world, to see the people walking along the street and the life outside, the life I have been missing these last several days.

In the evening Sarah read to me from 'Narnia', and then we had a glass of wine, and then we had a visit from Roger Alton, of the *Guardian*, who was very cheery.

Jeremy Paxman sent me some champagne with an amusing letter, which was kind, and I also had a letter from Ish [Kazuo Ishiguro] to say how glad he was to see me much better than he'd expected. This seems to be the general reaction from visitors, who expect the worst.

Saturday 19 August

Sarah took me into the square this morning, where it suddenly occurred to me that the russet brick of the National is the same russet brick as the russet brick of Pont Street and the Cadogan Hotel, a kind of Devonshire red, and of course built at about the same time. I found myself wondering about the architect involved (and the brickworks) and then my thoughts spun on to Oscar Wilde's arrest at the Cadogan. When I analysed this to myself I decided that it was because I felt as though I too had been arrested. On the way out we passed a man with his head stitched like a second-hand football the whole way round, but he was actually walking, and seemed to be okay. You do see the most extraordinary sights in the National.

In the afternoon I watched the VJ victory parade on television – Ghurkas and veterans all in their sixties and seventies, like my father. The thing about the veterans of the Second World War is the self-satisfaction they have, the look of real survivors from a world our world has forgotten. They seem curiously proud, though presumably their memories are full of pain and sorrow. You don't have to be in your seventies, either. How often as schoolboys did we parade in front of war memorials with the 'Names of the Fallen'. I realize as I watch that this is the world I grew up with at school, as a child or as a boy – a world of Spitfires and Colonel Bogey and American jeeps, Lancaster bombers and khaki, and the many war stories from people who had survived. To see the troops marching down the Mall was to see an empire in full retreat, oddly enough, and to see eccentric items of clothing one hasn't seen for years, topis and khaki felt hats and strange uniforms with brassy medals, full of memories but meaningless too, to a new generation. As I watched this parade the room was filled with the smell of cigar-smoke from the visiting Arabs in the hallway outside.

In the evening I read the first two chapters of Reg Gadney's new novel, but I still find I can't concentrate for more than 30–45 minutes at a stretch.

I can say now that I think he's going to come through this. I spoke to a friend of Steve and Cynthia's who told me about his stroke at the age of fifteen – one of dozens of accounts I have heard first and second hand – he was totally paralysed and couldn't speak or remember words, and now his foot doesn't flex on its own and his hand won't co-operate, but that's all. I can live with that sort of thing, but I feel this is a long slow march through a very humid jungle, full of insects. As Christine [*Robert's mother*] said: upwards all the way, but with jagged edges. Robert is becoming much stronger and moving his leg, but still not walking. His speech often sounds almost normal, but he is not talking a lot, and not quickly – I imagine because he is tired, but I am really not sure. He has a nagging, persistent fear that the change will be permanent. He is trying hard to be cheerful and succeed-ing mostly, but I can tell that he often feels quite blue. The most he will say, though, is that he feels fed up. I am slogging along, still exhausted, still waking up feeling worse than I did when I went to sleep. Every day no matter what, I wake up at five to seven. The heat is very wilting, so the windows are wide open. The noises, the cars, the traffic feel as if they are coming from the room. I am wearing swidgy yellow ear plugs and feeling ever weirder. Sara Mosle will be here this weekend, a wonder-ful help. It will be so nice to see her and it means I don't have to go home to an empty house at night. My parents-in-law reported yesterday that Dr Lees, the cool neurologist, spoke excitedly at Robert's progress, and said that at this rate he would be walking again soon. I assumed he wouldn't have said it unless it was very much the case, because from what I can tell, these guys are cautious and conservative and go far on the worst case side in making predictions.

MY DIARY: SUNDAY 20 AUGUST

At ten o'clock we went into the square, with Sarah pushing me as usual, and read newspapers until driven indoors by a gang of evangelicals singing hymns into a microphone, karaoke-style, on the other side of the square. Then we had lunch at the Queen's Larder, where there is a sign saying that the 'queen' of the Square is Queen Charlotte, George III's wife. Apparently when mad King George was in hospital here, during his time with Dr Willis in the 1770s, she used to keep delicacies for him in the pub (which became known as the Queen's Larder) and would visit him here. When I think of George and his wife I think of his delightful 'Mrs King'. After lunch I sunbathed in the wheelchair, and then fell asleep. Later, we went back to the room and I slept early.

On the whole, I do not remember my dreams at this time, and despite the extraordinary upheaval in my brain I cannot report any particularly vivid dream activity. If there is an exception to this observation it is that I had several sexual dreams, mostly adolescent fantasies. On several pages in my diary I find now that I've written, 'During my sleep I dreamed of sex once more.'

SARAH'S DIARY: 20 AUGUST

R. is beginning to clamour for big, fat non-fiction books, biographies and the like. 'Narnia' isn't doing it for him any more. He enjoyed the nostalgia of *The Lion, The Witch and the Wardrobe*, but reacted with highbrow indignation to *The Magician's Nephew*. These are good signs, I think. Everyone keeps asking me if he is going through personality changes. Quite a scary question, because the truth is I'm not sure: is he impatient and peremptory because of the combination of his normal self (before I came along) and the frustration of his condition, or because of a neurological problem?

Several visitors wanted to know if I had 'changed', a question that often came with enquiries about religion, and even now, two years later, it's a question I find hard to answer honestly. At one obvious level I have changed significantly; at another I feel myself to be just that: my self. For a while I had a strong fantasy of renewal and regeneration, and for a while it seemed as if I could begin my life again. Now, I know that this is just that, a fantasy, though a powerful one none the less. In one respect, however, I did change. I became less intolerant of difficulty.

MY DIARY: MONDAY 21 AUGUST

I have been nearly a month 'inside' today. Time has dragged very slowly, but I'm getting used to this slow passage of time, as I am to my situation.

My thoughts are still of the past, and of the 'truth' of the past. In some ways, I realize, this sequestration is parallel to the time I spent alone at school after my operation in nineteen-sixty-whatever it was. One thing that strikes me is that the Faber staff are being incredibly kind to Sarah, and that she and they have become friends, which is really rather nice. One of the great things about Sarah's having to look after herself in the outside world while I am here is that she meets my friends on her own terms rather than meeting them through me, which is probably a good way of doing things, and a good way for her to establish her own identity in London.

Last night I watched a programme about punks on the television. This brought back so many memories of first coming to London in the seventies, of living in the North End Road, near the Nashville Rooms, during the best/worst of Sid Vicious and the Sex Pistols. It's very odd how so much of the past seems to be coming back at the moment, at a time when I have so much time to think about the past and reflect on it all.

Then, a visit from Adam Phillips [*friend and psychoanalyst; author of* On Kissing, Tickling and Being Bored], who has a quite brilliant bedside manner, as I suppose he should. We talked about what it means to lose independence, especially for those of us who cultivate the idea of it; what it means to be a patient, and what it means to lie still in a bed for weeks, with no means of walking off our anxieties. Apparently, Adam says, Coleridge writes in his notebooks somewhere that convalescence is the time when we see the world the sharpest. He asked what I was reading, and if I was depressed. We talked about Africa . . . [*illegible*] . . . punishment, and the idea that one deserves bad luck. We left it that I would call him if I wanted to see him, and I made a note to do this. He asked if I felt that I would be forgotten, and I said that I did, occasionally. He asked about my dreams, and I explained that they were often very vivid, but couldn't at that moment recall any dreams of special interest. Adam recommended reading Oliver Sacks' *An Anthropologist on Mars*. Eventually he left, having calmed me down considerably.

Now it's lunchtime, and blazing hot outside. The drought continues. I still find myself longing for a nice small war on television. I explained to Adam my obsession with food programmes and the news. Also nature television. I can watch cookery programmes like *Ready Steady Cook* for hours, and take much pleasure in imagining the taste of the food, a taste that is now denied. I also like watching nature and travel programmes, and luxuriate in the view of the countryside one gets from television. This is another reason for watching Channel Four, which seems to me to be vastly superior to the BBC.

I've come to realize what it means to be an ill person, to be stuck in one place and unable to enjoy the world outside. Adam and I also discussed the way in which most doctors don't have a clue. He says that if you pay for health care and go on the private side, as I have, they are much more likely to discuss your chances, the prognosis and so forth, than if you go on the NHS, where they won't tell you a thing. Doctors have their professional pride: because they often don't know the causes of stroke, and its potential outcome, they refuse to be drawn into a discussion of what's happened. Doctors have their fantasies of omnipotence, too.

TUESDAY 22 AUGUST
Being a patient means having time to think, time to brood. It's a bit like being a baby again. All you can do while you are lying there is to organize your thoughts and make the most of your time, and of course, being alone in hospital (like prison) is not the same as solitude. There are constant interruptions from nurses and so forth, and there is nothing willed about it at all. You have to submit to the experience.

Now that I'm scheduled to go to the Devonshire [*Hospital*] for rehab, I am starting to feel very fond of,

1. the ward, and 2. the nurses. Julia came to say goodbye today, and said that I would soon be walking back in to see her. I'll certainly miss her, and Hanifa, and Mamie, to whom I have become very attached.

The press today is obsessed by the drought, which seems to be raging up and down the country. One of the worst things about this illness is that I shall have missed the best summer of my lifetime.

I have now been here almost a month. The most important thing is to explain the mood from day to day. Today my mood is much better. I saw Emma [*my assistant*] and Belinda [*the managing editor*] from Faber's this morning, and we chatted happily. This morning I had a new physiotherapy session, and the nurse said I would be going to the Devonshire on Friday. I am looking forward to this greatly.

In the afternoon I had a succession of visits from friends . . . [*illegible*] . . . ending with my dear brother Mark. I felt very cheered up by all these visits. [*My friend*] A. brought some soup, and cracked jokes, and stayed for ages, and was delightful. There's no doubt that visitors make a huge difference, and make the time pass more easily, though too many at once can be a strain and not enjoyable. People say you should visit the sick. That's true, but you should not drive them demented. I can be lonely here, but I also enjoy my solitude.

There's also the question of visitors' etiquette. When do they leave, and how soon? It is up to them to say when they are going to go, but I have developed a way of saying 'Thank you and goodbye', as a way of preserving my energy.

When asked by visitors at this time about my feelings, I liked to pretend to myself that I was taking a well-deserved break from my office, but in truth, when I look back on these days, I remember two kinds of anxiety. The first, which was quite irrational, was that my company would stop paying my salary and that I would not be able to afford to convalesce at leisure. In hindsight it was odd, I suppose, that I should be concerned with money and my bank overdraft when, physically speaking, I was incapable of tearing off a cheque from its stub. The fact is that even in hospital we cannot escape the tyranny of the mundane. Just as death and taxation are said to be always with us, so also are sickness and bill-paying.

The second worry, which was not answered by any evidence, was that my co-workers were merrily subverting my authority and opinions in my absence. A publishing house expresses a vision. During nearly twenty years I had played a central role in creating, developing and shaping this vision, generally through the books Faber & Faber had published. I became convinced, quite wrongly as it turned out, that everything I'd done was being scattered to the four winds. I was so ashamed of this self-centred anxiety that I could not bring myself to discuss it with anyone, not even with the chairman of the firm, Matthew Evans. It was not that I felt redundant suddenly, more that I had somehow lost control of an organization in which I had believed myself to be indispensable. I have discussed this aspect of my illness with many stroke-sufferers and they almost all confirm having experienced similar feelings of anxiety *vis-à-vis* the workaday world from which they have been disconnected.

The other aspect of my incarceration in the Nuffield was that I finally came to understand what the Thatcherism I'd lived through meant in practice. For a decade and a half the country had been privatized and de-unionized and monetarized and reorganized and, although I'd followed it in the newspapers, it had made little impact on me personally, except insofar as I was apparently better off (bigger salary, less tax, etc.). Now I could understand the true meaning of a privatized health service: invoices for every treatment, staff shortages, overworked ambulance crews, teams of sharp-suited hospital administrators conducting fatuous management exercises and the desolation of empty wards.

I lay, staring at the hospital ceiling, trying to remember, as a kind of mental exercise, the names of the writers I'd published these last sixteen years, country by country. Occasionally, I would spend hours checking through this list, staring out at the sky and wondering when I was ever going to be released from the torment of immobilization. Daydreaming was one way to escape; the other was my Red 'n' Black notebook.

MY DIARY: WEDNESDAY 23 AUGUST
One of the strange things is that when people come through the door, I don't know for a minute who they are, and it takes a while to remember who it is; sometimes I don't even recognize them, which is rather peculiar. It's at moments like these that I wonder if I'm losing my mind. Some days, madness seems just round the corner.

I find that I am feeling very tearful at the moment, not merely tears of anger, or rage, or depression: I just feel very emotional, and can cry about the smallest thing.

SARAH'S DIARY: WEDNESDAY 23 AUGUST
Feeling quite blue and tired today, as if grey storm-clouds were everywhere. I'm getting that helpless,

hopeless feeling again. I feel as if I'm all alone. I so depend on the last thing I have heard, the last person we have talked to, so that way my moods fly around all the time. If R. is glum and seems unwilling to try, I feel despair. If I talk to someone who says he is making good progress, I feel elated. A neurologist came in the other night and was so dour, so unsmiling, so creepy that it made me want to cry (R. said he was a typical Englishman of a certain sort, and that he could easily handle him). He talked about parameters and profiles, and then said that R.'s left hand would be 'useless', which was horrifying to hear. But then he amended it to say that it would be much better than it is now, which to my mind means that it will be better than useless. I felt so angry and scared and indignant on R.'s behalf. I'm sure these doctors have little psychological tricks for what they say. But I'm equally sure that they are uncompassionate, semi-aliens who just don't know how to deal with actual people. Maybe it's just too depressing for them giving bad news all the time, maybe it's easier to look at scans than to talk to patients.

MY DIARY: THURSDAY 24 AUGUST
This is my last day in the Nuffield ward. I had physiotherapy at eleven. Tomorrow I shall be going to the Devonshire at two thirty. They have booked an ambulance to take me. Julie Kavanagh [*friend, biographer of Frederick Ashton*] rang, and we talked about Raymond Blanc's stroke [*from which he made a full recovery*], then John Walsh [*friend; journalist*] rang, wanting to do a diary story in the *Independent*. I found talking to him very alarming and difficult, and felt very tired afterwards. Speech is very tiring, and I find that my volume is very

hard to control. My tongue often feels very heavy in my mouth, despite the therapy from nice Dr Click [*Whurr*].

I have developed a concept of the 'good' waiting period and the 'bad' waiting period. A 'good' waiting period is one where you know the outcome, and where you know that you are going to leave when they say you'll leave, or where you will be doing things when they say you'll do things, and a 'bad' waiting period is when you don't know what is going to happening, and you are just hanging about.

Tomorrow I shall have been here four weeks, and in summary I find that I have been amazed by the loving warmth and generosity of my friends and the interest of the outside world, stupefied by the boredom of the routine of the hospital, and the exhaustion of convalescence. The nights are often very difficult. I have become obsessed with the details of mobility, especially the wheelchair operation.

SARAH'S DIARY: THURSDAY 24 AUGUST
To the Devonshire rehab tomorrow. I find I get very nervous whenever anything new happens, and this particularly because it's a change in what has become a sort of refuge, and because it means a whole new round of tests where they evaluate R.'s condition. I'm so afraid of bad news – that they'll say he's not going to get much better, that he won't be able to walk well (or even at all) and won't be able to use his hand again. Doctors scare me, medical evaluations scare me, new predictions (or non-predictions or people looking sombre and negative and using words like 'useless') scare me, the future scares me. R.'s using his leg more, and leaning on his left elbow but still nowhere near walking. People keep telling us

stroke stories but it's still a complete mystery to me at least how he is supposed to walk. Were the strokes in those cases less severe than this one? More? Should more have come back by now? Or does that not matter so much? So much depends upon what happens at the Devonshire, and so I'm trying so hard not to let mine and R.'s expectations become unrealistic. I think R. needs to work and we both need good fortune and patience and perspective.

Pulling through. R. quite confident, at least to me, because he knows how scared I am. But it's so tiring, for both of us, and progress is so incremental. I don't know how much of a long view I need to take. I don't know what it's right to hope for – I have to learn how to hope for the best but prepare myself if it doesn't happen. And so does Robert. He seems sure that it will be okay, but I wonder if he really believes it, and I wonder how realistic he's being, and I wonder if his hopes, too, are going to be dashed in the end. I pray to a God I don't believe in. But I had an absurd thought the other day, that the thing about God is that even if you don't believe in him, he listens to you. Maybe there's some religion in me after all.

[9]

Death and Dying

August–September, 1995

We study Health, and we deliberate upon our meats,
and drink, and air, and exercises, and we hew, and we
polish every stone, that goes to that building; and so our
Health is a long and regular work; But in a minute a
Canon batters all, overthrows all, demolishes all; a Sickness unprevented for all our diligence, unsuspected for
all our curiosity; nay, undeserved, if we consider only
disorder, summons us, seizes us, possesses us, destroys
us in an instant.

John Donne, *Devotions*

Perhaps not surprisingly, in the aftermath of my stroke I
became quite obsessed with death, and with the skull
beneath the skin. This perception was enhanced by my
everyday encounters as a patient. I discovered then –
and throughout my convalescence – that we (and our
loved ones) are all unwell. I lost count of the number of
times people confided in me either the recent death, or
the profound sickness, of someone near to them, or their
own close encounter with acute illness. Some people
described transient ischemic attacks; several more told

me of friends or relatives who'd suffered a recent stroke (or heart-attack) and who had, none the less, gone on to make a complete/partial/rapid/gradual/impressive recovery. In short, my illness was an eye-opener not only to my internal world but to my external one, too. I felt re-enfranchized into a world of feeling from which I'd become dissociated.

So, when I look over my own past now, the figure of Death seems to be standing there at every turn, in one guise or another. Years before my own 'brush with mortality', I find that the theme runs like a dark thread through my imagination. Even when I was at home in England I was irresistibly drawn towards it. (My most recent novel, *Suspicion*, completed just before I fell ill, is narrated by a county coroner, an expert in untimely death. 'So often,' says my fictional *alter ego*, 'have I travelled the grim byways of mortality that there was a time when, against my will, I used to think of myself as the angel of death.') Perhaps this is a family trait. For some years, my mother had been the chair of a hospice in Cambridge. Not long before my first meeting with Sarah, I had spent a day at the hospice with Dr Tim Hunt, the resident doctor and an acknowledged specialist in death and dying. It was a day that came back to me many times during my convalescence, reminding me that, compared to terminal illnesses like cancer, the stroke-patient is, in the words of the Beatles song, getting better every day, better, better, better.

When I take my mind back to that outing to Cambridge, I see that then I was fascinated by imminent death, fascinated and scared, as those of us who have had little to do with it often are. Now that I've had a glimpse of this terrifying figure, an inkling of what it might actually be like to die, and have survived, I find that I no longer have that anxiety, but naturally I long to live. We all do, and the sudden, irretrievable finality of death remains so total, so colossal – a massive black wall, rearing up, tidal wave-like, to engulf us – that it's hard not to be awed by it, as we should be. 'Death,' observed W. H. Auden, 'is like the rumble of distant thunder at a picnic.' I have not lost my respect, of course, but I have lost my fear. I have known what it feels like to be carried away, helpless, towards oblivion and finding by great fortune the current slow and swirl towards the bank, leaving me sprawled, quite helpless, on a new shore.

The residue of nearly dying, and of being conscious through most of the experience, feeling detached and quite serene, is that the world still seems painfully vivid and precious. I have not, however, lost my fascination with death and dying, and when I was recovering in the National Hospital, my day with Tim Hunt remained an especially sustaining and important memory.

At the beginning of my visit to the hospice, a pleasant, single-storey brick building in the grounds of Brookfields Hospital, on the edge of Cambridge, Tim Hunt had reiterated to me that amid the manifold uncertainties of our take-off from this world there is one stark and unavoidable truth: the medical profession does not much care for the dying. Doctors are trained to diagnose and cure. Patients are conditioned to believe in the healing power of surgery and drugs. In medicine, death equals failure and dying is a reality that only a few can bear to contemplate on a professional basis. Doctors hate an illness they cannot cure, which is part of the explanation for the profound and chronic neglect of stroke-patients. (In many provincial hospitals, the out-of-the-way bed at the end of the ward is often still referred to as 'the stroke bed'.) But if, in the jargon of the National Health Service, 'no further treatment is appropriate', i.e. you are terminally ill, the most comfortable departure lounge is likely to be a hospice.

So how would you choose to die? Quickly? Peacefully? Surrounded by grieving relatives? The hospice caters to all our needs, providing comfort and dignity for the dying in their battle with the demons of fear, loneliness, depression, guilt, anger and chronic fatigue. It's a daunting task but one which has, in the last decade, begun to attract a new generation of doctors specializing in what is euphemistically known as 'palliative medicine'. Dr Hunt is one of the acknowledged pioneers in this field, a doctor of Death, so to speak.

Hunt, who has the dress and demeanour of a slightly mad professor (ill-fitting suit, wispy hair, flying hands, gangly walk), has treated about five thousand patients in the last ten years. Not one of them has survived. Yet many went to their graves firm in the belief that he is a 'magician', even a 'genius', words which I heard applied to him during my visit. Something quite odd, even uplifting, can happen when the process of dying is treated for what it is – a matter of extreme fascination. Hunt had been a protégé of the late Peter Medawar, whose autobiography, *Memoir of a Thinking Radish*, contains some characteristically acerbic pages on his own stroke and the quality of medical care he received in hospital. Hunt explained how, at his hospital, Addenbrookes, he'd become interested in this neglected area: 'I have to say we didn't look after dying patients very well. The usual sequence of events was that the consultant went round and he'd say, "That chap's very ill. Start the heroin." One day – I'll never forget this – there was a registrar who decided on this policy for a chap of thirty-six who was dying of a kidney cancer. At about five o'clock, the nurses came to me. The man wasn't in pain. Why should they bump him off, as they usually did? That's how I became interested in people who have been put on one side because they no longer present the challenge of diagnosis and treatment to the medical profession. It wasn't a high kudos thing to be doing.' Death, notoriously, has become an embarrassment, a taboo. Death is what happens to other people. Violent death occurs in faraway places of which we know little, East Timor, perhaps, or Indo-China. The older generation can remember standing in silence at the passing of a hearse, but in our time, at least until AIDS, the emphasis has been on cure, on long life. Fifteen years ago, hospices were seen as dormitories for the dying. As doctors became aware that there were some diseases that were beyond the power of the latest wonder-drug – multiple sclerosis, motor-neurone disease, various kinds of cancer – hospices became places where (thanks to the judicious use of analgesics) patients could continue to survive without the pain usually associated with terminal illness.

The manipulation of drugs, however, was not the whole story. Tim Hunt, in fact, is renowned for his ability to reduce a dependency on medication. What distinguished his work in the hospice was his minute attention to the neglected, mundane details of terminal illness. In hospitals, doctors tend to overlook the things that patients worry about the most: coughing, vomiting and hiccups. Symptoms of cancer, such as smell, used to be accepted as unpleasant but unavoidable. 'No one was interested in smell twenty years ago,' Hunt remarked. 'The stench from a fungating tumour. I remember this woman said to me, "What can you do about this terrible smell? I cannot bear to have anyone come near me." So I developed a new formulation to deal with it, and she became much more comfortable.'

The more Hunt investigated the taboos surrounding the deathbed, the deeper he went into the minds of the dying. 'For people who are terminally ill things are much blacker than they need be. They expect to die tomorrow or the next day. They see Death just around the corner. They can't sleep. How can you expect someone, even a healthy person, to feel well in the day if they don't sleep at night? Why don't they sleep at night? No textbook will tell you this. Patients will tell you. It's because they have a fear of dying in the night, of not waking up.'

Now, as I'd discovered in Queen Square, I found this to be true for myself. Some of my best and worst thoughts were those I had during the long loneliness of a sleepless hospital night. Hunt also told me that, contrary to popular belief, the terminally ill do not want crowds of visitors. 'Husbands and wives have a tendency to call relatives home for deathbed farewells. Actually, dying is a lonely business. The dying just want company. They want one person with whom they can share the silence and the darkness, a companion.' When Hunt had told me this, I had put it down as an interesting observation. Writing now, after several months in and out of hospital, I can acknowledge the wisdom of his comment: he was absolutely right. There were many days when I preferred to be left quite alone. (And I wasn't even on my deathbed.) On more than one occasion – and with rather guilty feelings – I would send people away who came to see me, including one of my dearest and best friends, blaming tiredness for what was actually an overwhelming need for solitude.

On the day of my visit to Cambridge, the sun was out

and Dr Hunt was in his element. In the hallway of Arthur Rank House, the atmosphere was casual and relaxed. There were children playing Snakes and Ladders, a middle-aged couple talking in low voices, a visiting priest chatting to one of the helpers, and a patient in a lint-white surgical neck support reading the *Observer*. Hunt, the master of ceremonies, whirled between the various groups, jollying everyone along. In the wards, the mood was quiet but not deathly. One birdlike woman, haggard and waxy with illness, almost unable to speak, was having her nails varnished by a Red Cross nurse. Hunt's hospice believes strongly in maintaining the dignity and self-esteem of the patients, even at the end.

In the consulting room, one of the biggest questions Hunt has to deal with is: 'How long have I got?' His first task was always to dispel fear, the apprehension of ignorance. He explained to me, 'You cannot say to a patient, "You're going to die in three or six months." It's highly disturbing to do that. The date gets marked on the calendar. I had this patient. He was so frightened he was trembling. He had conditioned himself to be dead in six months. What I do is I say, "I cannot see the end." I say, "Some days you'll feel grotty. Others you'll feel better." I encourage them to believe that they are exceptional. I try to treat the patients as I would want to be treated myself. Patients must feel that they matter. They need time. We spend all of our lives avoiding ways of dying. You cannot expect people to be prepared to die. What I do is I try to bring them into the decision-making. If you don't cover up or lie to them their hope is enhanced somehow.' Needless to say, this is a time-consuming procedure that fits badly with a time- and cost-conscious National Health Service where some consultants will dismiss a terminally ill patient in as little as five minutes.

Bigger even than the question of 'When?' is the question, 'How?' – 'How will I die?' To this, mercifully, Hunt could offer reassurance to both relatives and patients: 'I can firmly tell you that most patients will die in their sleep, a deeper and deeper sleep. This is a great relief to many relatives. Of course there are cases where death is uncomfortable, but this is often for psychological reasons.'

The battle with approaching Death rages fiercest in the mind, and Hunt had become expert in providing psychological reinforcements for those who wanted to fight. In the late afternoon I drove out with him into the sunny fens to visit two patients at home. The first was confined to her bed. She was troubled by a nagging cough. Her family had lost heart. She might as well have been dead. Afterwards, as we drove towards Newmarket in his cluttered, down-at-heel Metro for the second consultation, Hunt puzzled over two things. How, physically, to soothe the woman's cough? More important, how could he inject some confidence into her husband? 'You saw how he had given up,' he remarked. 'Look, this man's wife knows him better than anyone. She can read him so easily. She will see it in his eyes. She will feel she has been abandoned. There were no books, no newspapers by her bedside. He must learn to involve his wife in the world. Ask for her thoughts. She is still alive.' (There can, of course, be no evidence for this conviction, but I believe that Sarah's refusal to let despair get the better of us has been a crucial component in my excellent recovery.)

At his next appointment, the patient, a middle-aged mother of two, was shuffling about in a dressing gown.

She wore a surgical collar and was recovering from a course of radiotherapy. She had lost all sense of taste, a distressing experience with which I can now easily sympathize. Her GP had told her that this was an inevitable side-effect, but Hunt's reaction was quite different. He questioned the woman closely about her eating habits. Her husband participated eagerly in the discussion. Hunt said there were ways to stimulate salivation. Then, to everyone's amazement, he prescribed a diet of fresh pineapple – and good white wine. The transformation of the family mood was palpable. Now they had a project. The patient had something to look forward to. Her husband could go shopping. There was hope, after all. 'I want to put some of the responsibility back to the patients,' he explained afterwards. 'Involving the family in such matters is just as important as sending a get-well card.'

There's no doubt that Hunt can be almost spookily intuitive about his patients' state of mind, with a rare ability to calibrate the final moments to their advantage. 'The period before people die is fascinating,' he said. 'It's a great junction. If there's one word to describe what happens when you know you're dying, it's "reconciliation". This is not a spiritual thing, it's a matter of putting your affairs in order.' More often than not, Hunt finds himself an accomplice in all manner of settlements and resolutions.

Some of these deathbed scenes were worthy of Dickens or Chekhov. 'I remember one man, a Roman Catholic,' he said. 'He wanted to stop his wife remarrying after his death. So he put their house in the name of his children so that no man would be attracted to her for financial reasons. Then, two days before he died, he became very agitated. It turned out that the marriage had been terrible. His wife had wanted to leave. He was troubled with what he had done. He asked for first one, then a second, and finally a third priest, looking for assurances about his future that the priests could not give. That was a traumatic death.'

I wondered if those who have an active faith shuffle off their mortal coil with greater ease or dignity. Hunt shook his head. 'The sad fact is that those who have, so to speak, two Michelin rosettes because of their religious beliefs don't appear to have a better time of it. This is the truth. You can say, "How do you know this?" Well, I've looked after five thousand people . . .'

Those who are about to die are centre-stage in an extraordinary drama, and sometimes, like prima donnas, the dying manipulate the situation to cause maximum embarrassment. Hunt described how the deceased can ensure they are remembered long after their death simply by making hurtful and controversial changes to their wills. The deathbed can also be a place in which terrible, long-hidden secrets are revealed. Hunt told me, 'I remember a man with a wife and children. He was in great emotional pain. It turned out that the man had had several affairs that the wife knew nothing about and there were all these women who wanted to come and see him to say goodbye. I had to smuggle them in. You may say that this was wrong, but I felt I had to do what this man wanted. There was another patient. He was married, but for over twenty years he'd had a mistress in the next-door village, the love of his life. He was in terrible discomfort and pain. He wanted to be with her before he died. I had to get this woman in secretly. His own family had no idea. The man had this terrible regret that he had not shared his life with this other woman. Yes, those who tend the dying will be in receipt of many confidences.'

He began to tell me about his own father, who'd died recently. 'I think I practised what I preach.' Hunt's voice was sombre and low, but quite soothing. 'He'd had a stroke. I carried him up to bed. I said, "You've had a small stroke. You've lost your voice but there's a good chance of recovery." The GP wanted to send him to hospital. I said to myself, "Tim, here we have someone of eighty-six who's led a very active life and who couldn't stand to be in a hospital. There's a high chance he will have another stroke." That night I had to go and see another patient. At seven o'clock the next morning I went back to the house. My mother had her arms around him. He had died in his sleep.' For a moment, Hunt was no longer the hospice doctor but the bereaved son. Then he became the professional again. 'In a sense, that is what I want for my patients.'

When I look back over this encounter now I realize that, strange as it sounds, it was the only occasion I can recall in which someone actually described to me the effect of a stroke, its fatal propensity.

Now I'm an 'expert', of course, and during the long months of my year off, I often found myself drawn to all manner of books about illness, books about dying and books about death, from Elisabeth Kubler-Ross's trail-blazing *On Death and Dying* (also her eccentric treatise, *The Wheel of Life*), and Gillian Rose's *Love's Work* and Harold Brodkey's AIDS memoir *This Wild Darkness: The Story of My Death*, to C. S. Lewis's *A Grief Observed*. Of these, Lewis's meditation on the death of his wife, and Gillian Rose's profoundly affecting anticipation of her death by cancer stand out (with John Donne's *Devotions*) for their wisdom and poetry. 'I am bound,' writes Rose, 'to get love wrong, all the time . . . but still I keep wooing.' Rose observes that what she memorably calls

'Love's work', is 'humanity's survival mechanism', a conclusion I reached in my own way during my hospitalization. Finally, there was *The Diving Bell and the Butterfly* by Jean-Dominique Bauby, a French magazine journalist, whose story shadows mine in a number of intriguing ways.

'I had never even heard of the brain stem,' he writes, with an exasperated perplexity I fully understand. On the morning of 8 December 1995, Jean-Dominique Bauby, the editor-in-chief of French *Elle* magazine, woke up to a day like any other. But when he went to pick up his son from his estranged wife's house in the suburbs of Paris, pressing his BMW through gridlocked traffic, he suddenly felt ill and had to stop the car. Then he suffered a massive stroke and was unconscious for three weeks. When he came round in the hospital of Breck-sur-Mer, he was unable to breathe without a ventilator, unable to speak or eat unaided, or move anything except his left eyelid. He'd become, as his heartless colleagues, chattering in Les Deux Magots, would put it, a *légume*. The specialist doctors at Breck-sur-Mer, experts in stroke treatment, had managed to resuscitate him, and what they now told him was perhaps the most horrible news imaginable. 'You survive, but you survive with what is known as "locked-in syndrome". It is a small consolation, no doubt, but your chances of being caught in this hellish trap are about those of winning the lottery.' Almost totally paralysed, mute and half deaf, Bauby found that his cognitive skills were unimpaired and through his frustration came a resolve to prove that his IQ 'was still higher than a turnip's'.

The result was *The Diving Bell and the Butterfly*. Bauby planned his text in his imagination, then memorized each word, phrase and paragraph. A Paris publisher sent him an assistant to take down his words – Bauby would listen to a recital of the alphabet, then blink his left eye at the appropriate letter of the alphabet, one blink for Yes, two for No. Now Bauby could flutter free like the butterfly of the title from the diving bell (an odd metaphor) of his condition, and begin to narrate his experience. 'In my head,' he writes, 'I churn over every sentence ten times, delete a word, add an adjective, and learn my text by heart, paragraph by paragraph.' Slowly, the book took shape, and when it was published it was, in France, a *succès fou* and became an international phenomenon, with the added poignancy that its author died four days after his memoir's sensational publication (as if he had lived just long enough to know that his final message had got through).

Part of our fascination with Bauby and *The Diving Bell and the Butterfly* lies in the significance we attribute to his report from beyond the grave. He, who crossed over into the twilight world of neither dead nor alive, has had special access to the antechamber of life's great mystery; we, if we listen to him, may hear something to our advantage. That, I suppose, is our unconscious reasoning. The fact that Bauby has palpably experienced the extreme of suffering only adds to the authenticity of his utterance. Crucial to Bauby's significance is his harrowing immobility. As John Donne puts it in *Devotions*: 'When God came to breathe into Man the breath of life, he found him flat upon the ground; when he comes to withdraw that breath from him again, he prepares him to it, by laying him flat upon his bed.' Is it for the same reason that we find special consequence in the writings of Stephen Hawking?

And yet I found myself moved by Donne and strangely unmoved by Bauby. With Donne, we follow, because he is as we are: ordinary; when he writes of the 'variable and therefore miserable condition of Man' we know what he's talking about, and we share his perplexity. With extraordinary Monsieur Bauby we spectate, dumbly, from a distance, awestruck and horrified, no doubt, but not touched in any way that can register on the Richter scale of everyday human feeling. I had expected to be dead; I had been there; it did not interest me to go back, especially in the company of one so coldly cerebral as Monsieur Bauby (although he had very little choice).

Gradually, I came to terms with the fact that, although I had indeed survived, my old life was well and truly dead and buried. As I realized why this should be so, I began to face up to the reality of my new life. This was distinctly different from the experience of my 'new life' as a stroke-patient in Queen Square. In retrospect, I was beginning to do that from day one of my time in rehab.

[10]

Better Dead

25 August – 27 September

Meanwhile, where is God? This is one of the most disquieting symptoms. When you are happy, so happy that you have no sense of needing Him, so happy that you are tempted to feel His claims upon you as an interruption, if you remember yourself and turn to Him with gratitude and praise, you will be – or so it feels – welcomed with open arms. But go to Him when your need is desperate, when all other help is vain and what do you find? A door slammed in your face, and a sound of bolting and double bolting on the inside. After that, silence.

C. S. Lewis, *A Grief Observed*

My transfer from the National Hospital in Queen Square to the Devonshire Hospital, adjoining Harley Street, went smoothly. I said goodbye, with end-of-term sadness and excitement, to Cheryl, Phil, 'Phirrip', Linda, Hanifa, Mamie and especially Julia, whose sweet good nature had won both my heart and Sarah's. When I said goodbye to my physiotherapist John Marsden, he said in reply that he expected to see me back as an outpatient before too long. I found this an almost unimaginable thought. Dr Lees looked in for a final check-over, and then the Great Ormond Street ambulance took Sarah and me on the short trip across London to Devonshire Street. The trip through the backways of Fitzrovia was one I'd thoughtlessly made countless times in my car in the old days on hurried rush-hour journeys to west London, but now it seemed symbolic, a new chapter in a journey whose outcome was still dark and uncertain, though just to be moving, to feel the wind in the street and to see the blue of the sky as the stretcher was loaded into the ambulance seemed to offer a breath of hope, a glimmer of light in the prevailing darkness.

My new room, 304, on the third floor, was much smaller than the one I'd left – the ceiling low, the wood dark – and the street outside seemed much noisier. I missed the Queen Square nurses and the routine of the Nuffield ward, and felt rather trapped. I lay on my new bed, taking in my surroundings, while various members of the hospital staff came to introduce themselves: two black nurses, Cora and Dorothy, then the nursing sister, and then a nurse called Mary, an Irish woman, who told me she would be looking after me for the next several weeks. Gradually I became aware of what it meant to be in a small private hospital (compared to a private ward in a National Health hospital): a level of personal comfort, and twenty-four-hour attention, generally unavailable in the NHS. Finally Davina Richardson, the physiotherapist I had been told at Queen Square would be in charge, poked her head round the door. She looked very attractive in her grey hospital culottes and stripy-cream blouse. I found myself brightening at the prospect of physiotherapy with someone who seemed at once so friendly and intelligent. After these visits, I was soon very tired, and suddenly quite depressed. Sarah was wonderful: she settled me and my things into the room, and eventually I fell asleep. Fatigue was both a friend and an enemy in those early weeks.

During that first night at the Devonshire I dreamed very intensely, and found myself crying in my sleep. I cannot remember the dreams, but it was the first time I had dreamed so vividly since the stroke. I woke up with tears on my face.

When the nurse came in at eight o'clock next morning, and asked me how I was, I found myself saying to her, 'I am still alive.'

'Oh, I've never lost any of my patients!' she replied cheerfully.

The Devonshire is one of Britain's top rehabilitation hospitals, with superb physiotherapy facilities, a place favoured by injured sportspeople – and convalescent yuppie skiers. Its regular clientele, however, is made up of wealthy Arabs. During my stay, there were no sportsmen, and no skiers, just some sad paraplegic cases from Saudi Arabia, nearly incoherent victims of desert car crashes. The hospital itself, situated opposite Odins restaurant, a fashionable late-sixties hang-out, is a bit like a small private hotel, though at times the atmosphere on the shadowy, wood-panelled corridors was frankly Oriental, a claustrophobic mixture of bazaar and mosque. Confined to my room for most of each day, I gradually became aware of this when I was wheeled downstairs each morning for physiotherapy. The male nurse who usually took me down to physiotherapy was a wiry, gentle Arab called Mohammed – indeed, all the people who worked in the hospital seemed to be Arab, or Irish, or Greek. I soon guessed I was the only English person in residence. Sarah said she had seen an old colonel on the next floor, but since his stroke had knocked out his speech, we decided that I was the sole in-house representative of the English language.

I had chosen to come to the Devonshire Hospital (known to its staff as 'The Devvie') for its specialization in physiotherapy. My priority, from the first, had been to get myself back on my feet. The physiotherapy gym – a row of adjustable exercise benches and a collection of brightly coloured inflatable balls – was in the basement.

The first time I came into the gym and saw my fellow patients (of all ages) stretched out on their exercise benches, I thought I was hearing things. Was it really the case that this attractive nurse was weirdly urging her patient with the exhortation 'fuck, fuck, fuck'? What kind of advanced therapeutic procedure, I wondered, was happening? What was going on? I asked Davina, who explained, with much laughter, that the Arabic for 'up' was a word that sounded like 'fuck'. The nurse was simply asking her charge to lift his foot.

Sarah would join me down in the physiotherapy gym most mornings, politely deflecting questions from other Arab visitors about the number of children she had. Several old Arab gentlemen, attending brain-damaged teenagers, did not disguise their dismay at my apparent failure to have yet produced an heir.

Thanks to this regime, and Davina's expert attentions, my physical restrictions lessened, but with excruciating slowness. In hindsight, I see that she was concerned to get me standing and walking again. She was less concerned that my left arm remained lifelessly out of action (it was, in fact, almost a year after the stroke before I got the use of it back in a limited way). To me, however, the terrible frustration of trying to make a connection between my brain and my fingers, of imagining movement, while staring hopelessly at an immobile hand, was unquestionably among the lowest moments of these weeks. For much of the time, indeed, my lifeless left arm remained strapped across my chest to prevent accidental damage. Plus, there was the fact that I could still barely stand upright.

For the first twelve weeks after my stroke, I had to move around in a wheelchair, pushed by Sarah or by one of the nurses. The prevailing sense of helplessness was very difficult to come to terms with. I had no control over my feelings, particularly when we were outside, and I would rage horribly against whoever was pushing me. Nobody would say when, exactly, I'd be well enough to walk again, and at moments like these I saw a life of infuriating confinement stretching out before me, a vista of utter helplessness. Sometimes I wondered how I could possibly cope and more than once thought that if this was to be the best that my life had to offer, I would be better dead.

Later, when I read *The Diving Bell and the Butterfly* I came to feel ashamed of my mood at this time. Although I could understand and sympathize with what Bauby was describing, my afflictions, compared to his, were trivial. But never mind. At the time, like many stroke-survivors, I was shut away in my own sad little world, seemingly incarcerated at the centre of a miserable universe in which the phrase 'better dead' aptly summarized my feelings.

Fortunately, in the universe I could control – the tiny orbit of my hospital bed – I was not completely out of action. I could scribble in my Black 'n' Red diary, and write letters or postcards with my 'good' right hand; I could see friends and take an interest in the outside world, even though the world itself seemed terrifyingly noisy and overpowering whenever I was in it. Once I was into the routine of daily physiotherapy at the Devonshire, I had to face up to the slow process of recovery.

SARAH'S DIARY: FRIDAY 25 AUGUST
R. lies on his back while the physiotherapist moves his leg up and down. He can bend it but not all the way up. He lifts his butt up and down, up and down, and tries to put weight on the left side (he can). He's gaining balance and symmetry, she says, and strength. I ask Davina, the beatific physio, how she thinks Robert is doing. 'Very well,' she says. She's really pleased. 'Will he walk?' I ask. 'Yes,' she says. Then she says, 'Fingers crossed, he'll do fine.' Which sounds great. I feel temporarily relieved, then terrified again soon afterwards.

I think that one of the problems with stroke is that, as a condition, it offers a moving target. Compared to, say, cancer, stroke is not a degenerative condition. If you survive the initial crisis you are – with luck – constantly and imperceptibly getting better. I had to learn to adjust, and also to wait. Even now, two years later, I think the lesson in patience I learned during these weeks is the one that I value most highly.

Most mornings, Sarah and I would take the wheelchair to the delightful seclusion of the Paddington Street Gardens two blocks from the hospital. The air was now much cooler, and autumn was on the way.

SARAH'S DIARY: SATURDAY 26 AUGUST
Dull weekend due to the bank holiday and new routines to adjust to, including the tiny size of the room, which means that whenever Robert goes to the bathroom, the

bed and table and chair need to be moved. I opened the door this morning and sent a vase of flowers smashing to the floor. R. is making tiny incremental progress – he can stand more easily, seems to be able to bend his knee, but I so hate hovering over him and making him do these things, and I know it shows him how nervous I am. I have been rubbing his hand and foot which aren't moving to remind him that they are there, and that they are loved. I stare at R.'s feet and think I see flickers of movement but I don't want to depend on it or make a big fuss. Dream of being alone in crowds. I spent the afternoon at Marcus and Stephanie's [*American friends*] yesterday – two more strangers there – I felt very isolated, covered in a little invisible bubble of misery while they chatted on about work and pregnancies and babies. I joined in but felt I had a huge stamp on my forehead: Wife of Stroke Victim.

R. finally talked on the phone this afternoon to Peter Carey. No one can tell what an effort it is for him to talk so that he is understood. He has to think so hard about the things he has always taken for granted. I took him out in his wheelchair to a tiny green flowery park a couple of blocks away. It was agony – he becomes so acutely aware of the tiniest bump in the road, or the fact you can't get into most buildings, or do the things you might like to do. I read aloud again from *Charlotte's Web* in which we have reached the place where Charlotte spins 'some pig'. R. says discovering this book is the one good thing about having had a stroke.

The weather has suddenly turned autumnal after a dry, bright and very unseasonably (everyone says) hot August. It seemed to mock us, because we spent all of it indoors. I dread the change of climate, of being alone in the sad weather. It is as if we missed our chance to have a sunny, carefree time. At the moment I feel as if I'll never be carefree again.

My own mood seesawed wildly – at times I felt almost euphoric with relief and at the satisfaction of being alive, at other times almost suicidally depressed. I had a lot of bizarre sexual fantasies, mixed in with the general mood of depression. On my first Sunday, at three o'clock, I had a visit from one of the physiotherapists, Alex, a New Zealander, who put my paralysed left arm in a sling. With Alex, the exercises became almost sexual. It was strange to feel her breasts pressing against my hand, and to catch the scent of her body, though she did not seem to notice my reaction. I had a fit of giggles as she pressed down on my torso. The seriousness of the physiotherapy soon returned (I don't think Alex had any idea why I was smiling), but some of the positions she put me in were comically reminiscent of sexual foreplay, and I fantasized about asking her to have sex. The same afternoon, by chance, a nurse came in and gave me some Stroke Association literature, including a hilarious document entitled 'Sex after Stroke Illness', a comically old-fashioned leaflet – very sober and literal-minded, with definitions of orgasms and so forth.

That was also the day I tried to eat Sunday lunch at the Devonshire. Perhaps remembering the happy days of childhood, I chose roast beef and Yorkshire pudding. This was a mistake. With my left hand immobilized, I had difficulty managing the knife and fork and became terribly frustrated. Besides, I still had no proper sense of taste, and did not enjoy my food. I felt bored and tired and disaffected. I noted in my diary that, on a scale of ten, my mood was two.

It was a symptom of my mood at this time that I found myself at war with the nurses, and I complained bitterly about the cramped conditions of Room 304. I felt angry and helpless. To cap it all, when the catering manager, a friendly Greek, came in and asked how I was, he called me Mr Crumb. As I corrected him, endeavouring to keep my temper, I realized I'd reached a low point to be worrying about such matters of *politesse*.

Things slowly improved. I was beginning to make progress in speech therapy, though the effort of articulation remained a problem for me long after I left hospital.

Each morning, when I woke up, I would repeat as clearly and sharply as possible: *Round and round the ragged rocks the ragged rascal ran*; and then (Sarah's favourite):

> *Theophilus Thistle,*
> *The thrifty thistle-sifter,*
> *Thrust three thousand thistles*
> *Through the thick of his thumb.*

I was in the middle of these exercises one morning, lying in bed with my eyes closed, when I became aware that the catering manager was standing at the foot of my bed staring at me in amazement. It was clear from his expression that he'd decided I was not only sick but mad as well.

Veronica Noah, my new speech therapist, turned out to be firm, friendly and positive, not at all reluctant to say what was all too obvious to me: my speech was still badly slurred. That was quite normal, at this stage, apparently. Veronica, a brightly dressed, maternal woman with large spectacles, also told me I had a right to feel exhausted all the time. She was very direct and down to earth and breezily bossy, a change from some of the therapy I'd had at Queen Square. She was the first person who really spoke the truth about what had happened to me, and she gave me quite a hard time about my speech. Early on, she asked me to describe my day, then criticized the slurred way in which I articulated. As a contrast to Veronica, I think I found the nurses' and doctors' reluctance to commit to definite pronouncements about my condition and my likely convalescence the most frustrating part of these months.

SARAH'S DIARY: TUESDAY 29 AUGUST

I sat on a stool beside R. when he had physical therapy today. He lay on a table and tried to move his leg. He can bend the knee up and, once it's bent, he can keep it there. A contrast to the first weeks, when it would slide back down like an ice cube on a hot surface. His arm is in a sling because they don't seem to think there's any movement in it, and they're afraid it will flop around and be pulled out of its shoulder socket. He can't move his foot yet (though I thought I saw movement there yesterday). When we got back to his room he got out of his wheelchair and tried to get on the bed, and miscalculated and fell helplessly. He ended up on his stomach and couldn't manoeuvre himself around. His leg and arm got caught and it was very painful for him, and very sad to watch, like a beetle tipped on to its back, or a fish on shore. I feel like my heart is very slowly deflating. But even as I see him go through this I am filled with such love.

R. just phoned. When he gets tired, his voice gets fuzzy and slurred. They say that will go away over time but, like a lot of this, it's an alarming feature and you worry that it will be permanent. He's been moved to a better, bigger room, so some of the nightmarish circumstances of the last few days – having to move all the furniture around so he can be wheeled into the bathroom for his shower, for instance – won't be repeated again. He says he still feels blue. But he says his blueness has a bit of pink around the edges.

The part of convalescence that I found most profoundly humiliating and depressing was occupational therapy. Here, the admission of cerebral failure was even more stark. I was reduced to playing with brightly coloured plastic letters of the alphabet, like a three-year-old, and passing absurdly simple recognition tests. Sitting in my wheelchair with my day-glo letter-blocks I could not escape reflecting on the irony of the situation. If only Milan Kundera, Kazuo Ishiguro, or Mario Vargas Llosa, whose texts I had pored over with their authors, could have seen their editor at that moment!

SARAH'S DIARY: WEDNESDAY 30 AUGUST
R. took his second occupational therapy class today. Yesterday, he had to go through a list of letters and check off all the Es, and then look at a row of trees and put them in order of size – some people are so badly off, apparently, that they can't do those things. Today they taught him how to get out of bed – but he can already do that, too, using his good right leg.

My new room had a much bigger bathroom, and less street noise. On the telephone I found myself telling callers I was 'blue', which was an understatement. I realized I had to get used to a long-term approach. If I was lucky I might be on the road to recovery by Christmas, but not sooner.

[11]

Deficits

1–27 September

Neurology's favourite word is deficit, denoting an
impairment or incapacity of neurological function: loss
of speech, loss of language, loss of memory, loss of
vision, loss of dexterity, loss of identity . . .
    Oliver Sacks, *The Man Who Mistook His Wife For A Hat*

In the Devonshire Hospital, devoting two or three sessions a day to my gradual rehabilitation, I became more
than ever acutely aware of what I had lost, of my
'deficits'. I seemed to have been pitched forward into
old age, and much of my anger came from the daily war
between a youngish man's spirit and imagination, and
what I cursed as an old man's body. Outside my window, even the changing season seemed to conspire to
underline that I had fallen into 'the sere, the yellow leaf'.

When the early-September rain came, it was like a
curtain being pulled over the high season. Once autumn
arrived, I felt robbed of the hot summer, and this no
doubt contributed to my depression. Autumn had
always been, for me, a good time of year, and not being
able to have it, I felt very frustrated. Autumn was the

time of beginnings, of the new school year, of fresh starts, and yet here I was, trapped and helpless. I longed to get into a car and drive two hundred miles to the waves and wild wind of the West Country. Instead the Christmas holiday, then four months off, became my personal goal.

I told myself that if I could be home and semi-recovered by then, things would not seem so bad. Throughout my recovery I found it helpful to set myself limited short-term personal goals of the kind I had a reasonable expectation of achieving. At this stage, I still could not imagine being able to walk, though Davina reassured me that this would happen. Having a goal for the immediate future made the present more bearable, and gave me a target towards which to direct my convalescent energies. I told visitors to my bedside that my top priority was 'myself', and in the circumstances this assertion seemed neither self-centred nor unreasonable.

SARAH'S DIARY: FRIDAY 1 SEPTEMBER

I can't believe it's been the whole month of August. It seems like forever, actually. R. put weight on his weak leg today (with Davina's help) and was able to take steps with the other one. Better, he said, than he could do yesterday. I spoke to the occupational therapist who said walking depended on Robert – that if he did it his way, he'd be able to walk within a month, but badly, but that if he was patient and waited and did it the way he was told, he'd be restored 75%–90% of what he had before. It's hard to comprehend all this. I try so hard not to think about what our life is going to be like later, because it's wrong (or counter-productive) to flood my mind with enticing fantasies, and equally wrong to flood it with black, doomed scenarios. R. looks so healthy; it's hard to believe this has happened. I'm afraid for him to come home because the contrast for both of us will be so great, his condition now, compared to his condition before. The occupational therapist wants to come home and look at the house and see if we need to put a ramp in (for wheelchair access). Temporarily? I said. Temporarily, she replied. I feel close to panic all the time.

Meanwhile, as a milestone of progress, I was sent for another MRI scan. It was, I suppose, a measure of my recovery that I was now taking an interest in the technical side of Magnetic Resonance Imaging (MRI), a technique for scanning the brain which exploits the fact that hydrogen atoms resonate when bombarded with energy from magnets. Like its cruder predecessor, the CAT (Computerized Axial Tomography) scan – which I'd had on first admission to University College Hospital – MRI displays three-dimensional body images on a screen; its main advantage is that it does not involve radiation.

If my mind was sufficiently recovered to enjoy this kind of scientific information, physically I was still incompetent. I was still being bundled in and out of the ambulance on a stretcher. Now that I was much more alert than previously, I could take in, and respond to, the experience of MRI. The scanner – a narrow, cigar-shaped capsule – seems terrifyingly claustrophobic to some people. Sarah, for instance, said she could not imagine being in a space so narrow and cramped and loud, 'like blood pounding and people operating heavy drills and alarms sounding', but I found to my surprise that it was an interesting experience, not frightening at all. I think we both wondered what the scan would reveal. Would it, for instance, explain why my left arm was still not moving? My thoughts ran on: what if it never moved again? How would that change our lives?

The next night, Dr Greenwood, whose punishing work schedule with National Health and private patients always necessitated late-evening visits, came and showed us the result of the MRI scan. The clot – still a black blob the size and appearance of a Rorschach ink-blot on the negative – was much reduced in the brain. When I questioned him about my left arm, he admitted that when it came to the convalescent powers of the brain he and the other experts were still pretty much in the dark, though the current orthodoxy was to believe in cerebral 'plasticity'. Richard Greenwood was obviously a clever man, and I found myself wanting to impress him. I told him I'd come to the conclusion that having a stroke was like having one's personal wiring ripped out: everything stops, the electricity of one's body fails, and the wiring of one's association with the world also. So the things that had once seemed so important for everyday exist-ence no longer seemed important at all. At this time, I was in a mood of existential crisis, a mood that can still easily recur, lending the world a strange, provisional air, even now.

SARAH'S DIARY: MONDAY 4 SEPTEMBER
Robert seems to get a tiny bit better each day, and that does seem to be what they told us would happen, and the best we can hope for. Today he was actually sliding his foot around a little (with help from Davina), and taking the first tentative steps. He's not strong enough to do it on his own. As R. made what to me felt like a breakthrough, the two other mats in the gym were filled with two other stroke victims. One, a young Arab man,

was groaning and drooling and listing wildly to one side. He couldn't seem to move at all, and one of his eyes was mostly closed. He looked so weak and lost. The two therapists with him asked him what number his room was, and he couldn't (whether mentally, or just physically, I don't know) answer. They told him, and one said, 'I want you to remember that when you go upstairs.' She sounded like a nursery-school teacher. Behind him was an older man who can't move, either, and who just sat in his chair and stared listlessly. Occasionally he tried to mumble things, and the therapists tried to interpret what he was saying. Thank God, thank God, thank God, this hasn't happened to R. Compared to them, he's as good as sprinting in the 100-yard dash.

My convalescence continued, inexorable and infinitesimal from day to day: after about a week in the Devonshire, I had mastered the daily washing ritual. I could manoeuvre myself out of bed into the wheelchair, and wheel myself with one hand into the bathroom. There, I would have a one-handed shave and clean my teeth. I would gingerly transfer to the plastic chair under the shower, turn on the water – braving the first chilly blast of cold water – and wash my hair. Then I would pull the cord to call the nurse, take the towel, dry myself, transfer back to the wheelchair in the room, slowly get dressed, dry my hair with the hair-dryer, sit in the chair and write my diary. It's easy to describe, but in practice every step was painfully slow and laborious, fraught with the fear of falling over.

I was grateful, meanwhile, for the steady flow of visitors; occasionally I sensed that I'd become an object of mild social competition among some of my friends. I found that visitors in hospital are fascinating. Some people (whose blushes I will spare) became quite indiscreet, almost confessional, at my bedside, both much more personal and more forthcoming. I was told things in the privacy of my hospital room I would never have heard in a decade of drunken evenings. Perhaps, confronted by the stark and unavoidable evidence of human failing, my visitors felt obliged to expose their weaknesses and share their own private foibles. Such moments created some very special bonds with a wide range of friends and acquaintances, and sometimes with the people I least expected.

I remember that my friend the writer Michael Ondaatje, who turned up one morning unannounced, and who was usually so cagy, became positively voluble. He was passing through London en route from the filming of *The English Patient* in Italy, and spoke effusively about the performances of Ralph Fiennes and Kristin Scott Thomas, and about the magic of the Tunisian desert. It was wonderful to see him, and we talked for over an hour. Another visitor, who braved the crowd of robed Arabs habitually clustering in the hospital foyer and whose irrepressible presence brought great energy and joy into a black moment in my life, was Salman Rushdie. Of all the people who came to see me, it was he who somehow managed to leave behind his very considerable tribulations at the door and to focus his attention on me. I had been attempting to read his novel *The Moor's Last Sigh* but, physically unable to hold it open for more than five minutes at a stretch, had been failing miserably. I shall never forget the moment when Salman very sweetly read a page from the opening chapter, 'doing the voices' with characteristic brio.

One of my most regular visitors was an old friend, Brian Wenham, a distinguished BBC broadcaster who'd suffered a heart attack as a young man and retired early in his fifties. I cannot say exactly what it was that Brian brought to my bedside, apart from sympathy, several bottles of superb white wine and some very good jokes, but I always felt much better for his appearances. Brian always spoke of having a stroke or a heart-attack as like being caught in a 'biological car crash', that is, a totally random event, without meaning, and quite beyond our control, which was a helpful and consoling way to look at it. Brian Wenham died very suddenly as I was writing this book and his death removed one of the most vital props of my convalescent life, a mentor in the truest and fullest sense of the word, someone I trusted completely and who provided the kind of wisdom that no one else could match. I cried at his funeral in a way I had not cried since my days in the National Hospital.

After my visitors had departed, I would watch sports programmes on television, wondering when I'd be able to move freely again, and when my left arm would come back. (Even now, I still watch people running across the road or hurrying through the streets with envy for their spontaneity.) As Stephen Pinker points out in *How the Mind Works*,

Legs come with a high price: the software to control them. A wheel, merely by turning, changes its point of support gradually and can bear weight the whole time. A leg has to change its point of support all at once, and the weight has to be unloaded to do so. The motors controlling a leg have to alternate between keeping the foot on the ground while it bears and propels the load and taking the load off to make the leg free to move. All the while they have to keep the centre of gravity of the body within the polygon defined by the feet so the body doesn't topple over.

On countless occasions during my convalescence I became aware of the perils of losing my balance and helplessly toppling over as I struggled to relearn the fine art of walking, something I'd taken for granted for at least forty years.

The battle to recover the use of my leg was one thing; the quest for the use of my left arm and left hand was something else. I'd been told that neither would ever again be 'useful', and where some stroke-patients go into denial over the loss of previously functioning limbs maintaining, against all the evidence, that 'I never really used that arm/hand/foot etc.', I found that I could not accept this loss and would spend hours fruitlessly trying to think my way into reactivating my motionless hand, staring intently at its lifeless fingers.

It was the Greek physician Galen who pointed out the exquisite engineering behind the human hand, its astonishing capacity for manipulating an astonishing range of sizes, shapes and weights, from a log to a heap of seed. 'Man handles them all,' Galen noted, 'as well as if his hands had been made for the sake of each one of them alone.' So the hand can be shaped into a hook grip (to pick up a bucket), a scissors (to hold a cigarette), a three-pronged vice (to hold a pen), a squeeze grip (to hold a hammer) a two-fingered grip (to turn a key) a disc grip (to open a jar) and a spherical grip (to hold a ball), and each one of these everyday manoeuvres involves an astonishing range of cerebral activity. Needless to say, for as long as my left hand could perform none of these tasks, I felt profoundly depressed and disabled.

When my hand wouldn't respond, I used to say to myself that, at least, if I could walk and be independent, I'd be okay. I still had no real idea exactly how bad the stroke had been, or how it compared to others, but I was glad to be alive and was becoming increasingly determined about my recovery. I could sense tiny, almost imperceptible changes in my left side, and even though the regenerative wiring of the body and the so-called 'neural pathways' remained a mystery, I felt quite expert about my own capacity.

But at times, I still felt horribly frustrated. Every time I got into the wheelchair I felt vulnerable and helpless, stupid and ashamed. For some reason, I felt better when I was fully dressed in it, rather than just in shorts and a T-shirt, my habitual hospital garb, and my uniform for the daily round of physiotherapy.

SARAH'S DIARY: THURSDAY 7 SEPTEMBER

R. lies on the table and bends his knees up to his chest, in a modified form of sit-ups. Davina helps him by pushing the left knee up and supporting it as he leans his nose in. But gradually she takes her hand away – and he continues to do it. Each day, as he takes steps with his right leg, she supports the left leg less and less. It really is coming back. She says she feels things in the shoulder, and now in the elbow, but I don't want to think that way – I don't want it to be the only way of gauging achievement. So many of the achievements are mental, finding new attitudes about things or realizing that you can do things you didn't think you could given your level of mobility. He's starting to stand up and pee in the toilet now, instead of using the little bottle they leave by his bed. That to me is a huge achievement.

The truth is: we live in our bodies, and any failure of a bodily kind seem doubly terrible. The body fails; you fail. A stroke brings you face to face with these limitations: the human scale of everything that we do. Reduced to this amount of movement I began to wonder: How much space did I actually need? A single room? Ten feet by twelve? More? And what possessions did I really need? Marcus Aurelius had told me that 'Were you to live three thousand years, or even thirty thousand, remember that the sole life which a man can lose is that which he is living at the moment; and furthermore, that he can have no other life except the one he loses.' What did any of it matter if you are in a wheelchair, or confined to a bed? When you are reduced to one room, what are your true requirements? A modem? A satellite? I found I was watching television incessantly. I love reading, but often felt so tired and incapable that I couldn't read for long. It was too much of an effort to hold a book, and quite impossible to fold a newspaper. Meanwhile, with so much frustration and depression, my relationship with Sarah was going through some vertiginous moments. Both our diaries record its ups and downs at this time, the shift in the balance of power between us.

SARAH'S DIARY: SATURDAY 9 SEPTEMBER
We had a big fight this weekend when I insisted that R. go to the park. (It was a beautiful day, I think there must be something unhealthy and horrible about being cooped up in the same room for weeks on end.) He didn't want to go, and then I had trouble manoeuvring the wheelchair over the bumps in the street crossing. He began to snipe at me. I started to cry. But it precipitated quite a

good talk. R. said he felt helpless and angry. I told him that I was as unnerved by all this as he was, that his being immobile felt just as bad to me as if it were me immobile. What I couldn't say, though, was: I never learned to push a wheelchair that had my husband in it. I never expected this to happen, or prepared myself for it, or imagined it. Why do you expect me to know what to do?

I was terribly ashamed of the fury I'd directed at Sarah who was, after all, only trying to do her best. I rationalized that I had a right to be angry, but even now I still recall the moment with the wheelchair trapped on the street corner by the pedestrian crossing – me raging, Sarah in floods of tears – with horror and embarrassment.

As the September days passed, and my mood darkened, Sarah thought I should ask Dr Greenwood if I could see a psychotherapist. Despite everything that had passed between us, I still believed in my own powers of recovery and was unsure that the time had come to call in outside help. When eventually I did see Greenwood, and raised the question of my low spirits, we discussed my depression and moved on to the circumscribed world of the room, the cell, and the school dormitory. I compared my stroke to the experience of boarding school. It was not just that the architecture of hospital (corridors, staircases) is evocative of school. There were other, curious parallels: being in the hospital was like being sent away to school for a term, even though just at that moment I could see no end to being there. My answer to the question of psychotherapy was to say that I felt it would soon be time to see my psychoanalyst friend Adam Phillips again, and have another chat.

One of the high points of my recovery at this time was the inspiring kindness of my friends Don and Hilary Boyd who, seeing the depths of immobilized melancholy into which I'd sunk, simply breezed in one day and announced that they were taking me to the cinema. Don is a film-maker. From this outing (my first recreational moment since I'd been hospitalized) was born what we came to call the McBoyd Cinema Club, a regular Saturday afternoon movie-going fraternity of four which, throughout that autumn of 1995, attended some of the deadliest films of that year, possibly of all time, from *Braveheart* to *The Bridges of Madison County* and *Rob Roy*. However, it was from these outings that I learned what it might mean to be permanently disabled and in a wheelchair. I discovered, for instance, how awkwardly the world is constructed if you cannot walk, and how, on a crowded pavement, the majority of passers-by simply do not see the disabled person, and/or treat you with a mixture of ruthless disdain and pitying arrogance. Experiences like these made me more than ever determined to get on my feet again, if possible.

The conundrum of stroke recovery is that while one's conscious efforts are devoted to recovering one's lost self, the cruel fact is that this former self is irretrievably shattered into a thousand pieces, and try as one may to glue those bits together again, the reconstituted version of the old self will never be better than a cracked, imperfect assembly, a constant mockery of one's former, successful individuality.

As I felt stronger, I felt close to being able to do more work. I began to wonder if I should start to type up my diary. Or perhaps I should dictate it into a tape recorder? I couldn't decide, and in truth didn't really have enough energy either for one-handed typing or dictation. I wasn't sure, either, that my speech was up to a tape recorder yet. Time hung heavily every day. *Time* – the word appears throughout my scribbled diary: *Time*, *time*, *time* . . . Time the healer, time the gaoler. I still had no measure of my progress, and was resigned to taking things week by week, and day by day.

I found myself wondering what I should have done without Sarah: she was a miracle, a total support, a truly wonderful wife. When we'd first met she had liked to tell stories against herself to suggest her unfitness to function in the world (for example, the time when, as a cub reporter, she had attended a press conference about an unfortunate incident on Staten Island in which a man shot and killed his wife and then himself. Sarah had listened to the hard men of the press corps firing questions at the police spokesman – what kind of gun? when did the police arrive? where were the bodies? what were their names? etc., etc. – and had finally plucked up courage to ask a question on behalf of the *New York Times*. 'How many shots?' she yelled out. Dead silence. 'Who asked that?' barked the cop. Sarah mumbled her name and the *New York Times* and the cop said witheringly, 'Sarah, a guy shoots himself in the head, he shoots himself once.'). Now I was discovering that my apparently scatterbrained wife was secretly a triumph of organization and competence, as well as being supremely capable of soothing my manifold anxieties. When she read aloud in the evenings – we had moved on to *Pride and Prejudice* now – she made me feel calm and good again, and almost relaxed. The continuing routine of physio and speech therapy had become a source of comfort and solace, its very repetitiveness strangely reassuring.

Sarah's diary: Thursday 14 September

Strength is slowly, steadily returning to his leg. Davina makes him sit down and stand up for hours at a time.

After about two weeks in the Devonshire, I found that the toes in my left foot, formerly cold and lifeless, were starting to move. On 15 September, I noted in my diary that 'today Davina noticed that my toes were gripping the ground, just for a moment, blink and you'd miss it – but the first actual toe activity in a month.' This was an emotional moment for me, the first sign of recovery in the left leg. (When it was immobilized it was always 'the'; only when movement came back did I claim it as 'my'.) The excitement was intense. Later that same day, when Sarah was taking off my socks in the evening, we suddenly saw independent movement. There they were – my left toes moving! It was like finding life on Mars. All at once, I began to imagine that I might get regular use back to the other 'lost' parts of my body.

Sarah's diary: Friday 15 September

I was helping R. take off his socks last night, and – miracle – his three biggest toes wiggled! And then he did it again. I began to cry, which seems to be my reaction to most things these days. It's a tremendous effort to do things that aren't related to R.'s illness. I feel upset if that's all people want to talk about, and then upset if they don't talk about it, as if they had no right to go on with their lives while this horror was happening to us. So I force myself to see people and to accept invitations. But I feel sometimes like a cartoon character who runs off a cliff and begins to fall – but only after he's looked down and seen that he's walking on air.

After five weeks of an experience I'd come to think of as prison, I found myself wondering: does the flickering in the toes of my left leg mean the beginning of new life? I could spend literally hours staring at my immobilized foot trying to 'think' a connection between my brain and my toes. These were among the most frustrating moments of my recovery and I would exhaust myself in my futile efforts. This was indeed a humiliating lesson in one's impotence over one's body.

And now Sarah, ever the indefatigable researcher, found an acupuncturist, Dr Zhu, to encourage this recovery. Rather sheepishly, we decided to ask Dr Greenwood whether he would approve of our getting in touch with him. In my conventional English way, I was dubious of the efficacy of alternative medicine, but my feeling was that it couldn't do any harm, and given that I still had no feeling on the – my – left side, it might do some good. Despite Davina's supreme efforts my progress was still painfully slow. I remember telling Sarah at this stage that I was willing to trade becoming a pincushion for a bit of feeling and sensation in my left side. In orthodox medical matters I had hitherto been profoundly sceptical: now, as well as entertaining the possibility of acupuncture, I was reading books with subtitles like *The Breakthrough Medical Programme that Regenerates Your Mental Energy, Memory and Learning Abilities*.

SARAH'S DIARY: MONDAY 18 SEPTEMBER
Davina taped R.'s leg up with a bandage and helped him as he walked around a table! He actually did it. And I saw another flicker in his toes, too. I felt so proud and so happy and so hopeful, and R. was almost ebullient when we got upstairs.

As things come along more with his leg, I'm focusing all my worry and depression on Robert's arm, which hasn't shown much improvement besides the flicker of feeling in the shoulder that they started noticing early on. He has more feeling in it, he says, and they say that's a very good sign, as things go. They say it might come back, but it might not come back. At least there's still a possibility, and it's that that keeps me hoping. I think so hard about how bad it would be to have an arm that was totally useless. I suppose in the scheme of things it wouldn't be that terrible – you could still write, still read, still drive (apparently); it would just require finding new ways of doing the old things, which takes time and, much worse, is an alarming reminder that you're not the same as you were. You want so much to be exactly the same, to have things go back to exactly the way they were before, and they never will. But what I'm trying to tell myself is maybe that's not so bad.

As my stay in the Devonshire stretched into September, I found I lost my sense of time and could not, for some reason, keep track of dates. I woke up one morning wondering how long I had been there. Perhaps two weeks? Or was it three? Ever since the stroke had happened, I'd doubted my mental capacity, and now I became convinced, as I did periodically, that I was actually losing my mind. Actually, it had been little more than six weeks since the stroke itself.

I was glad that at least I had kept a record of this experience: regularly at nine forty-five I would sit in the wheelchair, write my diary and wait for the first session of physiotherapy for the day. It was remarkable what strength Davina had created in my left leg. My left toes were now working fully, which was exciting. The routine of physiotherapy was this: first, being trundled down the corridor in the wheelchair; then, down in the lift, for which we often had to wait interminably. Then downstairs in the basement we'd negotiate the double doors and face a blast of air-conditioning from the gym. Next it was off with the socks, off with the shoulder-brace and left wrist-splint and shirt (here, I was unpleasantly and unavoidably reminded of preparing for outdoor games at school). Then, I'd perform ten 'sit-to-stands', then ten more, then some exercises for my arms, then more lower-body therapy. Davina would grip my knees and buttocks and try to get my body to work. She would do this by urging me to attempt the action and then by making the movement herself where I was unable to respond. Every morning while I waited for physiotherapy I'd look at the TV section to see what was on TV to while away the evening. Such was life in gaol.

Dr Greenwood turned out to be totally supportive of the idea of acupuncture, and asked Sarah to ask Dr Zhu, the acupuncturist, to telephone him for his approval. The British medical profession these days is much more open to the idea of alternative therapies than in the past. Dr Zhu was, apparently, properly Chinese, and had trained in Shanghai, which was reassuring.

At the point at which Dr Zhu came into my life, my left arm was still hanging like a dead thing, its fingers seeming as cold and soggy as dead meat. My left leg was like lead, with no feeling or movement apart from the toes. My head ached intermittently. No one seemed to know whether or not I was improving, or if they did, they wouldn't say. I found the refusal of the experts to commit themselves immensely frustrating. When pressed, the physiotherapists said that they could see what they called 'flickers'. I could put weight on my left leg. With a bit of luck – 'maybe' – I would soon be able to walk. My speech was still slurred, and speaking was an effort. The most frightening headaches seemed to have gone. I wondered: were the headaches something to do with convalescence? On some days, my legs ached as if suddenly released from cramped quarters. Despite Dr Lees's words when I first went to the National Hospital, any new headache made me afraid. Was this the warning of another stroke? A precursor of a fatal recurrence? I think Sarah felt the same.

Time did not seem so bad now as in the days past. I had been brought closer to many people, including Sarah, whom I loved anyway, but who now seemed totally indispensable. I had also been made aware of things I did not know about; I was older in experience. I had not changed much otherwise – I looked much the same and still felt reasonably young at heart, though often terribly frustrated. If this was a brush with death, I knew now that it could have been much worse. So it was a timely reminder, a tap on the shoulder, a clearing of the throat behind me, a *memento mori*. I also felt as if I had been given a glimpse of old age – the helplessness and dependency and the waiting for things to happen. Before, in my 'old' life, I had always been the youngest in any group; now I would feel like the oldest, at least in experience.

SARAH'S DIARY: WEDNESDAY 20 SEPTEMBER

I dreamed that I was in an elevator that was barrelling up and down in a skyscraper, out of control and not stopping at the right floor, and I began to panic. There was a stranger in the elevator and I ran over and threw my arms around him in fear. When the elevator began to calm down, he still wanted to hug me, and I didn't want to. When it stopped at the right floor, he stalked away.

Robert is only slurring now when he talks too fast. His breathing is the only thing that seems to be still affected – he runs out of breath at the end of sentences – but it's very discouraging for him, and hard for me, because I want so much for it to be fine. He calls at work on our special line and my heart lifts and when he can't make himself so well understood I feel so sad.

The routine went on. Breakfast at eight o'clock (Alpen, grapefruit and coffee), then shower and shave, transfer back to the wheelchair, dress and dry, then sit in the wheelchair and make notes, and wait for the physiotherapist. My moods fluctuated wildly: one morning I had a blow-up with Catherine, the occupational therapist, as I was coming out of the shower. She had come to inspect my feeble efforts at dressing myself (to evaluate the likelihood of my return home), and was driving me mad by watching me struggle into my clothes and offering no help. This was an example of 'tough love', and to me it was absolutely infuriating.

Catherine: 'Everyone is concerned that you are over-using your right side.'

Me: 'Who is everyone?'

Catherine: 'The nurses.'

Me: 'But the nurses change all the time. How on earth can they have any opinions worth having?'

Catherine (defensively): 'Davina is very concerned about the overuse of your right side.'

Me: 'She's never said so. And what do you mean, "overusing my right side"? All I've got is my right side!'

I sank into a furious silence. I felt as if I had been treated like an idiot and a child. After this the atmosphere between us became very cool and difficult, a breakdown in relations that was entirely my fault – Catherine is a fine and dedicated professional. I felt better for having written it down in my diary, and added, as a PS, 'Thank God for Davina!' In the end, I was saved by Dr Greenwood's arrival. He seemed to know how vile my mood had been. Greenwood and I then discussed (a) my mood and (b) the possibility of psychotherapy. I mentioned my friendship with Adam Phillips once more but said that I was against seeing a shrink: I couldn't imagine what we would talk about, or how it would be helpful. I knew I was supposed to feel angry about my situation, and depressed, but when I did get angry, it was fairly unspecific, and came in moments of frustration, rather than all the time. On the whole, I said, I accepted my fate, and was trying to work within the restrictions that had been set down by it. I repeated that I didn't see how therapy would help. Greenwood said that we were approaching an exceptionally difficult phase that was typical of stroke recovery. He was quite specific about this, and it was clear that he believed this would be a period as trying to Sarah, the carer, as for me, the convalescent. I found him wise and sober and helpful. I had come to trust him completely; and I was determined to get through this phase without becoming overwhelmed by depression and hopelessness.

SARAH'S DIARY: THURSDAY 21 SEPTEMBER
I watch Robert do his physical therapy and get so alarmed when Davina says things like, 'Your knee's not really coming in.' What does that mean? Still nothing in his arm, and Davina is saying if it comes back at all, it might take months, not to expect anything day to day. Robert can shuffle around if he's wearing an enormous

bandage that supports his leg, and if Davina walks along behind him, supporting his waist. He's been very grumpy and sniping at me a lot. I feel – I feel depressed. Dr Greenwood said we're approaching what's in some ways the hardest part, because the more Robert improves the angrier he gets about what he still can't do.

When I did not sleep well, when I watched the light under the door and wondered when dawn would come, I found my night-time full of fears and thoughts about my future. Perhaps this was a sign that I was finally getting better. Life seemed to be inching slowly towards normality at last; the possibility of going home seemed more feasible. In my daily visits to the physiotherapy gym, I found that I could nearly walk, but my left foot was not strong, and, lacking muscle control at the ankle, dragged badly. As Sarah had noted, the more I got better, the greater my frustration.

It was time for a haircut. Each morning my hair was taking longer and longer to dry, and then I realized – a sobering thought – that it had last been cut just before I got married. When I rehearsed these long, strange weeks since our wedding – our honeymoon in Morocco, our first days at home together in London, the party we'd planned to give for our friends who'd not managed to come to Philadelphia – I recognized that we had been strangely lucky. I felt so close to Sarah now, and hoped that when we got home together we should be closer still. I was sure that the experience had been very good for our marriage in the long term, and we used to say to each other that if we could survive this we could survive anything.

The next big excitement was the arrival of Dr Zhu. He was distinctly Chinese, dressed very plainly in a grey-green shirt and a black tweed jacket, and dark green felt trousers. As soon as he arrived he produced an article about his work from *The Times*, rather like an author producing his reviews. This amused Sarah and me greatly. He asked the nurse to take a Xerox copy of the article so that we could keep it. I lay on the bed in my underpants and shut my eyes, and then quite suddenly he told me that he had put a needle in my arm. I had felt nothing. I was quite alarmed, but lay there patiently. After my experiences at the National, Dr Zhu's needles seemed comparatively unthreatening. Millions of people had had this treatment; there was no need to worry. The acupuncture itself was like a series of tiny mosquito bites. Dr Zhu put two or three in my arm, and several in my leg and ankle on the left side, also one in my belly and one in the top of my head, which was a bit more unnerving. After about twenty minutes he removed the needles. I felt very lazy and sleepy after this and wondered if this was connected with the acupuncture. Dr Zhu said he would come again on Tuesday, and then again next Saturday. The evening after his first visit, I seemed to have a slight tingling in my right arm, which, presumably, had something to do with the acupuncture.

SARAH'S DIARY: MONDAY 25 SEPTEMBER

A good weekend. Dr Zhu, the funny little acupuncturist in a black jacket and tie, came by and stuck tiny little needles up and down Robert's left side. He said the stroke had thrown his body out of balance, and the idea was to bring the balance back. How this is achieved with puny pins that you would use for sewing buttons on is beyond me, but whatever. If I support him, Robert can walk a few steps. We're getting along much better – I just snap back at him, and he knows I'm not going to put up with any bad behaviour. I can see a tiny, tiny glimmer of light down at the end of the very long and dark tunnel. Robert will start coming home soon on weekends. Big adjustment – creeping up the stairs, hobbling into the bathroom, being tired all the time – but it's progress.

Finally, as planned, I spoke to Adam Phillips about psychotherapy. He told me that, these days, hospitals are all into therapy in a big way; he advised me to wait till I really wanted to do it, which exactly reinforced my opinion. I think Sarah found my reluctance to admit a need for psychoanalytic help extraordinarily incomprehensible, but such help is not part of my culture and I took the view that there were enough people fussing over my needs already. In physiotherapy, in which I was now participating enthusiastically, I was learning to negotiate the hospital stairs, with immense difficulty, and beginning to feel more stable on two legs.

One of the innovations employed by the Devonshire in convalescence was the video camera. I still possess a VHS cassette of my pathetic efforts at walking during these weeks. When I watch it now I can hardly imagine being so enfeebled and helpless, and see with shock the lines of despair on my face.

I found myself thinking that it would be nice to get home, where I would feel more independent. I had reached the stage where I was feeling more energetic internally, and fed up with the hospital/prison routine. Getting up in the mornings was hard. All I wanted to do was lie in. I found the shower and shave routine an absolute tyranny, and I longed for a bath, for a long soak.

By the end of September, I was beginning to take unsupported steps, but my left leg flailed out wildly and it was hard for me to retain my balance. I'd been at the Devonshire about a month when Dr Greenwood convened a conference of my various physical therapists to evaluate my progress.

SARAH'S DIARY: WEDNESDAY 27 SEPTEMBER
We had a case conference last night, a meeting where all the therapists sit around and talk about the patient. They're all so dour. Dr Greenwood said Robert's arm would never work again. Part of me wants to just prove him wrong. We were all sitting there waiting for Robert, and he came in with Davina, walking unsteadily, making a triumphal entrance that seemed to announce, 'No matter what you say, look what I can do.' My heart lifted so much, and we all had a good laugh about Robert's shoes. He's bubbly, now that he's starting to be able to walk. Life suddenly looks good, and I feel as though I'm slowly thawing out and rejoining the world again.

Chris Cunningham was my Irish nurse during this phase of recovery, and I came to like her immensely. She was friendly, bright, and very encouraging. Each morning we now did what Chris called 'a soft-shoe shuffle' into the bathroom. 'Don't tell Davina,' she'd say. It felt pleasantly illicit to take steps in the privacy of the room, and I had the constant fear of falling over, but I enjoyed having my little secret with Chris, and I looked forward to having the morning session with her. Dr Zhu, who now came three times a week, was always very calm and professional. He put his needles in my arm, leg, belly and, finally, head. The last one was always alarming, although I didn't ever feel much more than

163

the mosquito-bite sensation. After bending over me for some minutes he would stand back and count, one–two–three, up to fifteen, then he would do a few more. Finally he'd be done, and I'd lie there, feeling drowsy. Dr Zhu wanted to know if I could feel the energy passing down my left leg. To encourage him I would say, 'Yes', though actually all I could feel was the continuing ache of the muscle and the bone. Nothing seemed to be happening, but the truth was that, since his first visit, I had been walking more confidently on my left leg, so perhaps this was a victory for acupuncture. Who knows? I used to tease Davina about Dr Zhu's extraordinary skills, which became quite a byword in her department. (Dr Zhu treated me for about three months. Sarah and I became very fond of him; we learned that he had fled Shanghai to live in the West, and when we began to feel sorry for him, enduring the life of exile in Britain, were relieved to discover that he had a beautiful Welsh girlfriend to whom he was engaged to be married.)

The more I thought about my returning movement, the more I found that when I was watching TV I tended to focus on what people were doing with their arms and legs. I still look at athletes on television with a kind of wistful envy for their ease and mobility. As far as the outside world was concerned, I was still at death's door. Occasionally I would get a letter from the outside which I didn't understand. People would write and say, 'I am praying for you.' What on earth did this mean? Such people obviously believed in God, or said they did, but it made no sense to me. Alas. Prayer is not about answers, as I see it, but questions. We pray to resolve things that trouble us within. Not for the first time, I found myself comparing my room to a monastic cell. So, now: what size was this room? Ten by ten, perhaps. Is that the size of a cell? My mood was now much better, calmer and more philosophical. The end, i.e. getting home, was in sight, even if I was going to have to learn to adopt a different pace.

[12]

Slowness

28 September – 7 October

> You will never get it, if you don't slow down.
>
> Paul Auster, *Smoke*

In preparation for the next stage of convalescence, at home, Davina arranged for me to be taken back to our house in St Peter's Street to see how well I could negotiate the stairs and handle the complexities of domestic life as a 'disabled person'. We went early one morning in the Devonshire Hospital car, taking the road to Islington, with Davina driving. I directed her along the familiar back route, enjoying the Dickensian twists and turns of the road; it was such a thrill, after so long indoors, to see the old sights again. In Danbury Street the rowan trees were full of fruit, and the mellow autumn sunlight reflected brilliantly off the Islington stucco. Sarah was waiting for us at No. 41. To my amazement, I found I was able, with Davina's supporting help, to walk very slowly and unsteadily across the pavement to the house and up the steps to the front door. It seemed years ago that I had been carried out of there on a stretcher. Still upright, I made it into the ground-floor living room and sat down. The atmosphere seemed cold and shadowy. It was odd, and upsetting, to be back in the room in which I had been lying for so much of that distant Saturday; it was hard to shake off the terrible memory of that experience.

We sat, with cups of freshly brewed coffee (an extraordinary luxury, to me) and explored the possibilities of my being at home. My own feeling was that I would be more confident being there. The worst of it would be dressing and bathing. Finally, after a tour of the house, with Davina measuring up for rails on the stairs, and a grab-rail by the bath, we went back to the Devonshire, where I suddenly felt profoundly tired.

I had been out of action for nine weeks. In the scale of things this was not so long. Soon, perhaps next weekend, I would be going home. Dr Greenwood was now proposing to start me on one aspirin (75 mg) a day, to thin my blood. Just a precaution, he said. I found that as the day of my departure drew closer I was in a worse mood about everything and obsessively anxious to leave the Devonshire. I realized that by the time I did get home I should have been in hospital for the length of an English school term, twelve weeks. I couldn't wait to get out: each day seemed longer and more boring than the last, and, to make the time pass, I watched more and more TV. One of the after-effects of my stroke is that I've remained quite a telly-addict where previously I'd scorned watching TV.

SARAH'S DIARY: MONDAY 2 OCTOBER
Robert's making really good, steady physical progress: he can walk on his own, if he knows he'll be able to grab on to something, and when he wears the bandage [*on his ankle*] that mimics the brace, he can even walk up

and down stairs. He jerks his leg forward and has to think about where to put it down, and how to make it hold weight while he takes the next step. His knee and ankle are weak. He's still very tired, and I keep worrying that he'll always be tired. And nothing much happening in the arm; Catherine, the occupational therapist, gave me what looks like a junior vibrator with instructions on how to use it to stimulate Robert's arm. You rub it back and forth in different sections thirty times in a row. It runs by battery, so no fear of electrocution. We're getting ready to bring Robert home. He says it worries him, coming home and being able to do so much less than he did. But not really less, is what I think, when I'm being cheery about this. He won't be able to open jars or carry the groceries or get dressed very easily, but he'll be able to work, and to drive (we hope), and to read and write and talk and think and make love, and be just the same as ever. We went home yesterday for the day, and it was sheer bliss.

They've done a refit of our house, putting in new rails along the stairs and steps in the bathroom to help Robert haul himself around. £700, but it doesn't look too alarmingly disabled-fitted; the banisters are nice wood and make a pass at fitting in with ours. Robert still very tired and, as the day of coming home approaches (next week, we think), getting more and more grumpy, in part because he's reached the end of his tether at the hospital, and in part because of fears of coming home. I've seen him really lose his temper a few times, where he bangs his arm down and just explodes. It can be because I drop a glass of orange juice, or because he can't do something, but it's very upsetting. I know it's because of his illness. But it makes me really scared, anyway.

I'm bad-tempered, too. But there are good moments, and good hours, and good days, and Robert in general being very sweet and very brave. I suspect that going home won't be as bad as I dread. But I have more dreams of murder – last night that it was Mom who murdered someone, but somehow I was guilty, too. It's the third time I've dreamed I was a murderer and nobody knew it. Robert is going to have to wear a brace in his shoe that's made of plastic and goes all the way up to his knee. The point is to support his ankle, which is still very weak. He may have to use a cane, but actually that might make it more difficult, because it's another thing to think about, and according to Davina, it throws your balance off and gets you into bad muscle habits. He can now make his way slowly, slowly across the room into the bathroom on his own – no more wheelchairs in the evenings.

People forget about the relatives of stroke-sufferers. Of course they have their moods, too, and their own convalescent cycle of readjustment.

SARAH'S DIARY: TUESDAY 3 OCTOBER
For some reason it was much harder than I would have thought to adjust to his paralysed left arm, which doesn't work at all. It's as if everything has been distilled down to his arm, that it's not working has come to symbolize everything awful about this experience. People say you go through a period of mourning for your lost powers. Perhaps I've been putting that off for myself, and now that he's coming home finally have to face up to what's happened. Poor Robert. I worry so much about him. Poor me, who's not handling this part very well.

Sarah was right to identify my left arm as the source of anger and despair. Although it was lifeless, it was not without feeling: at times it could be excruciatingly painful. In addition it had developed a swelling (bursa) on the left elbow, which had become tender and very vulnerable. On those occasions when I banged my arm inadvertently, I would rage in a fury at the excruciating pain.

Eventually I was allowed to go home. At noon on the appointed day, 5 October, Greenwood's office rang to say that I would have to wait for an extra two hours to see a doctor about my bursa. This meant that we had to wait till six o'clock, and arrange for the car to come at six thirty. Sure enough, by six thirty there was no sign of the doctor, and the car was waiting downstairs. The delay became profoundly frustrating; all I wanted to do was leave.

Finally the doctor, a Mr Huskisson, arrived at about a quarter to seven. He took one look at my arm, and said that it was fine to leave it alone, that it was a benign bursa, and not to worry. That was it. He was very cheery, competent and matter-of-fact. The thing that struck me was that, after so many weeks of the doctors' not saying what was wrong with me, it was peculiar to have somebody who knew exactly what was wrong, and who could, if necessary, prescribe an exact cure. This is the contract of medicine, the contract between doctor and patient that had been missing for so many weeks.

So then I limped, with the greatest effort and difficulty to the third floor elevator, making my farewells to the nurses on duty as I went. Downstairs, I negotiated my way slowly to the car, which was being driven by an Iraqi who was himself recovering from major back surgery. It was exhilarating to be in a civilian vehicle again, driving through the streets of London and seeing the signs of the rush-hour. Even the delay on the Marylebone Road seemed pleasant, and I enjoyed looking at the office workers hurrying through the darkness towards Euston Station. Then we were going up Pentonville Road, and turning into Upper Street, with Sarah in the front, chatting away to the driver about his recovery, following her natural instinct to interview anyone with a story. So then we were driving down Upper Street, and inching along the Essex Road, and turning right into St Peter's Street, and suddenly I was home, and walking down the pavement slowly with the Iraqi driver carrying my bags into the house as if I'd just been away on a long trip.

We went into the living room together, sat down, and drank the champagne S. (a friend) had given me at the Devonshire, and toasted the future. I felt very perked up by everything, and immensely relieved to be out of the hospital at last, and with no sign of having to go back, either. Then we had supper, and finally we went upstairs to bed. And this was a new, almost undreamed-of luxury, to lie on our double bed, to stretch out, and to feel less cramped than I had for so many weeks.

Lying in bed on my back, looking at the ceiling, I remembered again the day it all happened, and reflected on the nature of time. In some ways this whole experience had been like a punctuation mark in the middle of my life. For years I had lived freely, and at will. I had been independent, able to do what I liked whenever I liked, and had travelled widely around the world. Now I needed help with everything, including getting dressed and bathed, and the idea of leaving the house was unthinkable – almost frightening, really.

It is, perhaps, not possible to overestimate the significance of a serious stroke in the life of the average person.

It is an event that goes to the core of who and what you are, the You-ness of you. First of all, the event happens in your brain which is, without becoming unduly philosophical, the command centre of the self. Your brain is you: your moods, your skills, your character, your intelligence, your emotions, your self-expression, your self. When all that fails, you are left with the question: what was the cause? The doctors can answer questions about blood and veins and arteries and cholesterol, but that, as a friend of mine put it so aptly, is 'just the plumbing'. You – the you that's survived this upheaval within – are still left with the question: why? Before you can begin to get to why? you have to ask yourself: what? What was it that I went through? What is its significance? What does it mean? These are questions which bring us inexorably back to Why?

In my case, since the doctors had failed to find a reliable explanation for my stroke, I came to the conclusion that it happened as the outcome of a profound internal dissatisfaction with my way of life, my goals and ambitions, my achievements such as they were. Before the stroke happened, I'd reached a point in my professional life when I could almost literally not see my way forward. So it came as a physical punctuation mark, a reminder from my body to pause and to take stock. What I needed was a season of vulnerability. In the language of psychobabble, I needed to get in touch with myself again, and perhaps – who knows? – only a catastrophic physical breakdown could achieve that.

In contrast with the hospital, being at home was wonderful: I could look out of the window and see trees, and leaves, and blue sky, and the movement of people. I could, with some effort, be either downstairs or upstairs. For some reason the idea of walking down to the kitchen seemed one level too far, but I could struggle laboriously upstairs to my sunlit study, and sit at my desk, write things down, and feel able to express myself again, which was exhilarating. In my curiosity about the outside world I became obsessed by the people living in the houses that backed on to our little garden. I developed what I thought of as a 'Rear Window' fixation about their daily movements and routines. It was not until, some months later, when I was coming and going more easily, that I lost the urge to stare fixedly across the gap between the houses and spy on the lives displayed before me.

How did this stage of my convalescence proceed? At first, it was a massive relief to be home again, a milestone in my slow return to the world I'd lost, but then depression began to set in. I became more and more obsessed with my disabilities, and more and more frustrated. And yet, if I could look at it objectively, there was much to be thankful for. In the first months of my convalescence I found I was doing a number of things that in August I had imagined I might never do again. I made a call from a pay phone. I took a train. I flew in an aeroplane. I went swimming. I ordered a meal in a restaurant. I made love to my wife. In subsequent months I continued to repossess my experience of the world. I went to the opera (*Don Giovanni*). I walked alone to post a letter. I got my driving licence back. I made – and kept – an appointment to get my hair cut. I took a (to me) perfectly hair-raising journey on the London Underground. I went to the dentist. Slowly, I recovered pieces of my old way of life, bit by bit, as if reconstructing a scattered jigsaw. But 'slow' was the operative word.

Six months before, I had been able to slip across the street to post a letter in the time it now takes to type this sentence. When I got home, after my time in the Devon-shire, to cross the street and achieve the same result I would have to raise myself up from my chair, find my cane, limp to the front door (say, three minutes), nego-tiate the steps to the street and make my way to the corner (roughly, five minutes), then hobble back and collapse exhausted on a sofa in my living room, as though I had just run a marathon. Every day I was acutely reminded that there was a world out there, a world I could not be part of in quite the same way. In my new mood of self-examination I was inclined to say, So what? One tangible effect of my illness has been a more Zen-like response to the pressures and anxieties of the world.

The truth is that in my 'old' life as a fit person I had become a monster of irresponsibility. For years I had lived for my freedom. I would look up and see the jets circling over London and say to myself, 'There is no reason why I should not be on a plane to anywhere in the world, at an hour's notice.' I revelled in ways of escape. Psychologically speaking, I carried a passport and a wallet full of international credit cards. Before my stroke, I'd been dissatisfied with my lot; in hospital I'd come to recognize that I'd been ambushed by the 'adventure' I'd been looking for, and was travelling into a new and strange interior: my heart. Now, my passport was in a drawer and I had not made even a domestic credit-card transaction in four months.

In my new and vulnerable condition, I became dependent on my wife and together we discovered an intimacy that, if things had been different, might have taken years to establish. Sarah, who had married me, she says, in part because I seemed 'strong and vigorous', was now seeing me at my weakest and most exposed. It was hard for both of us, and it demanded constant readjustment. Once I left the hospital and came home, I needed Sarah for so many humble everyday routines: to help me in and out of the bath in the morning; to make our bed; to get me ready for the day. Strictly speaking, I could dress myself, but in practice, I could not do without her: I could not tie a tie, or button a cuff. When, finally, I put on my shoes it was Sarah who would ease my feet first into my socks, then, with the AFO 'splint' that supported my ankle and foot, into my shoes, and knot the laces. If the morning post brought medical bills to pay it was Sarah who tore the cheques off at the stub, sealed and stamped the envelope. What else? It was Sarah who had to put the breakfast on the table and who brought home the food for our evening meal. Additionally, I had to learn that everything takes time.

I became friends with slowness, both as a concept and as a way of life. In the past I had been noted for the impressionistic speed with which I could accomplish things. At first, the contrast with my present way of life was a source of great frustration. At times I felt an anger inside me, a rage that could come out in sudden and terrible ways. I had to learn to be patient. In English, of course, the adjectival and nominal meaning of 'patient' comes from the Latin for 'suffering' – *patientia*. A patient is by definition 'long-suffering'. It was then that I realized what Dr Greenwood had meant when he had warned me about this post-crisis stage of recovery. 'You are,' he'd said, on one of his evening visits to my bedside, in a phrase that both Sarah and I found extraordinarily apt for our situations, 'about to go through the rapids.'

[13]

The Rapids

8 October – 12 December

The black dog I hope always to resist, and in time to drive, though I am deprived of almost all those that used to help me . . . When I rise my breakfast is solitary, the black dog waits to share it . . . Night comes at last, and some hours of restlessness and confusion bring me again to a day of solitude. What shall exclude the black dog from a habitation like this?

Samuel Johnson, Letter to Mrs Thrale,
28 June 1783

In her study of Sylvia Plath and Ted Hughes, *The Silent Woman*, Janet Malcolm quotes from Hughes's poem, 'Sheep' (about a lamb that dies inexplicably soon after birth):

> It was not
> That he could not thrive, he was born
> With everything but the will –
> That can be deformed, just like a limb.
> Death was more interesting to him.
> Life could not get his attention.

Janet Malcolm goes on: 'Life, of course never gets anyone's entire attention. Death always remains interesting, pulls us, draws us. As sleep is necessary to our physiology, so depression seems necessary to our psychic economy. In some secret way, Thanatos nourishes Eros as well as opposes it.'

Depression is as old as the Greeks. In the fourth century BC it was Hippocrates who coined the terms *melancholia* and *mania*, and there were days when it seemed as if both had been invented to describe my state of mind. According to Andrew Solomon, an expert in the condition, between 6 and 10 per cent of all Americans now living are battling some form of this illness. Anyway, Dr Greenwood had been absolutely right. After the Devonshire, a new depression rose up and engulfed me like a wave. The fragile vessel of my personality was swamped and buffeted from all sides, and the months after I began to understand that I'd never be quite the same again were to be among the worst of my life, beset with frustration, irritation and the fear of failure. At times, even while I knew that the facts of recovery were on my side, I found myself thinking: My life is over. At the age of forty-two, I appeared to be reduced to the condition of an old man with a cane, watching the world go by, musing sadly on the past. I had been dumped unceremoniously in the land of the unwell (to me, it is no 'kingdom') but it was not until I came to this new place that I realized what a charmed life I'd led. For forty years I had hardly seen a doctor or a hospital. Suddenly, my physical condition was top of the agenda every day of my life. What's more, I was not going to wake up one morning and find myself magically restored to health. The changes in my condition were infinitesimal, obvious only to those who, like Sarah, observed me from day to day. The frustration of this, I decided, was a bit like losing your wallet.

And it was like losing your wallet *every day*. Your wallet *and* your Filofax. The same sense of 'Goddammit!' and that sense of 'Oh, no!' – all those telephone numbers to call, all those connections to remake. All those little short-cuts that make everyday life bearable. Occasionally, when I lay in bed – the bed in which I awoke on that summer morning so long ago – I would think, Perhaps I am dreaming. Sometimes I would say it out loud: Am I dreaming?

Sleep was now my friend, but if I dreamed then I do not recall my dreams. In my depression I was drugged by sleep, drugged and oppressed and anaesthetized and stupefied by its powers. I spent hours and hours asleep. I could sleep late into the morning. Or I could sleep before lunch, and in the early afternoon. I could sleep as the day faded, and again before nightfall. I could sleep early or late, regardless of whether I had spent even twenty of the previous day's twenty-four hours unconscious. The sleep monster had me in his jaws, and I was happy to be under the covers with him. When I worried about becoming narcoleptic, I repeated to myself what the doctors had told me in the National Hospital: that sleep was the brain's way of recuperating from the 'insult'.

Perhaps (I would think on coming to), perhaps I shall wake up and find that the effects of the stroke will have gone away. Yes, perhaps it could be like the ending of the corniest short story: 'And then I woke up, and it was all a dream.' Some aspects of these months became muddled and confused. Time lost focus; events telescoped. Did that really happen? Was this really the case? But no, I was not dreaming, I was changed for ever.

Now that I write this I know that what happened during the night of 28/29 July was an irrevocable moment in my personal history. Sometimes it is difficult for me to acknowledge the importance of what has happened. I come from a tight-lipped culture in which the standard response to misfortune is to assert that one is 'fine', or that one is 'perfectly okay'. It is, of course, massive denial to claim that one is coping when plainly one is not. For me to admit that I was often scared and lonely during these long winter months was as difficult as it was to admit that I could, sometimes, feel a profound anger towards the world that had done this to me.

When, shortly after coming home, I was able to discard my wheelchair, and began to think about going back to work, it seemed for the first time in months that I might make a reasonably full recovery. With my cane, I could sustain a very short, leisurely stroll. I was once more getting out and about in the world, the world I thought I had lost, and which, with Sarah, now seemed to me more precious than ever.

Meanwhile, we both continued to write our fragmentary diaries. Depression hovered over Sarah, too, she who is normally the cheeriest of souls.

SARAH'S DIARY: WEDNESDAY 18 OCTOBER
I feel numb and sleepy all the time; it's hard to work up any enthusiasm for anything. I'm so relieved that Robert is home but in my relief I'm finally feeling the sadness I know I've been beating back all this time. I suppose I have to let myself get through this, too.

My own diary at this time contained pages of unprintable fury, interspersed with an obsessive account of my physical weakness. I had spent my weeks at the Devonshire learning to stand and walk again, but while my left leg had responded to treatment, my left arm was still lifeless and inert. In this condition, my left wrist was vulnerable to spraining and my left shoulder, bearing the full weight of the left arm, could still seem incredibly painful, especially at night. My depression deepened further, and Sarah took the full force of it.

SARAH'S DIARY: THURSDAY 19 OCTOBER
Robert is feeling very sad about his arm, and I am, too. I think I've made my peace with it not coming back. But Robert has to make his peace, too. He tosses and turns at night and worries about it, and I think he's doing what I've been doing: using it as a symbol for all of this, the pain of loss, the unfairness of this happening. When I look at our actual situation now, I don't think it's that bad. But the emotions surrounding it are.

Sarah continued to search for ways of improving the situation, using all her journalistic skills to check out new treatments.

SARAH'S DIARY: FRIDAY 20 OCTOBER
A visit to the Disabled Living Centre, situated very inconveniently for any disabled person, a 15 minute walk from the Westbourne Park tube stop. No park in sight. A sad neighbourhood with 'To Let' signs in most of the shop windows, and shuffling old people with plastic shopping bags. The centre was filled with really ugly shoes, and devices meant to help you out. A lot of them are for wheelchair people; but we need stuff for one-handed people. Hooks to help with buttons; special shoelaces and big shoehorns; reading stands – they have

them all, and a dim woman who sounded stricken and said she was just volunteering for the day, so she really couldn't answer my questions so well. But she was incredibly sweet. All the stuff was laid out like a sad rummage sale, and I felt sorry that more people weren't there for what was supposed to be a Come On In open house. None the less, I left feeling heartened, with a small armful of catalogues and sense of purpose and a feeling that we really can do this.

Looking back, it was Sarah's determination that was so vital during these difficult weeks. Like many stroke-sufferers, I was so exhausted by every tiny detail of everyday life – even the energy required to get up and cross the room to answer the front door or the telephone – that the stress of ordinary life seemed overwhelmingly daunting, and the idea of addressing a self-generated programme of rehabilitation almost impossible. The more I sank into inky black inertia, the more Sarah battled on.

SARAH'S DIARY: SUNDAY 22 OCTOBER
We just have to grit our teeth and get through this period, both of us. I have to adjust to my new multi-purpose role: wife and lover and cheerleader and physiotherapist and cook and housekeeper and nurse and all around drudge. So I have to separate out my distaste of all that from what's happening with Robert. He does get better but it's terribly slow. I worry about his anti-depressants because they make him so dopey at night. I worry that we'll never be back to normal. I love him so much. Outpatient physio began today, and it was very encouraging. Robert has energetic, no-nonsense Sue Edwards, who'll whip him into shape, if anyone will. She worked

on his arm and, wonder of wonders, we actually saw things happening. Little things, but still things. He moved some of his fingers. He moved his elbow the tiniest of bits. I am flabbergasted.

Now that I was home, my physiotherapy was conducted at the outpatients' department of the National Hospital. It was decidedly odd, having spent the summer being wheeled in and out of that gloomy Victorian vestibule with its marmoreal Rolls of Honour to the casualties of the two world wars, now to be awkwardly limping in there through the wheelchair-friendly automatic doors with my stout NHS-issue rubber-tipped cane. At first, I was oppressed by memories of the worst days of August, but as I regained the physical use of my left side I began to feel more positive and optimistic. Sue Edwards, the most recent in what I see with hindsight was a long line of first-class stroke-rehab doctors, was indispensable to this. Under her robust and expert direction – she had no time for convalescent faint-heartedness – I began to make quite speedy progress towards my ideal of self-sufficiency.

For instance, once I'd suffered the stroke, I'd been obliged by law to surrender my driving licence to the Licensing Authority in Swansea, and when I'd been in the Devonshire Hospital, one of my goals had been to be able to drive again. Now that I was venturing out and about in a limited way, I was eager to secure my licence as a disabled driver, and I arranged to be tested at the Banstead Mobility Centre, some twenty miles from Central London, in Surrey.

SARAH'S DIARY: THURSDAY 2 NOVEMBER
I'm scared to death that it won't work out, that they'll

tell him he isn't ready yet, and he'll fall into a funk. I would have thought it was too early, but he was so eager; it was impossible to prevent him from going. I hope, hope that it comes out all right.

For me, however, this was another milestone in my return to everyday life. One morning in November, I made an early start and, alone in the street outside for the first time in weeks, nervously took a taxi down to my assistant Emma's house in Balham, getting to South London by about eight fifteen. Emma gave me coffee and croissants, and then we went on down into Surrey in my Faber company car, with Emma driving. It was exceedingly strange to be back in the old car again, and yet stimulating mentally. In those first weeks at home, the excitement of doing 'old' things for the first time once more never went away, and gave the world a thrilling vividness that it had never had before.

The rush-hour traffic was heavy, but eventually we got through Norbury and places like Carshalton and Wallington, and reached Banstead, where the famous Mobility Centre is situated. It is in the grounds of a former children's polio and TB hospital, on a hill, as so many of them had been. We drove round a circular avenue between autumnal trees. There were little red-brick houses dotted around the grounds, former children's wards. After a certain amount of difficulty we presented ourselves at the Mobility Centre and waited to be called for the examination. This was my first encounter with the world outside hospital, and it was an exhausting experience.

The first test was 'orthoptics', and here I was relieved to discover that, despite everything, I still had perfect sight, and that my left and right fields of vision had not been impaired by the stroke, as will happen to so many. From orthoptics I went down the corridor to a physiotherapist and a driving instructor. The physiotherapist checked out the weakness on my left side, then the driving instructor seated me in a simulator and tested my reactions in various hypothetical driving situations – a woman and baby crossing the road unexpectedly, a cat running out suddenly, a truck braking and so on.

The instructor said my reactions were pretty quick – quicker actually than the national average, he said, i.e. less than half a second. Then he showed me how easy it would be to adapt my car for one-handed driving with the installation of a remote control (like a TV zapper) on the steering wheel. I was very encouraged by this, and optimistic that I could soon get back on the road. I was sent outside to wait for the actual driving-test stage of the day. Eventually, I was put into a car with the special adaptation made to the steering wheel, and then we drove round a little testing circle a few times, an exercise I found exhilarating but profoundly tiring. Finally the instructor told me that if I had been attempting a real driving test I would have flunked, mainly due to my failure to look in the driver's mirror. None the less, he said he would recommend that I had my driver's licence adjusted, so that I could drive my car. This was a great relief, since without Banstead's (or its equivalent) approval, you are basically grounded.

For quite different reasons, I think Sarah and I were both pleased that I had passed the Banstead tests without too much difficulty.

Perhaps it was not a coincidence that, after my day at Banstead, in physiotherapy I achieved the great milestone of at last getting my left arm to move. It sounds trivial, but after so many weeks of having it hang lifeless by my side, unresponsive to all attempts to move it, the moment when I found I could raise it, even a few inches, was quite extraordinarily exciting. I wrote in my diary, 'Sue Edwards is a genius, and gets movement where nobody else seems to find it. Sarah was very encouraged by all this, and remained wonderfully optimistic throughout the session.'

Apart from the trips to the outpatients' department of the National, there was the continuing routine of home life.

SARAH'S DIARY: FRIDAY 3 NOVEMBER
This is what it's like at home. We wake up at about eight and snuggle for a bit. Snuggling is hard because Robert hasn't found a way yet to be comfortable with his left arm. He's protective of it and when I touch it, either on purpose or by mistake, he gets very defensive. Then I go downstairs and make breakfast: cereal for Robert, and a big pot of coffee in the green art-deco coffee-warming pot, and I bring it up on a tray, with the mail, if there is any. Robert lies in bed. Then, slowly and with great difficulty, he takes a shower, and I help him dry off and get dressed, again very slowly. Then he dries his hair and I make the bed and try to clean up a little. I try to do things but am so keyed-in to him that when he calls out to me I feel like I should be there before he has finished articulating my name. It's very tiring. There are so many dishes to be washed all the time. All the things that we used to share I have to do now. It means buying lightbulbs, and taking out the garbage, and carrying boxes up and down the stairs, and stripping the bed, and leaving money for the cleaner, and calling the taxi, and remembering about the dry cleaning, and remembering that we need new keys made, and making all the meals, and

organizing, and buying the newspapers and throwing them away after we've read them. I'm not very good at it, and I never liked doing it much. Robert hates it that I have to do it, too, but it's easy for him to slip into the habit of me doing everything. I feel weepy a lot and often find myself bursting into tears when we're sitting together, out of love for him and latent fears from what happened, that I could so easily have lost him. I feel by turns very sad, and slightly resentful, and very, very happy. He walks better and is slowly getting more energy, but it seems to come and go: some days he's great, others very dull.

After sleeping for hours at a stretch, I never knew, when I woke, how my mood might vary, or how much energy I might have. I seesawed between listlessness and little bursts of effort. When Sarah and I went out, I found the effort of movement, with my cane, incredibly exhausting. I felt awkward inching my way down the street, and would often not go out until after dark when I would try to navigate my way to the street corner, a distance of perhaps a hundred yards. I was still mortally scared to attempt to cross the road, and would stop at the corner, catch my breath, then, very carefully, turn around and shuffle home. After such expeditions I was always exhausted, but pleased to have achieved something.

SARAH'S DIARY: TUESDAY 14 NOVEMBER
I don't know how much depends on mood and how much on other things, like sleep, or on ineffable factors that we can't quantify. R.'s arm is gaining in some strength, but still can't be used for anything. Yesterday we went to see two movies – *Burnt by the Sun* and *The*

Madness of King George, and we had to walk all the way down a long street together to get to the cinema (the traffic was too congested for the taxi). It was very hard for Robert and incredibly slow, and it's alarming for me to see how precarious you are when you walk down the street with a bad limp and a cane. When people wouldn't step aside to let him go I glared at them and tried to make them feel bad. I love Robert's cane and think he looks very distinguished with it.

The struggle of everyday life together brought us closer and closer. Sarah noted that 'When A.A. [*a friend*] asked me how I was today, "We're fine," I replied. There's no more "I" when it comes to questions of being fine or not; there's only "we".' It's hard, even two years on, to appreciate how much mental and psychological effort became invested in my nearly useless left arm. I monitored its progress minutely. Sue Edwards was now saying that she could see more than just 'flickers' of activity. I was beginning to be able to squeeze with my fingers, but not yet extend them, and could move my elbow a bit. And next to the frustration of this slow recovery was, just below the surface, rage.

SARAH'S DIARY: THURSDAY 16 NOVEMBER
Robert shows big flashes of anger, particularly when things hurt him (when the hair on his leg catches in the brace, or his elbow or shoulder is jarred). Part of it is the pain, and part the feelings of helplessness and physical weakness I'm sure he feels. He's mad too, because he thinks people (me) are poking at him and telling him what to do all the time, and he hates it and lashes out at me. I think this is normal, but I wish he would talk to someone about it. I don't know the right things to say.

He hates admitting weakness. He's made quite big progress in walking – he can now begin to lift his foot up. Slowly, slowly, it's looking like less of an effort. And last night he pulled his arm up at the shoulder, and then lowered it back down! Very exciting. Physically, Robert is improving very noticeably. It's his spirits that need bolstering these days; he looks terribly depressed, and wakes up with what seems to be overwhelming lethargy and *anomie*. I feel like I'm sniping at him all the time. I want him to have the will to do this himself and feel bad when he doesn't. But I don't know quite how to handle it.

This is an authentic record of this most difficult stage of convalescence, and now that I come to write it down I can only add in hindsight that the worst of stroke is the aftermath, when you feel you are on the scrapheap. For me, the lifeline in all this was the thought that I could one day write down my experience, as a reporter from that foreign country, the world of stroke.

By mid-November we were beginning to make plans to take a proper holiday at Christmas. Our idea was to go away and recuperate in the sun and by the sea, probably in the Caribbean. Having missed the summer and the long holiday we'd booked as part of our wedding celebrations, we felt we deserved this. Afterwards we planned to come back via New York, to see Sarah's parents and some of our American friends, and thus slowly begin to reconnect with the world from which I had been severed these last several months.

At home in London, I was fortunate to have a steady stream of visitors, friends and professional acquaintances. Many of these were people my own age who were curious, I think, to see how one of their number was getting on. At least that was how it seemed to me. One of these asked me straight out if I'd felt any self-pity. I replied that I could honestly say to him that I did not. Irritation, yes. Anger and annoyance, yes. But not self-pity. It was, however, a good question. Looking back now on the whole experience, it seems like a rather substantial punctuation mark in the course of a long life. At least, I hope so. I began to develop a silly superstition that, just as this had happened when I was forty-two, so I would die when I was eighty-four; one of my visitors told me that Bernard Shaw says somewhere – I have not managed to trace the reference – that to be seriously ill in your forties is to toughen and prepare you for a long life. I also told my friend that I was interested to observe how one of the effects of catastrophic illness was to turn complexity to simplicity. When I reread my journal now, I am surprised how detached I seem to be about my experience, but that, I suppose, lies in my nature.

In my blackest moments I felt that perhaps my life's significance was bound up entirely in my experience of and response to this 'brain-attack'. Sometimes, I felt as though I'd spent twenty-something years of effort and literary endeavour to find myself shut into a pigeon-hole marked 'young stroke-sufferer'. In my better moments, I knew that I should be grateful to the stroke for giving an enhanced value to my life and for the reminder that one should take nothing for granted. I think I was always given to rumination; now I am more reflective, and less impetuous. I was always happy on my own; now I feel, having survived, that my self-sufficiency had a purpose as a kind of training for the terrible isolation of stroke and its aftermath. I am less impatient; I let things take their course.

One of the effects of a dramatic stroke like mine is

that you feel shaken free from the concerns and obligations of the world. You care less. Matters that used to seem important no longer seem so crucial. And in one important way, I feel absurdly privileged. I also feel I've become a very minor expert in a subject of extreme fascination, the catastrophic failure of the brain.

Once I was home in St Peter's Street, and alone with myself again, my first thought had been to review the weeks leading up to my stroke in the hope of finding a clue that might yield some kind of explanation for my sudden plight. Other thoughts crowded in. All my life I'd been fascinated by the dramas of the mind, and I'd often feared that I too would one day have some kind of nervous collapse. The stroke seemed like a massive fulfilment of that fear, and once I was home, with time to reflect on things, I became haunted by the terror that I might now actually go mad.

Back in the bed from which I had fallen all those weeks ago at the end of July, I was forced once more to confront the question the paramedics had put to me as I lay on the floor by the grandfather clock in the shadows of evening, an inch or two from death: What's your name? or to put it another way: Who am I? It was a question that would nag throughout my year off, and even now I am still not free of a persistent, and possibly pointless, anxiety about the existential and psychic meaning of my illness.

[14]

Seizing the Carp

13 December – 5 January 1996

> I don't know *why* we live – the gift of life comes to us
> from I don't know what source or for what purpose; but
> I believe we can go on living for the reason that (always
> up to a certain point) life is the most valuable thing we
> know anything about, and it is therefore presumptively a
> great mistake to surrender it while there is any yet left in
> the cup . . .
>
> Henry James

The more I faced up to what had happened, the more
I found my 'black dog' mood beginning to lift: somehow, somewhere, I found a new determination to get
through. In the middle of December we set off for
the Caribbean for a holiday in the sun, a generous gift
from my mother-in-law. This was what Sarah liked to
call 'seizing the carp'. Sarah's love of language, its
quiddities and absurdities, was one of the qualities
that had drawn us together, just as her obsession with
grammar and spelling is one of the things that gives us
both so much harmless enjoyment. Before I fell ill, we
used to joke about *carpe diem*, a Latin tag that became,

for both of us, 'seizing the carp', i.e. living life to the full.

It was hard, in those first few months of recovery, to imagine seizing anything, but I am glad we did what we did. Still nervous about negotiating even the pavement outside my house, I was extremely apprehensive about going, but once we'd established that British Airways had wheelchair facilities, we set off in a spirit of adventure. A holiday that for ordinary people would seem like pure junketing became, in my enfeebled state, a huge effort of will-power, but it did make a big difference, and was an important milestone on my return to health.

Even the mundane experience of flying became a moment of extraordinary release. All too soon, it seemed, we were circling to land at Bridgetown, Barbados, in the balmy Caribbean twilight, and I was being helped by kind hands into a wheelchair to make the journey through the terminal to a waiting car. Sarah and I quickly discovered that this was the fastest route through any immigration line; later, when it was no longer necessary to ask for wheelchair assistance, we used to speak nostalgically of the days when we'd been treated like VIPs. It was quite dark when we arrived at our hotel, but we could hear the ocean waves beating on the shore and knew that after so many weeks of drab greyness and oppressive restriction we would, in the morning, be greeted by the tropical warmth and dazzling equatorial sunlight of Barbados. For the first time in weeks, I did not feel exhausted by the prospect of the day, or the effort of getting through it.

It was luxurious in so many respects to be away from the UK in December, but the real joy of our holiday was the opportunity for daily swimming in the soothing waters of the Caribbean. At first I was nervous to do this, and felt intimidated by the waves' power to knock me off my feet, but gradually I became confident about floating on my back in the water, paddling with my right arm and kicking, where possible, with my left leg. Walking on the beach was still a huge effort. I could make progress over the sand only by supporting myself on Sarah's arm, but in the water I was free. Floating on the crystal water, and staring up into the dazzling empyrean, I could almost forget what had happened and feel, for a few moments, that I was myself again.

We had nearly three weeks in Barbados, and by the time we were ready to come home, I felt renewed and positive – prepared for the next stage of convalescence. It seemed appropriate that the New Year had arrived. Together, perhaps, we would find a new purpose.

On my return to London, I discovered a new mood of acceptance inside myself. Okay, I told myself, so things were not so bad. I could hobble about, with a stick. My left arm, though still paralysed, was beginning to show flickers of life. I was now being told that in the long run I should make a 'fairly good' recovery. In other respects, I was beginning to feel pretty much myself, and the dramas of the past several months were beginning to seem in retrospect strangely dreamlike, even hallucinatory. Perhaps, I thought, in the end, I would look back on the whole experience as an interesting episode that would make me realize more than ever what an extraordinary place the world was, and how lucky I was still to be in it.

The next milestone, in January of the New Year, was my return to work, to the offices of Faber & Faber, about six months after I'd fallen ill. This I found extraordinarily difficult, despite the generous and friendly support of my colleagues on the staff. Initially, I felt incredibly remote from the business of the office, and often terribly tired. The mundane matters of executive life now seemed utterly unimportant to me. Looking back on it now, I see that I was a long way short of competence to function in a busy office, and yet until I was actually at my desk in my old room there was no way of gauging the extent of my convalescence.

Associated with my alienation from the everyday concerns of Faber & Faber, there was also the question of shame. This was one of the most unexpected and yet most crippling of my psychological afflictions at this time. An eighty-four-year-old stroke victim, Edwin B. Jelkes of Decatur, Georgia, explains in his unpublished account of his illness (one of the many very moving stroke-related documents I received during my year off) how 'shame' afflicts the recovering stroke-sufferer:

> At some point in time after the reality that you have actually had a stroke sinks in, you progress to a state of being ashamed to be seen by anyone and are afraid to get out of your stroke shell. This fear of being seen grows until the mentally healthy person gets tired of being ashamed. Hopefully, this tired feeling leads to adventure, and adventure leads to small trials. Desire to get back into the real world that was so natural to you before the stroke finally overcomes the embarrassment you feel, and you step out. And then the fun begins. It took me two months before I mustered enough courage to get out of the house and go somewhere. I chose a movie away from town where I would not be seen by anybody I knew (still ashamed but not so bad).

In this state of mind, simple things, like a visit to the next-door office, seemed like major expeditions, and duties that in the past I'd managed with ease now seemed burdensome and difficult. Sarah told me that I looked distinguished with my stick, but I was embarrassed by and ashamed of it. I also found that to conserve my energy I had to stay immobile at my desk, and try to use the telephone to conduct business as much as possible. Here was another problem: my speech was still slightly slurred and I had difficulty in constructing complex sentences. I could easily imagine what I might say – I would, for instance, find no impediment to committing my thoughts to paper – but then have the greatest difficulty in expressing the thought in spontaneous speech. I noted in my diary that 'limitations of mobility and articulacy strike at the heart of who one is as a person'. I was comparatively fortunate in this; those who suffer a left-side stroke will, characteristically, experience far greater obstacles to speech recovery.

Actually, what could I now do? I could walk with a stick. I could move my left arm about a bit, with difficulty. I could close the fingers of my left hand, but not open them. My mobility was much improved, but I still needed the AFO splint strapped to my left leg to achieve real movement, and I could only wear it inside an extra large pair of Adidas trainers.

Sleep continued to be one ally in my convalescence. I still slept long and heavily. I would go to bed at ten and rise twelve hours later, feeling heavy and sluggish. This, I suppose, was depression. I know now that I was much more depressed than I realized at the time.

Dr Greenwood had referred, imaginatively, to 'the rapids', but in practice I felt as though I was becalmed, as idle as a painted ship upon a painted ocean.

Like a prisoner in a cell, I had good days and bad days. On bad days I was terribly aware of my body and its limitations; I was acutely aware of what I could no longer do. I fought the constraints and regretted the past. I mourned, I grieved, and I wailed inwardly. And just as prison throws you back on books and the constantly reiterated assertion 'This is not the end', so in the aftermath of my stroke, I read voraciously and refused to admit defeat. There would, I told myself, always be the good days. On good days, I did not fret over the uselessness of my left arm or left leg. I was at peace in my body, and my mind was keen and alert. I felt complete, alive and good. Such days were rare. Tiredness was always creeping up. If I could vanquish tiredness, I told myself, I would be fine. I admonished myself not to be impatient. Everything takes time. Time can be your friend as well as your enemy. *Time, time, time* . . . When would I ever feel myself again? On some days, when I woke, even the smallest thing seemed impossible. I fretted over arrangements and logistics, and the world seemed so threatening.

The worst of any day was always getting started, finding the energy to haul my body to the edge of the bed and struggle into the bathroom. For several months I was able to run myself a bath and gingerly climb into it, but I then lacked the strength to get myself out and had to be hauled out backwards by Sarah, an ignominious procedure that neither of us enjoyed. Bathing became less of a drama when Islington Council supplied me with a plastic shower chair specially designed for use by the disabled. When I had the strength to stand upright in the shower, I soon discarded this chair, but Islington Council never forgets. More than a year later, I received the following letter (from the Neighbourhood Services Department & Community Health Service):

Dear Sir/Madam,

We write to recommend that when using bath or shower equipment with drainage holes or slots, towelling or similar protective material should be placed between the seat and the user's body. This prevents testicles, or any other part of the body in contact with the seat, being forced through the drainage holes or slots and becoming trapped.

It is also recommended that all types of bath and shower seating equipment should be regularly inspected to ensure there are no sharp edges or potential areas of entrapment. If you discover any please inform the Duty Officer on the above number.

This letter is in response to recommendations made in a safety notice (MDA SN 9709) published by the Medical Devices Agency Adverse Incident Centre.

Yours Sincerely

Amita Randhawa, Team leader (Job Share)

In the world of medical disability, there are some things you simply could not make up.

I found, as I reached this stage of recovery, that it was comforting to be in the company of those who'd experienced and understood what I'd just been through. I became more and more interested in what had happened to me, and involved in stroke-relief organizations. I was visited by a former lawyer named Donal O'Kelly who was in the process of setting up a young-strokes pressure group, Different Strokes. I'd first come across him in the Devonshire Hospital when he'd sent me a photo of himself, and a note suggesting that we get together some time soon. His picture seemed rather promising, I thought. We seemed to be the same sort of age, forty-ish, and he looked pretty fit to me. Just then, that was something that mattered. I was terribly lost and lonely and was very glad to hear from someone who seemed not only to understand how I was feeling, but who also offered a ray of hope for the future. When, in due course, we did meet, we found that we had a lot in common and arranged to stay in touch. Donal suggested meeting up one Saturday, and mentioned a venue at the Tottenham Court Road YMCA.

The first time I met Donal and his friends, a mixed group of young people who'd survived recent such brain-attacks, I was astonished to learn that an affliction which had seemed horrifyingly exceptional to me, and which I'd always believed to be an old person's illness, was actually rather common among the younger generation.

On the face of it, the people who gathered at the YMCA (under the organization of Different Strokes) seemed like any other weekend fitness group. There was Liz, a delightfully attractive Anglo-Italian tour guide. She had been just twenty-four when she was struck down in Milan on 5 March 1994. She'd had a bad migraine for twenty-four hours and when she came to get out of bed she fell over, more or less unconscious, and couldn't get up. Her boyfriend called an ambulance, and she spent the next five weeks in Milan's university hospital before she was shipped back to the Home Counties. Liz had had a blockage in her left carotid artery, and though she'd been on the Pill, she says the doctors still cannot find a medical explanation for what happened.

Amanda, from Toronto, was not much older, slim, dark and seemingly normal. She was twenty-six when she'd been struck down, in her sleep, with a right-side hemiplegia on 11 November 1993. 'I don't remember the first two days,' she says now, 'and for a long time I didn't even know I'd had a stroke. All the doctors could say was "You're so young."' After ten days in hospital and three months in rehabilitation Amanda was able to walk and talk again, but she could not feed herself properly or get dressed on her own and relied on her mother to look after her. 'She'd watch over me,' she says. 'It was terribly frustrating; it felt like being a child again. I'd forget to do things, or leave the gas burning, and she'd be behind me checking that I was okay.' Like many young strokes, she says that the worst of the aftermath was feeling as if she'd become a different person somehow: 'adapting to a whole new you'.

Liz, who has a dark-eyed Italian look, with boyish romantic curls and clear pale skin, nods vigorously here. 'You wouldn't recognize the way I used to be,' she says. She'd been a tireless worker and partygoer, getting by on four or five hours' sleep a night. The effect of her stroke was to paralyse her speech, slowing her processes of articulation almost to a standstill. Hesitantly putting one word in front of the next, so that you can almost feel the enormous effort of will that lies behind the simplest everyday statement, she says, 'I still have difficulty finding the words. I have to think, think, think, three or four times before I speak or write. My reading's getting better but it's still slow.' There have been times in the past three years when she thought she'd never recover. She has run the familiar gamut of post-stroke emotions: anger, despair, frustration and constant depression. She has now reached a point of reconciliation within herself, but feels that there's a medical time-bomb inside her waiting to go off (unlike many young stroke-sufferers, who can be fairly certain there'll be no relapse, Liz had a small second stroke in January 1997).

'I think I'll live for the day,' she says. 'I don't make many future plans.'

Basil is another of Donal O'Kelly's Saturday afternoon team who has to think hard when I ask him about the future. 'I still get very severely annoyed,' he says, after a long pause. 'I have to take it from day to day. In my thoughts I can become very aggressive. I ask myself: why has this happened to me?' Basil has Jamaican parents and, at the time he fell ill, was about to take a place on a TV *Gladiators* show in Australia. To meet Basil, a very good-looking athlete with immense charm and physical presence, you'd never know he'd suffered any affliction. Actually, he says he 'nearly died' on 11 March 1995. Over two years later, he's unable to work (he used to be an engineer) and has to supplement his modest earnings by occasional stints of lucrative modelling. He comes to the YMCA every Saturday because it's the one place where he can swap stories with people like himself. In theory Different Strokes is about exercise; in practice, it's the talk that's really therapeutic, breaking down the isolation that so many young strokes feel.

Liz, for example, believes that her illness came between her and her old friends; it was as though they were frightened by what had happened, frightened and unable to cope. She still finds it 'nearly impossible' to meet new people, and says sadly that 'I tend to stay as lonely as possible', even when she plucks up the courage to go clubbing like any normal twenty-something. She says that the problem with the men she meets is that they have no idea what's happened to her or what she's gone through. 'They can't handle it,' she says, choosing each word with care. 'They shy away and the next day they just won't speak to me.'

The stigma the stroke-sufferer experiences is something no doctor will tell you about, but it is a common complaint among younger people, who are more likely to be still forging new relationships, and to be active in the world, especially those, like Basil, who appear to make a full recovery. Today, he is the picture of fitness – until he starts to walk. 'When I got the brain-attack,' he says, 'it felt like I was drunk. My limbs went haywire.'

When he came round he discovered his life had gone haywire, too. His ten-year marriage collapsed ('my wife couldn't take it any more'), many of his friends let him down, and he began to feel, he says, that 'I was no good to nobody.' Things were so bad that 'I considered committing suicide.' He got through the first part of convalescence, but still admits to feeling 'severely bitter', another common reaction among young strokes, but not generally recognized in the wider world.

Donal, who has also become quite expert in the statistics of this brutal affliction, told me that each year in Britain some ten thousand people of working age will have a stroke – nearly two hundred per week, of whom one in five will be under forty.

Regardless of age, the physical and psychological damage is the same. The majority of stroke-survivors will have a paralysed arm and many will be unable to walk normally. Liz, Amanda, Basil, and many others like them, suffered blindness, aphasia and various kinds of paralysis. Those who suffer a 'right-side stroke' seem to find fewer threats to long-term recovery.

The psychological and social damage of stroke is immeasurable and often it will harm those who are affected even more than the quantifiable physical damage. Between 30 and 50 per cent of patients will experience clinical depression; about a third of these will still be suffering from clinical depression after one year. As many as 80 per cent do not return to their previous vocations.

Amanda, twenty-seven, is not untypical. When she was struck down, Amanda couldn't walk or speak, and her hearing and eyesight were also affected; she found the experience profoundly distressing and humiliating. A year after she fell ill, Amanda decided she had 'to make a new start', and left Toronto for London. 'I was determined to get better,' she says now. 'I couldn't relate to my old friends any more. I had to get on my own two feet.' When she started coming to Donal O'Kelly's afternoon sessions at the YMCA, she was delighted at last to discover some young people whose experience put her own sufferings into perspective.

Finally, there was Donal himself, who'd brought us all together. Perhaps his story was the most remarkable of all. In June 1993 he was a successful barrister, forty-three years old, recently divorced, without children, a member of a busy chambers. Aptly enough, he was cross-examining a police sergeant about a 'vigorous arrest' in a North London courtroom when he felt a pain in his neck and then, as he puts it, 'all the lights went out'.

He goes on, 'I was loaded into the ambulance, unable to move and unable to speak. I was taken off to the nearest hospital and carried into casualty still wearing my barrister's outfit. My words were not coming out right and the staff assumed that I was a drunken actor. Then I felt that pain again and, unable to breathe, my limbs seized up, I passed out and was gone for days. When I woke later I was paralysed on both sides. It was as though my brain had closed down so that I couldn't take on the enormity of what had happened.'

After two months, O'Kelly was discharged from hospital, feeling shattered and bereft. He'd discovered that for long-term illness the National Health Service was of little practical assistance and he'd used up much of his savings to pay for private physio and speech therapy. Back in the world, putting his life together, he found that the established stroke organizations did not seem terribly interested in young people who'd suffered as he had.

Gradually, the idea grew in his mind that he should devote his energies to the cause of young strokes. 'At first I worked as a volunteer with the Stroke Association. I wanted to do more for young strokes, but I got nowhere. Basically, I think they thought I was after a job. Anyway, after a national conference in November 1995, which wasn't a huge success, a lot of people who'd come expressed dissatisfaction, and out of that dissatisfaction Different Strokes was born.'

However, when Donal described the extent of his initial disability, I felt encouraged. He had been blinded (his sight soon returned) and paralysed, yet now he was walking unaided, and his speech seemed normal, if slightly hesitant. Donal's example was one that persuaded me to believe in the potential for recovery. Now I go quite regularly to Different Strokes, and Donal and his friends make me feel immensely welcome. When you are recovering from a stroke, the world seems a hard place, and sometimes I would think: No one understands me, or what I've been through. It was good to have Donal's friends to share my experience with.

Soon after I went back to work I was thrilled to

receive, in the post, my disabled person's orange parking badge. (This was one of the few felicitous side-effects – almost a perk – of the stroke, a *laissez-passer* that, in some provincial towns, changes hands for £1000 on the pensioners' black market.) The orange badge would enable me to park, I believed, pretty much wherever I wanted. Never mind that it was associated in my mind with elderly people in the high streets of the Home Counties. Perhaps I was at last coming to terms with my situation. I soon discovered the limitations of the Orange Badge in the borough of Westminster. Thus:

> Dear Sirs
> I wish to appeal against a parking fine awarded to me today (see enclosed ticket). I was disabled by a stroke in July last year and received an orange badge in December. I have been using this in my home borough of Islington for the past several weeks. When I came into central London today I was unaware that the Orange Badge is not recognized in Westminster and parked on a single yellow line in order to shop in Covent Garden.

A few days later, a small victory: I received a note confirming that I would only have to pay half the fine (£30).

During the working week, I continued to make my regular trip to Faber & Faber, usually after a daily session of physiotherapy. One day in February of that first year, I went to a publishing party, supporting myself with my cane as usual, and found myself being asked, 'Did you hurt your leg?'

'Yes,' I replied, moving away, 'but it will get better.' I felt obscurely angered by this innocent question, as if I wanted recognition for what I'd been through. Why did

I feel angry about such things? Why did I expect people to know? Shouldn't I be glad that my recovery had gone so well?

As I resumed my old life, two things struck me as symbols of that lost world. First, shoes; and second, clothes. Throughout my time in hospital I was either barefoot, or I wore cosy thick white gym socks, but never shoes. It was physically impossible for me to pull a shoe on to my paralysed left foot. Now that movement was returning I was wearing shoes again, shoes I'd not worn for about six months, footwear that seemed strange, even exotic. I felt like a child discovering the adult world of mobility. There was one pair of black shoes, in particular, which I found almost impossible to put on. I'd bought them perhaps two weeks before I'd fallen ill and worn them only once. They seemed to symbolize that lost world to which I could never return. (Some months later I gave them away.)

With clothes, the feeling of alienation was even more acute. For weeks in the Devonshire I'd worn shorts and a T-shirt. Now I was learning to pull on a shirt, fumbling right-handed with the buttons, occasionally dragging myself into a suit, a strange garment that seemed to belong to quite another person, and then struggling hopelessly with a tie. Until my left arm began to move again, a well-tied tie was an impossibility. I came to accept that I'd have to go to work in an open polo shirt.

Meanwhile, I was still having physiotherapy treatment at Queen Square, and being reminded, by the interest taken in my condition by various experts, that this was a research institution. On 13 February, Sue Edwards took me to see John Rothwell, a research doctor who was testing a system for 'transcranial magnetic stimulation'.

I found him situated at the top of 23 Queen Square, above Dr Greenwood's office. He worked in a room like a train-spotter's garage, full of Meccano-style shelving, wires and computer parts. It was hard to imagine, looking over the chaos and clutter, that this was the centre of a highly sophisticated inquiry into the workings of the brain. Amid a litter of reused items, Rothwell was conducting experiments into the vitality of areas of the brain. The chair in which I was seated had been filched from an old Jaguar. Rothwell, a cheery, chatty character, a kind of neurological Dr Who, attached electrodes to my arms and began sending magnetic signals to my brain, stimulating different parts of the body – left arm, left leg, etc. – in an attempt to determine exactly which part of my brain was no longer functioning. At first I did not find the low level magnetic click on my head much of a problem, but when he turned up the power to get a response from the damaged right side of my brain, it became troublesome and anxious-making. I felt, not for the first time, as if I was a stroke-recovery guinea pig. Sue Edwards and her colleague Jo watched in fascination. During one break from his investigations, in response to my questions, Rothwell produced a section of a brain in a bottle of formaldehyde. This was the first time I had seen the crucial organ separated from its protective skull and I was fascinated. Rothwell's sample brain looked like a giant grey nut; it was cut in half like a Damien Hirst. Rothwell pointed out the damage to the basal ganglia, identical to my stroke. It was shortly after this that I arranged, courtesy of Michael Dunnill, a distinguished Oxford anatomist, to visit the brain sections on display at the College of Surgeons in Lincoln's Inn Fields.

Sarah, meanwhile, was determined to uncover the

cause of my stroke. In quest of this, and with Dr Greenwood's blessing, we paid a visit to Mr Thomas at the Lindo Wing of St Mary's, Paddington. I showed him what I could do. This was February 1996, and at this stage, I walked with a stick and a limp, moving better when my arms moved freely. I could now flex the left wrist and move my fingers, though I could barely grip a sheet of paper in my left hand.

Mr Thomas looked at my MRI scans and suggested that he could perhaps see signs of a tiny congenital abnormality in the veins of my brain and suggested that I get my blood retested by his colleague, Dr Hannah Cohen.

So, sure enough, three weeks later in late February, we went back to St Mary's for another consultation, and another blood test. Dr Cohen's concern was that I might have a blood deficiency known as Lupus Anticoagulant, which would make my blood prone to clotting. Dr Cohen was perceptive, friendly and articulate, but her account of what my blood might be like left me depressed and fearful. If I had a clotting abnormality, I'd be treated with warfarin (rat poison) to thin the blood. I nearly fainted as she took blood, and felt woozy afterwards at the thought of the inevitable blood-monitoring that might be necessary in the future. For many stroke-sufferers, a daily dose of warfarin is a routine treatment, but its effectiveness depends on close scrutiny of the blood, and runs the risk of causing internal bleeding. Mercifully, the upshot of several complex tests was that I was declared to have absolutely normal blood.

Aside from these investigations, for the first time since I returned to work, I began, as the spring of 1996 unfolded, to think seriously about leaving my workplace of twenty years. What I'd suspected in the National was true: I was no longer able to acquit myself as editor-in-chief of Faber and Faber in the way to which I'd become accustomed in the past. Stroke-sufferers, generally, have to face up to the issue of their interrupted careers. In the end, despite the support of my company, I was no exception. There was, I should emphasize, nothing remarkable about this. Almost all those who suffer stroke and survive the 'insult' end up making a change of direction, and I believe my case was typical. Partly, this is because however much you recover, you are likely, physically speaking, to be impaired from functioning as you did before. So stroke-sufferers often find themselves working in charities, or for the health services, or for the disabled. It's as though, having been granted a window on to the world of the physically disadvantaged, we are unable to remain indifferent to the plight of such people, and insist on taking up a kind of dual citizenship. As ticket-of-leave citizens from the land of the unwell, we have been so profoundly affected by the experience it's almost the only thing we can think of. And then there's the confidence question: it's probably the only thing we think we're good for.

I realized, as I got better, that I was wanting to say goodbye to a person who had, in a sense, died nine months before, and I had to say goodbye to his life as well. I came to believe that just as a part of my brain was now irretrievably dead, so a part of my former activity and lifestyle was defunct, too.

The more I returned to my old life, I was struck by the fact that my life had become divided in two, before and after. The life 'after' was my life with Sarah, and it was mine to define as I chose. I felt like an adult now, and I could apply my intelligence to making it how I wanted, to suit my capacity. There would, I told myself, be no compromises and no connection with my 'old' life. That was in the past, for better or worse. In some ways, it was like a second chance. This turned out to be hopelessly optimistic. You can no more shed your past, this side of the grave, than you can change your personality. Elsewhere, I wrote myself a question: What are the themes of life now? and answered:

1. mobility
2. typing
3. speech
4. energy
5. versatility
6. sadness (regrets)
7. anger
8. readjustment (patience)
9. frustration
10. memory
11. slowness
12. slipping/skipping/ease
13. sleep

Thoughts such as these were still on my mind when, in the course of that spring, I arranged to have lunch with my friend Alan Rusbridger, the editor of the *Guardian*. I remember thinking, as I waited for Alan to arrive, that just six months earlier in the depths of my hospitalization such an encounter would have seemed not merely surprising but quite unthinkable. I was even more surprised when Alan asked me, almost casually, if I would like to become literary editor of the *Observer*, Britain's oldest Sunday newspaper. I was so astonished by this suggestion that I could not for a moment think of an answer.

In the event I said, 'Yes', to this wonderful offer. I was sad to leave the world of Faber & Faber, in which I'd been so happy and fulfilled, and where I'd found so many friends, over many years. After all I'd gone through, I was apprehensive about joining the *Observer*, but my anxieties proved groundless. I quickly discovered the exhilarating speed and freedom of working on a newspaper, mixed with the delightfully stimulating camaraderie of the newsroom. I had for so long dreamed of making a career change, and now, it seemed, my cherished dream was coming true.

[15]

An Aspirin and a Glass of Wine

May 1996 to July 1997

> He looked about in that very place for his own image;
> but another man stood in his accustomed corner, and
> though the clock pointed to his usual time of day
> for being there, he saw no likeness of himself among
> the multitudes that poured in through the Porch. It
> gave him little surprise, however; for there had been
> revolving in his mind a change of life, and thought and
> hoped he saw his new-born resolutions carried out in
> this.
>
> Charles Dickens, *A Christmas Carol*

The dream of leaving has always been such a powerful
fantasy for the busy professional. How often, during my
years at Faber, did I hear friends and colleagues express
the desire to take time out from their overcrowded
schedules and make the time to recharge their personal
batteries? The dream of renewal, like the dream of
leaving, remains the pipe-dream of the disgruntled professional. 'I just need time,' people will say, 'time to get
my head together.' But of course, generally speaking,
we carry on, because that's the way we're made, and

because the commitments and responsibilities of life demand it.

When, however, you suffer a stroke, or an equivalent catastrophic physical breakdown, you experience the dream of leaving as a nightmare. But perhaps only such a crisis can precipitate change.

My shift of focus, from literary publishing to literary journalism, had been prefigured in my journalistic forays to places like Cambodia and East Timor. I was more than ready for the transition and, besides, there was a sense that the publishing world in which I'd grown up was changing. I no longer felt at home in a new literary environment dominated by the bottom line and the restrictive scrutiny of accountants and financial directors.

Everyone wanted to know if I'd changed. When I answered that, essentially, I thought I had not, I was aware that my old self had been left behind somewhere on the staircase of 41 St Peter's Street. Sometimes, in my more sentimental moments, I felt I was like Tom, the sweep's apprentice in Charles Kingsley's Victorian classic, *The Water Babies*. Perhaps I had left my sooty clothes on the riverbank and become purged and renewed by the waters of ill-health; perhaps – who knows? – my stroke had been a blessing in disguise.

The first year after illness struck was dominated by the struggle to become physically better. The second year – once I was back to an everyday existence – would be all about psychological well-being and the battle with the demons of despair and depression. But now, at least, I could begin to mix hope and optimism with sadness and gloom. In many ways, it was this mixture that would characterize the tone of much of the second year after my stroke.

Donal O'Kelly tells a nice story of the time he saw the great blues guitarist B.B. King at a live performance. B.B. King, the master of blues desolation, appeared on stage in an electric blue suit, with his hair coiffed in perfect ringlets, the effervescent picture of the successful star. He was, says Donal, obviously conscious that his audience would be not unaware of the contrast between his melancholy blues lyrics and his ebullient demeanour. Approaching the microphone, he addressed the front row of the stalls with a winning smile. 'To play the blues,' he said, 'you gotta know the bad times, but you gotta know the good times, too.'

So, of course, it wasn't just a year off. It could not, could never, be any such thing: the idea that, after a twelve-month break, one could seamlessly resume the life one had left behind was ridiculous. To illustrate this, I should enumerate the small but significant ways in which there can be no return.

First, and most obviously, I am typing this with the variously available fingers of my right hand; my left is intermittently useful to hold down the shift key, but it lacks the sprightly dexterity of old. Another thing: in the past, I used to enjoy holding a pen in my right hand. Now that pleasure has diminished, and (though my right side was not affected by the stroke) my handwriting is more difficult to read than ever.

Next, the left side of my face is still mildly frozen. To the untrained eye, I appear normal, but an expert can detect the slight paralysis of my left-side features. In the same category, my speech sounds normal to outsiders, but to me it is vulnerable to stuttering and slurring, and I now have regular speech therapy to correct the deficit. I still prefer to speak sitting down, where the weakness on my left side is less exposed, and find it difficult to stand upright and hold a sustained conversation. Interestingly, it was my speech therapists, whose skill lies in the art of communication, who were consistently the most helpful to me at every stage of recovery. It was they, for instance, who spoke most frankly about my 'deficits' and encouraged me none the less to believe in myself. What else?

I can walk for an hour or so, at a slow pace, with rests, but I cannot walk briskly, and the idea of running out to the shops for a pint of milk, or the newspaper, is unthinkable.

At the end of the day I can still feel profoundly fatigued, and in need of a rest.

My appetite for alcohol, formerly substantial and generally associated with much conversational late-night drinking, has dwindled almost to nothing. After about six months, my tastebuds returned to normal.

My interest in alternative therapies, and in the complementarity of Eastern and Western medical traditions, has become a significant part of my reading. In the absence of clear answers from conventional medicine, I am quite ready to take spin on the wheel of holistic treatment.

I still find that, although to outward appearances cured, I lack the sharpness and edge I believe I used to have. My confidence in many areas has not fully returned. I feel weaker, less competent, less commanding and more vulnerable. All of the above can equal the word that begins with D – depression. At times, I plunge into an abyss of depression, finding it difficult to emerge and then only with the greatest effort of will. For some months I experimented with Prozac and Zoloft. I also explored the potential benefits of several American drugs: Luvox, Xanax, Paxil, Navane, Valium, BuSpar, and Wellbutrin but found that I disliked the side-effects, and eventually switched to that gentle alternative, the herbal remedy, St John's wort (*hypericum*).

I no longer complain, as I had in the past, of the threat of boredom. Now, everything in the world seems precious, special and fascinating.

Outwardly, then, I am fine. I can meet people who do not know me, and pass for an unafflicted forty-four-year old. Inwardly, I still have something missing. I believe, in time, that this inner sense of deficiency will fade. When I try to characterize it to people who ask about it, I say that sometimes I feel like the pilot of an aeroplane who on looking over his shoulder in the cockpit sees his tail-plane and the end of his fuselage suddenly blown away, but who finds, amazingly, that although his plane has gone into a 'graveyard spin', somehow it has not crashed. Today, I feel like a pilot who is nursing his crippled craft to a safe landing somewhere unfamiliar, but close at hand.

I take virtually no medication. My doctor tells me that a daily aspirin and a regular glass of red wine is probably the best kind of long-term treatment.

Like many forty-somethings, I wrestle with broken resolutions about taking exercise. In my case, the excuse I have is that swimming is the only activity in which I can achieve something like a normal exercise routine. So I swim. Not as often as I should, but perhaps at least once a week. Swimming has certainly helped to strengthen the muscles in my disabled left side.

I began the story of my stroke with a question, Who am I?, which I have attempted to answer, in my own way, through the stories that make up this narrative. As I have shown, a stroke will open up an almost unending vista of questions about yourself, and your significance. If your stroke was serious and you manage to survive, as

I did, you become, as I've explained, shaken free of the concerns of everyday life. And yet the question Why? continues to hover over almost every day of your life, though before you can begin to get to Why? you have to ask yourself What? What was it that I went through? What exactly is its significance? What does it mean? These are questions, alas, which bring us inexorably back to Why?

In my case, since the doctors have failed to find a reliable explanation for my stroke, I like to think that I was profoundly lucky. If there is a God, he is remote, detached and impressively hands-off. I am inclined to say that at first I did not think there was anyone out there for me, and then that I had been cruelly punished without reason, and yet, finally, that there was an odd kind of purpose to everything that happened.

Even now, completing this chapter as the second anniversary of my stroke approaches, I can see that, much as I might hope to relegate this personal catastrophe to a file labelled 1995–96, in truth its effects will be with me for much longer. Two months after I came home I found myself wishing that I could somehow sustain the state of convalescence. I would read over my diary – noting how much progress I'd made – and feel almost nostalgic for the vulnerability and alertness of the first few weeks. When I was no longer a dramatically ill person and had become just a forty-four-year-old, nearly middle-aged man with a limp and a mild speech imped-iment I somehow wanted more. I wanted to retain my singularity. It was time to recognize that I was back in the world, but even here there were stages of rehabilitation.

At first I was glad to be home; then I felt imprisoned; then I became depressed; then I found myself reliving my first day again and again. I could not walk up the stairs without seeing my naked body curled foetally on the mezzanine. I could not lie in bed and escape retracing my confused journeys across the map of the ceiling that long ago Saturday. Whenever I stood on the front step, I saw my helpless body being stretchered out by the paramedics in the summer evening light. I watched TV a lot; I read familiar books; I sat in my armchair and entertained kind visitors. Otherwise, I did what I could to lead an ordinary life.

I have come to believe that by stressing normality and activity the stroke-sufferer has a better chance of recovery. The brain and its workings remain a mystery to doctors, but I am certain that adopting a vigorous and positive attitude to recovery actually assists the process of renewal. I cannot prove this; it's what I believe to have been true in my own case. Of course, there are countless sad examples of people who do not recover their faculties, but, as a youngish man, I'm inclined to believe that the more I use my brain in everyday life, the less likely I am to lose it. Sue, my physiotherapist, had a phrase for this. 'Use it, don't lose it!' she liked to say, cheerfully whacking my left leg with the flat of her hand. Gradually, I came to compile a personal list of Dos and Don'ts for the convalescent stroke-sufferer.

Under Dos, I listed the following:

1. Try alternative therapies like acupuncture.
2. Find out as much as you can about your illness.
3. Take the initiative.
4. Accept help from friends and relatives.
5. Trust your body.
6. Give yourself time.
7. Meet and talk with other stroke-sufferers.

My personal Don'ts were simpler and more fundamental:

1. Don't despair.
2. Don't imagine you are forgotten.
3. Don't surrender.

In hindsight, I believe that I've been 'away' to a
prison, or a war, and come back, sadder and perhaps a
little bit wiser. I'll probably not see the meaning of this
event in my life for some years, but one thing is certain:
even if, nearly two years after my stroke, the experience
is beginning to seem just that, part of experience, still it
has meant a lot, even as it is slowly becoming absorbed
into the pattern of my personality.

Now, when I meet people for the first time, I no
longer feel, as I did at first, that my stroke stands
between me and the outside world like a pane of frosted
glass. I can be myself again. When strangers ask me how
I hurt my leg I can now say, without awkwardness, 'Oh,
I had a stroke a couple of years ago,' and move on to
other topics. 'What,' asks the *Mahabharata*, 'is the greatest miracle of all?' and then provides the inspiring
answer: 'Each day death strikes, yet man lives as though
he were immortal.'

I no longer think I am immortal (as I did in my
twenties) but life has returned to normal, more or less.
True, I have to plan my movements more carefully than
before and I cannot spontaneously do things I'd like to
do as of old: I cannot spontaneously go for a long walk,
or run through the park on a bright Saturday morning,
but as Sarah likes to chide when I wail about this, 'When
did you ever do those things, anyway?' She christened
this the 'Waterstone's sensation', after the bookstore on

Islington Green, at the top of St Peter's Street, a distance of perhaps four hundred yards from my house.

Before my stroke, I had always loved to browse at leisure in our two small neighbourhood bookshops, Angel Books and the Village Bookshop. It so happened that when I was in hospital the bookselling chain Waterstone's opened a huge new store in a deserted building on the bad, neglected side of Islington Green, a two-minute walk from my house. In my 'old' life, I would have stopped in at the first opportunity and enjoyed browsing the shelves, buying paperbacks I'd never read and perhaps getting to know the staff. Now, frustrated that this simple detour on my way home had become an exhausting half-hour excursion fraught with difficulty and exhaustion, I regretted my lost freedom to do as I pleased. Yet, as Sarah likes to point out, in my 'old' life, I would have sandwiched such a visit into the texture of an already overcrowded day, probably found fault with the selection and availability of the books and come home denouncing the way the book chains threatened the livelihoods of the independent bookshops. None the less, this 'Waterstone's sensation' occurs often enough each day to be worth noting. It offers an insight into the restrictions of old age, the dependency that comes with the loss of mobility.

Besides, for all the things I've lost, there's so much that's been gained. My stroke came as a punctuation mark in the course of a busy life. At the time, I thought it was a full stop, but it turned out to be a comma, or at worst an exclamation point. For a long time, I felt cursed. But then I would recognize that I had this consolation.

I suffered this blow, or calamity, less than two months after getting married. I had been absolutely sure of my love for Sarah in a way I had never been absolutely sure before, and yet who knows what the crisis might have done to our relationship as newlyweds? We knew and loved each other well, but no better than two people who had criss-crossed the Atlantic for a year in a highly charged romantic daze, and had spent barely one calendar month in each other's company. When Sarah was summoned back from San Francisco, she did not know what she might find at the other end of a long plane ride. Her new husband might be a vegetable. He might be dead. As it happened, I was conscious and alive and she, for her part, rose to the occasion with grace, humour and courage. Now, when I wake and find her breathing quietly next to me, every day seems like a blessing.

None the less, until I had reached 29 July 1996, I did not feel released from the malign aura of my stroke. After that anniversary I began to feel better. Besides there was someone other than myself to think about. By the end of July 1996, Sarah knew that she was expecting a baby.

She broke this news to me casually one evening as we were watching a video. Sarah, I remember, was eating a piece of fruit (one of Sarah's most endearing habits is the way she squirrels away food for hungry moments. You can be absorbed in a film at the movie house and suddenly find, from the rustling at your side, that Sarah is about to take a bite from a piece of cake or fruit she happened – just happened – to have in her pocket), and when I observed that this would be good for her, she replied, 'Good for both of us, I'd hope.'

The news of the baby in our lives came, I believe, not a minute too soon, before I turned into a monster of dependency. Now, suddenly, all the focus was on Sarah.

Her welfare was top of the agenda, and it was now her well-being that mattered. In the next several months we went for the usual battery of tests and were relieved to be told that the baby (we had opted not to know its gender) was doing very well.

After the frustrations of stroke recovery, it was wonderfully reassuring to visit a clinic and to receive specific answers to simple questions, in other words to receive a diagnosis on which one could rely.

We would lie in bed and think about the future. We would lie in bed, read the papers, try to enjoy our freedom and imagine what life was going to be like when 'TK' (named after the journalistic abbreviation for copy 'to come') actually arrived.

Meanwhile, as we waited, we read in the newspapers that women's brains actually shrink during pregnancy. This, Sarah reported (for the Internet magazine, *Slate*), was why, as a pregnant woman, she felt 'so spaced out and inept'. So why haven't we mailed our Christmas cards yet? Because my brain is too small!

As the moment of TK's arrival drew nearer, traditionally a time of joyous anticipation, Sarah became more and more conventionally baby-centred. She told me one weekend in January that all she wanted to do was yell at me because the house was such a mess. This 'nesting instinct' – the time that you put charming little touches to your delightful home, floral borders in the baby's room, ruffled scraps of fabric glued to the window-frames – seemed so far from Sarah's nature that it was almost comical to behold. When, I teased, would she start needlepointing animal cushions or stencilling scenes of sweet wee fairies dwelling under toadstools? She replied that at least I should consider picking the mail off the floor. 'I think,' she observed on one occasion, 'that you're an even bigger slob than me, and you leave trails of paper behind you wherever you go, like a snail.' Well, quite so.

When Sarah went to the doctor, some two weeks before her due date, she was told that there was no sign of imminent labour. 'Perhaps,' she wrote in *Slate*, 'perhaps I'll be pregnant for the next fifty years, getting bigger and bigger and evolving from my current status (youngish, smallish water buffalo) through the really mammoth parts of the animal kingdom (aged enormous whale).'

These last weeks were so strange for both of us as we stood on the edge of this precipice, not knowing when exactly she would finally go over the edge into parenthood. It was like waiting for a guest who would be staying with you for the rest of your life, said Sarah, and – the joke is – YOU DON'T KNOW ANYTHING ABOUT HIM (or her).

And still, after what had seemed like years of outpatient visiting, we were attending hospital classes. My recovery from my stroke can be measured by the level of my disaffection on these occasions. In one survey of fathers' attitudes towards labour, most of the men questioned said they were thrilled to be present, looked forward to delivering one single-handedly at home, wished they could have a baby themselves, etc., etc. But 3 per cent replied that they got sick. My mood at these childbirth classes was somewhere between wanting to have the baby myself and feeling sick.

Sarah says that my attitude to these antenatal sessions was that of a political prisoner undergoing the torture of watching videos of other prisoners having electrodes attached to their private parts. My customary response was to lie on one of the beanbags provided for the mums (we were all supposed to sit on the floor) and fall asleep. Sarah likes to say that I would wake up when the po-faced instructor's flip-chart presentation moved from 'pain relief during labour' to 'parking near the hospital'.

The final session was especially gruelling. We were shown videos of several women actually going through childbirth. Stephanie, the first case, had decided only to take nitrous oxide and apparently spent half a day moaning and whimpering or laughing pointlessly as if she was insane. As the other cases unfolded, and we watched scenes of heaving and panting, unbearable pain and carnage, it occurred to me that, whatever else I'd gone through, it had been essentially pain-free.

Sarah was surprisingly tolerant of my response to the trauma of the antenatal class. She contrasted my behaviour with that of another man she'd heard about. This father-to-be arrived at his childbirth class and proceeded to sit stiffly in the only chair in the room, looking increasingly unhappy. The instructor noticed this and felt she should confront his repressed, but obviously intense emotions.

'What are you thinking?' she asked him gently.

'I was just thinking,' he replied, 'that I'd like to go skiing.'

At home, now, it was Sarah who was having the sleepless nights, caught in the antenatal limbo, that two-week border between the past and the future, lying in bed, as she put it, 'like a giant walrus marooned on the rocks'. When she confided her thoughts to her *Slate* diary at this time, it was an apt summary of our time together:

We've had a strange three years. I moved away from New York and into Robert's house in London just a year after we met. We got married six months later, and then he fell spectacularly ill, and while he's better now, I'm not sure I am – though I can usually push it down pretty far, I suspect I'll always feel unsettled and scared.

A few days after she'd written this, Sarah turned to me one Saturday morning, with a strange expression on her face. 'Time to get going,' she said. Now, for the first time in months, I was the one who was looking after her. It was a joyous moment. As I steered the car, with Sarah, the beloved whale, beside me, towards her maternity hospital, my view of the city streets was veiled with tears. No question about it: my year off was coming to a close.

[16]

Candlemas

2 February 1997

The blossom is out in full now ... it looks like apple blossom but it's white, and looking at it, instead of saying, 'Oh, that's nice blossom' ... I see it as the whitest, frothiest, blossomest blossom that there ever could be ... Things are both more trivial than they ever were, and more important than they ever were, and the difference between the trivial and the important doesn't seem to matter. But the nowness of everything is absolutely wondrous.

Dennis Potter, *Seeing the Blossom*

Our baby was born on Candlemas, Sunday 2 February 1997. We named her Alice.

Afterword

Until I was forty-two, I had virtually no personal experience of serious illness and very little knowledge of death. Metaphorically speaking, I went to weddings, not funerals. To my generation, Death was as remote as the obituary pages of the newspaper. My life, and the lives of my generation, were barely troubled by mortality. Unlike our parents, we hadn't had a world war to intrude the realities of existence into the unruffled texture of everyday life.

When I fell ill, I discovered all at once that I was quite definitely not immortal. You can say that I must have been blind, deaf and dumb, and to that I plead guilty. In mitigation, all I can offer is that old charmed life I'd been leading, a life that was, I suspect, not so very different from the lives of any number of thirty- and forty-somethings in the West: hedonistic, heedless, happy-go-lucky, helter-skelter, at times hellraising. Anyway, I survived to fight another day. I digested the painful lesson of 28/29 July 1995, and embarked on a slow and psychologically painful convalescence. It was during those months that I began to learn something else, rather less obvious, about the human condition.

The world is terribly unwell. This, I discovered, is not just a matter of physical decay. Wherever I went I found people telling me of their illnesses, their breakdowns, their crises, and their bereavements – their suffering. I don't flatter myself that I'm an especially sympathetic figure, it was simply that, by virtue of my 'brush with death', I'd become an involuntary representative of that world of the shivery hush that precedes the arrival of the coffin.

I quickly lost count of the number of people who confided in me either the recent death, or the profound sickness, of someone near to them, or their own encounter with acute illness. Hume Cronyn, the veteran American actor, described his feelings on the death of his wife, Jessica Tandy. A woman whose husband had dropped dead one day in the kitchen described, in the most moving possible terms, the slow process by which she had become reconciled to her appalling loss. A friend I'd lost touch with wrote to confide her battle with breast cancer. And so on.

During these months I had, meanwhile, been battling to commit my recent experience to the pages of this book. Wrongly, I assumed that, one day soon, my convalescence would end and I could put all this stuff behind me. Wrongly, I assumed that once my book came out I would be able to close this chapter of my life so far, turn a new page, and move on.

It was not to be. *My Year Off* was published in Britain and then in America, with subsequent editions in Australia, Canada, and South Africa. Overnight, it seemed, I became engulfed not just by the world's unwellness, but, more generally, by its universal pain. The daughter of an old schoolteacher wrote to describe the 'devastating psychotic breakdown' that had culminated in a suicide attempt from a second-storey window. From Athens, an actress, confined to bed for a year with TB, wrote to share her 'parallel experience'. Mrs D also offered 'a similar experience' in a long and beautifully handwritten letter. 'I, too, despaired,' she wrote. 'The uncertainty of a full recovery hung over our family life and made me angry with my husband and children.' A well-known biographer described how illness had 'sabotaged my mental and communicative powers'. From New Jersey, a retired dentist described how, in the aftermath of spinal surgery, he spent seven months of physiotherapy getting to the point where he could rise from his bed and walk. And then there was this, from a mother in Wales:

We, too, have become inhabitants of the world of pain. In December 1997 our lovely daughter Veronica was diagnosed with leukemia after three months of being ill and doctors dismissing her symptoms . . . Veronica was transferred to Cardiff. I gave up my job to look after her and we rented a house in Cardiff . . . Chemotherapy devastated Veronica; the loss of her looks and even more the loss of her fertility threw her into a terrible depression. All her friends and colleagues rallied round and phoned or wrote almost daily but she did not want to see anybody.

A year ago last week she suffered a stroke (the doctors were unsure what caused it), quite mild compared to yours but equally debilitating. Her right side was affected and she could not speak or swallow very well; she went down to 7 stone in weight. However, thanks to her youth and the efforts of therapists, she recovered her speech and her movement relatively quickly and seemed to be rallying round. She finally persuaded the doctors to give up her anti-depressants, her hair started to grow again and she agreed to start seeing people again. By the end of March she appeared almost normal at her twenty-fourth birthday celebrations. After a whole month's rest she had to start radiotherapy . . . Somehow one of the drugs affected her very badly, she was in so much pain it was awful to watch her . . . She had to be hospitalized again. While in hospital she contracted a serious infection which she could not fight (her immune system was non-existent) and on 19 July she died of pneumonia . . .

Now we are living in hell. Or rather, it is like living in two worlds: we see the 'normal' world and we are able to integrate in it, we do 'normal' things, which provide us with some respite, but at the end of it all we have to come back to the other world, our private hell. Life does indeed go on, as everybody keeps telling us, but there is no joy in it for us, it is all mechanical. Veronica used to cry pitifully in her worst moments and say, 'I want to be normal, Mummy'; at other times she used to say, 'I wonder if I'll ever be happy again', and that is how I feel now. I feel that I'll never be happy again, there is nothing to look forward to. The feelings are so complex. Grief, although overwhelming, is not all. There is also a feeling of failure at not having been able to save her and there is guilt, of course, guilt that we are here 'enjoying' a good meal or reading a book when she is in her grave. My poor, poor child, so lovely, so kind, she has been cheated of her life.

There is such a deafening silence about this world of pain, about those people like us who have to live their lives in that world, being 'brave' as it is called, perhaps putting on an air of 'normality', of 'happiness' because otherwise it makes others feel too uncomfortable.

I was still digesting the anguish of this terrible communication when, about a week later, I received this, from the North of England:

> My friend had a stroke last December. Aged thirty-six, she lives in a rented house. She was in a coma in intensive care for three weeks and nobody seemed to know what was wrong with her. She didn't speak and her eyes rolled around in her head. . . Now she is paralysed on her left side. She cannot walk or stand and has to be lifted with a hoist from her bed on to a wheelchair and from her wheelchair on to the toilet. She has been terribly frustrated, angry, tearful, despairing and demanding throughout her convalescence . . .

Now, not a day goes by without someone writing to me, or telephoning, or e-mailing with their observations. Unwittingly, I find I have become a lightning conductor for that thunderstorm of physical calamity that is raging just over the horizon. This, from a bookseller in the Midlands, is typical:

> I, too, suffered a stroke, or brain haemorrhage, some ten years ago. . . I was in a coma for fourteen days, and missed Christmas, the New Year and Lockerbie. When I finally came round, I was paralysed down my right side, and the doctors told me that if I did have an operation to clear the rest of the damaged tissue, then I was likely to suffer a further attack, and as the doctor in charge of my case would have it, I would not reach thirty. . . With all the dangers this entailed, I nevertheless had three holes drilled into my skull, that they might locate the precise location of the corrupt cells. . . It hurt

like hell. . . I was constantly throwing up. . . And yet it seems to have done the trick. . . It has been a very slow process. I am aphasic. . . I know what I want to say, but have trouble in putting the words together. . . Of course there is the relief that I have been spared to fight another day, but there are other days when I am possessed with an utter fury . . . And there is nobody to turn to in Birmingham . . . no meetings, no contact, no help. I have often felt a little alone in my affliction . . .

In a similar vein, this arrived last week from a thirty-eight-year-old man in Australia:

I had a right-hand-side stroke that left me paralysed . . . Reading your book was a horrible fucking nightmare reliving all the horrors of the 'biological car crash'. I live on the beach three hours south of Sydney and I jogged every day, swam in the ocean, and had no stress and whammo, my brother found me lying on the kitchen floor. Well, I'm home now living happily . . .

These are not friends or relatives (though I've heard from them, too); these are people living in what I've come to think of as the world of pain, calling out to someone they think – rightly or wrongly – will understand their plight and sympathize with it. The incidence of physical suffering is a lonely mystery; perhaps sharing it lightens the burden. And then there is the great enigma of that involuntary separation inflicted by the death of those without whom we would never have wanted to live. I have had letters from widows, orphans, hospital workers, carers, parents. This especially distressing letter, in the spidery writing of the dying, arrived from a London hospice:

I am a terminal cancer patient of seventy-two with tumours on the right side of my brain who has undergone an experience of collapse somewhat similar to yours. I am extremely grateful to you for using your expertise in reporting back from post-stroke country so as to make it plain to my family and friends what I am going though.

I try to answer these letters but, compared to the stories I'm hearing, my experience has been trifling, as more than one correspondent has pointed out. Sometimes I feel ashamed to claim fellow-citizenship with these sufferers, but there it is: they are writing to me and there's not a thing I can do about it. I have a card on which I scribble banalities. 'I'm glad you liked the book. Thank you for writing. Your letter touched me.'

The truth is: it did.

As well as looking at the world through the eyes of someone who might have died, I have acquired a quite new view of it. Of course I recognize that people will want to communicate with those they feel are sympathetic to their plight, but now I have come to believe something different. It's this: that despite the stupendous contemporary journalism of feelings, there is still a vast unarticulated story out there that gets no publicity, a story of almost unendurable pain and desperation. Sure, I've been to Hell and back, but these people are living there every day of their lives or, as Eliot puts it, 'living and partly living'. Oddly, the more everything is reported, analysed, expounded, categorized and explored in newspaper column after column, and the more people feel able to express whatever they think, the more deafening the general silence that hangs over illness and ill-health. There is a sea of horror lapping at the edges of the everyday world, and these messages in bottles are floating in on every tide.

These are the messages from what I now think of as the world of pain, messages that describe the suffering of strangers. I have learned three things. First, that the world's front-line pain is the pain of AIDS, cancer, heart disease, and stroke (the big killers). And then, behind the lines, there's the pain of despair, loneliness and loss: the aching void in the lives of the bereaved.

Second, I now know that we are all, in some sense, in the doctor's waiting room. I used to be indifferent towards, and frightened of, illness. Now I recognize it as part of the human condition. Illness is OK. There's nothing wrong with infirmity. It's part of the way we are.

Third, and finally, there's the recognition that, despite the extraordinary progress of medicine, and despite all the safeguards we have built into the way we conduct our lives, we are still in the world of our ancestors. In those far off Anglo-Saxon times, life was characterized by the poet as a sparrow fluttering out of the howling storm into the brightly lit mead hall, circling through the laughter and the smoke for a moment, before disappearing once more into the dark. Sometimes, when I read these letters I've been getting, I sense that dark just beyond the window.

May 1999

Further Reading, Some Useful Addresses and Acknowledgements

READING LIST

Arthur Ancowitz MD: *The Stroke Book* (New York, 1993)

Marcus Aurelius: *Meditations* (London, 1995)

Paul Auster: *The Invention of Solitude* (London, 1982)

Jean-Dominique Bauby: *The Diving Bell and the Butterfly* (London, 1997)

Harold Brodkey: *This Wild Darkness, The Story of My Death* (London, 1997)

John Donne: *Devotions Upon Emergent Occasions* (Cambridge, 1923)

Steven L. Dubovsky: *Mind Body Deceptions* (New York, 1997)

David Hughes: *The Little Book* (London, 1993)

Dharma Singh Khalsa: *Brain Longevity* (London, 1997)

Joseph Le Doux: *The Emotional Brain* (London, 1998)

C. S. Lewis: *A Grief Observed* (London, 1961)

Peter Medawar: *Memoir of a Thinking Radish* (Oxford, 1986)

Sherwin B. Nuland: *How We Die* (New York, 1994)

Stephen Pinker: *How The Mind Works* (London, 1998)

Roy Porter: *The Greater Benefit to Mankind* (London, 1997)

Elizabeth Kubler Ross: *The Wheel of Life* (London, 1997)

—*On Death and Dying* (London, 1966)

Oliver Sacks: *The Man Who Mistook His Wife For A Hat* (London, 1985)

—*An Anthropologist On Mars* (London, 1995)

Susan Sontag: *Illness as Metaphor* (New York, 1977)

Weiner, Lee & Bell: *Recovering At Home After A Stroke* (New York, 1994)

USEFUL ADDRESSES

I gratefully acknowledge the assistance of Donal O'Kelly and the Different Strokes organization in the compilation of this dossier.

Different Strokes, Sir Walter Scott House, 2 Broadway Market, London E8 4QJ. Tel: 0171 249 6645

The Disability Information Trust series of leaflets, Mary Marlborough Centre, Nuffield Orthopaedic Centre, Headington, Oxford OX3 7LD. Tel: 01865 227592.

REMAP GB, 'Hazeldene', Ightam, Sevenoaks, Kent TN15 9AD. Tel: 01732 883818

Disabled Living Centres Council, 286 Camden Road, London N7 OBJ

Keep Able, Fleming Close, Park Farm, Wellingborough, Northants NN8 3BR. Tel: 01933 679426.

Nottingham Rehab Limited, 17 Ludlow Hill Road, West Bridgeford, Nottingham NG2 6HD. Tel: 01159 452345

The Stroke Association, CHSA House, 123–127 Whitecross Street, London EC1Y 8JJ. Tel: 0171 490 7999

RADAR (Royal Association for Disability and Rehabilitation), 12 City Forum, 250 City Road, London EC1V 8AF. Tel: 0171 250 3222

ACKNOWLEDGEMENTS AND THANKS

I gratefully acknowledge thanks to Faber & Faber for permission to quote from 'Sheep' by Ted Hughes.

Among the many relatives and friends and, in some cases, complete strangers, who offered support and encouragement during my year off I would especially like to thank: Roger Alton, Paul and Siri Auster, Julian Barnes, Glen and Carol Baxter, Stephen and Flo Bayley, Peter and Hilary Bazalgette, Blanche Belliveau, Merrill Berger, Don and Hilary Boyd, Will and Susan Boyd, Melvyn Bragg, Sally Brampton, Breyten Breytenbach, Bill Buford, Georgina Capel, Peter Carey, Ian Chapman, Elizabeth Clough, Amanda Conquy, Arnulf Conradi, Chris Corbin, Jenny Cottom, Charlotte Cory, Bill and Steffy Cran, Jan Dalley, Michael Dibdin, Ray Dolan, Brian Dunn, Hillary Durgin, Peggy Edersheim, Valerie Eliot, Jack Emory, Morgan Entrekin, Julio Etchart, Liz and Martin Evans, Matthew Evans, Dr T. E. Faber, Anne Louise Fisher, Gary Fisketjon, Peter Florence, Robert Fox, Robert and Elizabeth Frayling Cork, Reg Gadney, Malcolm Gladwell, David Glynn, Jaco and Elizabeth Groot, David and Eileen Hammond, David Hare, Robert Harris and Gill Hornby, Monica Hart, Ian and Victoria Hislop, Julia Hobsbawm, Gerry Howard, Tanja Howarth, Ted and Carol Hughes, Will Hutton, Kazuo and Lorna Ishiguro, Edmund B. Jelkes, Howard Kaminsky, Pat Kavanagh, Julie Kavanagh and Ross MacGibbon, Dillie Keane, Garrison Keillor, Kate Kellaway, Jeremy King, Jean Korelitz, Sarah Lawson, Mario and Patricia Vargas Llosa, David Lyall, Sarah McCrum, Stephen and Emily McCrum, John McGahern, Joanna Mackle, Christopher and Koukla MacLehose, Mark and Trish Malloch Brown, Adam Mars-Jones, Belinda and Colin Matthews, Lucy Maycock, Caroline Michel, Peggy Miller, Rohinton and Freny Mistry, Arshad Mohammed, Lorrie Moore, Patricia Morison, Sara Mosle, Andrew Motion, Paul Muldoon, Ivan Nabokov, Deborah Needleman, Sue New, Rebecca Nicholson, David and Gwyneth Nissan, Redmond O'Hanlon, Donal O'Kelly, Michael Ondaatje, Helen Osborne, Bruce Palling, Tom and Giti Paulin, Jeremy Paxman, Doug Pepper, Adam Phillips, Caryl Phillips, Emma Platt, Jonathan Powell, Craig Raine, Jon Riley, Kathy Robbins, Deborah Rogers, Jane Rogers, Richard and Ruthie Rogers, Jacqueline Rose, Elizabeth Ruge, Alan and Lindsay Rusbridger, Salman Rushdie, Stephen Segaller, Clive Siddall, Sarah Spankie, Sarah Stacey, Norman and Christine Stone, Peter Straus, Roger Straus, Alison Summers, Jocelyn Targett, Peter and Helen Thompson, Hans and Susan Utsch, Ed Victor, Jacob Weisberg, Edmund White.

I have already mentioned the doctors who treated me, but I would especially like to thank Davina Richardson, Andrew Lees, Richard and Ruth Greenwood, Sue Edwards, Sam Machin, John Land, my acupuncturist Dr Zhu, and my speech therapists Veronica Noah, Renata Whurr, and Christina Shewell. Almost as important as the medical experts were the literary people who guided me through the writing of this book. First and foremost I must thank Binky Urban, Peter Straus, Gerry Howard, and most particularly Louise Dennys, who had the idea in the first place. Thanks, too, to the staff of my agents in London, Peters, Fraser and Dunlop, especially Michael Sissons, Anthony Jones, Carol MacArthur and Charles Walker. Finally, a special thank you to my all friends at Macmillan in London and WW Norton Inc. in New York.

Dedalus Original Fiction in Paperback

THE DREAM MAKER

Mikka Haugaard was born in Denmark in 1953. Her father is Danish and her mother American and she grew up bi-lingual. She studied classics at Cambridge University and did research in Roman history. She now teaches classics and psychology at a London school and lectures for the Open University. She is married with two children.

Dedalus published her first novel *Gabriel's Bureau* a dark, fast moving thriller in 2005.

Mikka Haugaard

The Dream Maker

Dedalus

Published in the UK by Dedalus Ltd,
Langford Lodge, St Judith's Lane, Sawtry, Cambs, PE28 5XE
email: info@dedalusbooks.com
www.dedalusbooks.com

ISBN 978 1 903517 56 7

Dedalus is distributed in the USA by SCB Distributors,
15608 South New Century Drive, Gardena, CA 90248
email: info@scbdistributors.com   web: www.scbdistributors.com

Dedalus is distributed in Australia by Peribo Pty Ltd,
58, Beaumont Road, Mount Kuring-gai N.S.W. 2080
email: infor@peribo.com.au

Dedalus is distributed in Canada by Disticor Direct-Book Division
695, Westney Road South, Suite 14, Ajax, Ontario, LI6 6M9
email: ndalton@disticor.com   web: www.disticordirect.com

First published by Dedalus in 2008

The Dream Maker copyright © Mikka Haugaard 2008

The right of Mikka Haugaard to be identified as the author of this work has been
asserted by her in accordance with the Copyright, Designs and Patent Act, 1988.

Printed in Finland by WS Bookwell
Typeset by RefineCatch Limited, Bungay, Suffolk

A C.I.P listing for this book is available on request.

For Adam and William

1

The stranger in my bed

"I do like Max," said the sultan. "I even prefer him to Ali Baba, but I don't know about Boris."

"He'll grow on you, and anyway you can't have Max without Boris," replied his wife, the beautiful Scheherazade, holding tight the reins of fiction. "The choice is yours . . ."

And the sultan knew that she had won because no treasure in the world, be it gold or emeralds, can compare to a good story.

★

I'm going to start with the present. The past will catch up with us soon enough.

A few hours ago I was standing in a small shop down the road, a little lost and a far cry from sober. Leaning on the counter, I discovered that I needed help. I wanted to go home. I had something to go home for, but I had forgotten what. The owner knew me well. I was relying on that.

"What have you done to yourself?"

Done? I'm not much in the doing business, not these days, but I felt my face, wondering how much had happened to it.

"I think someone hit me," I said. "Down by the river. I remember a little bit of that."

The man behind the till shook his head.

"Your eyes are all swollen and you need a doctor with that nose. Steve will take you home."

His son shrugged his shoulders and didn't move. He'd seen me too often, hardly able to stand but insisting it was otherwise. His father was more tolerant.

"Help her home. She can't walk. She won't make it on her own. Take her shopping, will you? A mango and a piece of cheese. What kind of shopping is that? She doesn't eat and look at the state of her. You should take care of yourself, Rachel," he said to me kindly. "Help her Steve. Can't you see that she needs help?"

"How did she make it here then?"

"A miracle. There are always some of them around."

And, as if to confirm what he had said, I began to slide slowly, very slowly, till I found myself lying on the floor.

"Ophelia," I said searching for dignity, "lay among the flowers like this. Her body drifting with the current and surrounded by flowers. Her hair . . ." and touching my tangled knots, my sad strands, I continued, "her hair enclosing her face like a lion's mane."

I reappeared in my flat clutching Steve's arm.

"Are you all right?"

This is what they all say before they go, a shy question mark at the end begging the answer they always get. Yes, I'm all right.

A man's body lay on my bed. Was I all right, was he all right?

"Who is that?"

"Let me think . . ."

But nothing came to me. I couldn't remember him at all.

"Shall I wake him?" Steve asked.

"I don't know."

The man on the bed sat up suddenly looking at me and expecting recognition.

"A friend of mine," I explained trying to remember who he was and peering at him with blurred vision. "A good friend of mine."

"Since early this morning." he smiled. "Very early this morning. You could say last night or dawn. I brought you home."

Home. Not much to say about that. Not much to say about

this high-ceilinged room with its bed, table and chairs and enormous bookcase. The photographs on the walls, I shall say something about them of course. In due course. Everything in due course.

"I brought you home."

"Thank you," I said humbly watching Steve leave closing the door carefully behind him. "Thank you."

"Is that mango for me?"

"Yes," I lied.

"I had hoped for something more to eat. You mentioned a Chinese takeaway."

In my state? Surely not? Even a miracle could not have guided my tottering steps and steadied my poor frame for that epic journey.

"A Chinese takeaway?"

"Well I wasn't sure you would make it. But you insisted."

"I'm afraid that all I've got to repay you with is this, this mango." I sat down heavily on the bed.

"I'll have it then – just the mango. The other stuff I'll give you back."

"The other stuff?"

"The string of pearls."

"The string of pearls?"

"For taking you home – and for a fuck. Yes, love." He smiled mischievously. "But you can have them back. What's in the bag?"

"Bread and cheese. Did you say for a fuck?"

"Yeah – you wanted that. And in what state, in what state." He shook his head absorbed by the bread and cheese.

"You should see a doctor when you have sobered up."

My poor body. And not for the first time. Hamlet was right. Get ye to a nunnery. Fat chance.

"There is butter in the fridge. I'll bring knives and plates so we don't mess up the bed." An attempt to regain a little

11

ground. Some dignity here. I rose and waved feebly at the kitchen.

"This is a comfortable flat."

He cut the cheese carefully. Had I asked him to stay?

"A very comfortable flat."

Apparently.

"You have a lot of books."

"I write books."

"Write books?"

"I am a dream maker."

"Did you write this? 'She couldn't take her eyes off his suntanned body and her kisses, like playful butterflies, woke him with their soft touch'."

The book lay open on his knees; bread and butter on one page, while he read the other with difficulty. The grubby sheets covered his legs, and with a laugh he wiped his hands on them mocking my timid smile.

"Yes," I said proudly, "I wrote that."

"That's not you. That's Tina Faithful. Pure Tina Faithful." He read on, " 'She looked long and hard at his buttocks before tapping her long nails teasingly on his thigh. "Shall I draw blood?" she asked. Before he could answer . . .'" He whispered, "That's Tina Faithful, that's her style." I thought I heard the word 'inimitable'. "And look," he closed the book to reveal her name heavily embossed on the cover.

Silently, my mouth full of cheese, I pointed to the inscription on the first page in a large clear schoolgirl hand. "Thanks for all the help. Tina."

2

Please touch me

Tina Faithful looked into her huge handbag expecting to find everything there.

"I was sure I put the contract in here. Anyhow, I've been told that it says all the usual things, and the advance is brilliant, although they can't be sure that it'll sell because it's a first book."

It did sell. Boy, did it sell, but I shall never forget Tina standing there with her bag on the table; the only table in that flat.

"They've given it to us in cash. I suppose they took one look at me and figured that I didn't have a bank account. Maybe they even think that I don't know what a bank account *is*. They want the book, but they spoke to me like a piece of shit. Anyhow here it is: five thousand pounds."

She opened the bag and I remember the revelation of money, the feel of cash. Slowly she extracted the bundles placing them on my side of the table, pushing them over towards me, waiting for me to take them and laughing in my eyes. Or at my eyes. My tired eyes. I continued smoking.

"Count them Tina. Count them for me. Just count them slowly for me."

"You're beginning to sound like that book – like the book you wrote. Count the money yourself. Five thousand pounds. Have you ever seen so much cash?"

There on the breakfast table I rearranged the bundles, placing them between the mug of coffee and the ashtray counting slowly while Tina looked at me triumphantly as if she herself had printed the notes. And I paused between each thousand with a humble flourish, as if each represented one of my wild phantasms, my lightly spawned creations, my women

15

of easy climaxes, and my men whose terse dialogue anticipates even terser action. And the name Faithful, that's mine too. She has supplied some of the plot and all of the research. She has discovered all I had to know about guns and explosives and banks and money and smuggling. Before I was rich, when the Max trilogy was only an idea, she persuaded someone to pay for my visits to Los Angeles, Saint Petersburg and Cairo, and introduced me to someone who claimed to have worked for the KGB. But I have peopled this rich landscape and supplied her with my fantastics.

At the bottom of her bag, Tina found the contract which said that she would get twenty percent of my royalties. That seemed a lot for her name and her assistance, but my present preoccupation was the money, the bundles of cash which seemed to dwindle in the counting.

"But Tina, I asked for more. We have so many debts. You should have asked for more."

"More than five thousand?"

She made the figure sound huge. "It's a first book. That's why he won't give more as an advance. And . . ." she paused drawing an envelope out of her bag. "Here's a thousand, just from me. The money in this envelope is just from me because of our partnership."

She smiled a little uneasily putting the envelope firmly on the table, anticipating my answer, and, next to it, a bottle of champagne. I took the envelope and I drank the champagne. I knew that she had stolen the money, and that she had probably stolen it from me. But that is Tina . . .

Tina, my Tina, my friend of easy promises and unfailing determination.

"The problem with you," she would say trying to survey the chaos of my life, "the problem with you . . ." and then she would stop and look uncertain as if she had found herself suddenly in a strange place where the relationship between the total and its parts is too elusive. I would sense her mind ticking, adding and subtracting, wondering whether I was worth so much bother; because I can be such a nuisance, such a waster of other people's patience. A relentless consumer of time, other people's time. But the more she thought, the less she had to say.

"Well, one of your problems is that you drink."

"Really? Thank you Tina."

Tina, my friend from schooldays. Murphy was her name. Is her name, except on the spines of books. In most lessons we sat next to each other, and ours was one of those friendships that grew out of childhood and never lost the mystery of childhood.

And I'm not one for mystery, I can tell you. I have no patience with mystery, but I've allowed a little bit of it in my life. Just a little bit, and Tina is one of those little bits, Tina and the count, that old liar, and Max, of course; Max shares this dimmed glow although he's fiction and one shouldn't, perhaps, lump real people and fictitious people together. I'm not one for mystery, and I'm not one for intimacy, but I know that everything is always better if someone touches me: a hand on my shoulder, a hand on my hand, my legs, my body. It's amazing what touching can do to this old wreck.

We were arm in arm, friends nudging and giggling and sharing secrets which Tina also shared with the world, and had to share with the world because of her natural exuberance, the wonderful excess which was Tina. Is Tina.

She was most herself in the morning, feet dangling, sleep heavy, elbows on the bed, but ready to see you. Always ready to see you, brushing aside that sleep for the comings and goings of the day. She was Tina when eating in unashamed bursts of pleasure, licking her fingers. She was Tina when unravelling the sad plots of her stories with the feigned astonishment of a failed birthday party magician. "And you won't guess what he said."

And finally she was Tina the wrecker, Tina the greedy.

All this happened over several years involving many people, but as one of them is a lover and the other a son – within such a grand context I'm rather marginal – it has a certain ebb and flow about it which commands attention. One might even say a certain grandeur.

"What are you writing, you drunken old cunt?" Demands yesterday's saviour lying on the bed, petulantly consuming cheese for lack of anything better. Why do I invite such language? Or am I not listening? Did he say cow?

"The story of Tina," I reply, "Tina Faithful. You'll want to read it. And even if you don't want to read it, I'll want to write it. There is an alluring fire in the writing of it that will keep me going, I can tell you. And that's what it is about, keeping me going – which is a lifetime's occupation and with a poor reward, if 'drunken old cow' is all you can say."

Why can't I say cunt? But I have an aversion to such words. He rises languidly out of the grimy sheets which enfold him – mind you his body hasn't seen a shower too recently – stretching his young body with its fine masculinity.

"Please," I want to say, "please touch me."

"Have you got another dressing-gown," he asks, "or is there only the one you are wearing?"

3

Killer hands

I'll begin with childhood. Dabbling briefly in that distant time, I will resurrect only what matters. A few facts, a few feelings and the events of a particular day.

Tina was Tina Murphy and her mother was Julie, a good-looking woman with a large round face, solid temperament and warmth; someone who knew how to laugh and I have always been addicted to laughter.

"I don't know where she has got it from," she would say of Tina. Tina, her favourite, her youngest child; youngest of five. "I don't know where she has got it from. And I don't know where she is going." Mr Murphy didn't share her admiration. He was a quiet man with quick bursts of anger and contorted feelings. He didn't much like his lively teenage daughter, instead he admired Axel their lodger who seemed to us to be always lurking somewhere silently in the house. His tiny room had been converted from a bathroom to allow for more space and a weekly income. That had been the plan, but Axel didn't fulfil this plan because most weeks he didn't pay, and Mr Murphy, a man for whom no detail was too small, didn't notice.

"I don't know where she has got it from. Not from me at any rate. I'm a loser."

She loved to ponder Tina's future, so different from her own. She relished unfavourable comparisons that emphasised her own smallness and the wonder of this child, her Tina, but Mr Murphy would not understand

"What are you talking about? Going *where*? Got *what*? I can tell you what she's got: she's a bitch, that's what she's got. She can be a real little bitch." He would stop talking as suddenly as he'd begun; a quick eruption of words and, then, all sense of purpose gone, he would no longer be looking at you, but at his hands. His huge hands, that we called killer hands. Tina had told me about his killer hands.

"Your mum is a slag," I had said, unsure of the meaning of the word. "A fat slag."

A shrug of the shoulders. No denial. "My dad can kill people. He can kill your dad. He can kill your mum too. He has killer hands."

"Really Tina?" I whispered, getting close and feeling a darkness descending on this comfortable bit of my world, the nursery with its toy train in which we were the only passengers. It was raining and we could hear drumming on the roof and the sound made an island of our safe cupboard. I think I must have been about five and here was Tina inviting admiration and awe with her obvious handle on the world. She *knew* killer hands. I didn't know anything.

"Really?"

Tina had no doubt. "He has killer hands," she repeated without hesitation.

Since then I had been fascinated by Mr Murphy's hands, those big slabs of hands which he would keep occupied whenever he was expected to speak.

On this particular day Julie was, as usual, full of her admiration for Tina, but Martin Murphy wasn't having it.

"I wonder what she is going to be. I wonder where she is going."

"She isn't going out," said Mr Murphy suddenly, as if provoked, his hands covering an amazing amount of table. "She isn't going out."

"I didn't mean that sort of going."

"What other sort of going? What other sort of going, for Christ's sake?"

"Going and becoming. Going and becoming. What is she becoming?"

"Nothing, by what her teachers say." His hands stopped. "And she isn't going out," he repeated and kept repeating, insisting on the literal meaning of words.

"She is not going out. No, she is not going out. No she isn't. She isn't because of last time."

"But she's going with Axel."

Axel Winter the lodger. I can see him sitting in one of the old armchairs in the Murphy's lounge looking at his shoes, his hands resting on the arms of the chair. Axel was studying for a degree in History. He came from Germany and I have no idea why he was living with the Murphys but for some reason Tina's father really cared for him. No one could have had less in common with Martin Murphy than Axel Winter but Axel would listen to him with deference, and say, "really Mr Murphy?", with hardly a hint of a question mark, in a way that made you laugh.

"That's all right then. He's not like *you*. He's careful."

"Who says I'm not careful?"

"I do," said Martin helplessly surveying his dead killer hands, "I do."

"You idiot. Who else says I'm not careful?"

"I don't care who says what. I know what I know."

He looked angry and frightening. I took hold of Tina but she was enjoying herself. She always had an instinct for people's impotence, and she couldn't leave it alone, particularly where men were involved.

"He drinks. Axel drinks – he drinks himself stupid, and he will pass no exams will Axel Winter."

That, of course, was to go too far.

"He is *not* at lectures. How can he pass exams when he's not at lectures?"

"Shut your mouth," he repeated drumming the table. "Shut your mouth."

"Answer me then!"

Of course, he didn't have an answer.

We left, and I could feel Tina's fear. As a parting gesture, she said playfully, looking him straight in the face, "Drinks, drinks himself silly your Axel. Smells too."

Cornered, Tina's father banged his fists on the table and started shouting at us. I can't remember what he said, but the gist of it was that we were both bitches and Axel deserved better. It was all a lot of theatre and look at me, but at only fourteen I thought there was something fine in that performance and something sensual about his pain.

"He smells," repeated Tina, "Axel smells. He could wash."

She had dismissed him, but I could hear her father hurling words, continuing the battle, helplessly denying what even I knew was undeniable, that this Axel was a loser, but I was impressed and taken in by him and, of course, I wanted him to notice *me*. Sitting on the stairs, I enjoyed the hurly burly of his anger and its rise and fall punctuated by hopeless violence as whatever he could lay his hands on hit the walls.

"The bitch!"

Silence. Tina smiled.

"I don't know why he cares, but he does. Cares for Axel and gets really angry when I tease him. He's an idiot."

"He is?" I asked full of admiration for her certainty and wanting details.

"What are you talking about? He is what?"

She was always losing the thread of a conversation, or acting as if there wasn't one, and would look at me with amused curiosity, bite her lip and close her eyes as if my serious face was just too much for someone with her knowledge of the world. Then she would laugh and reveal her play-acting by repeating whatever she had said with a firmness which was somehow explanatory.

"He's an absolute idiot! Don't you see?"

And then I always did see, had to see. And there was never anything more to say, but on this occasion I had decided to do something on my own. I wanted to take the place of Axel Winter. And it didn't matter that he was an idiot, or her father. The man himself scarcely mattered at all – what mattered was the strength of his feelings and these I had seen in the raw. No one had ever noticed me in such a way.

I was fourteen and I couldn't escape my mother's looming presence. There was only her – men came and went, sometimes making their first real impression in their departure. I knew this was my chance of getting what she wouldn't or couldn't give, and, of course, something more. There was sensuality in his pain. "Please touch me," I wanted to say.

My mother's life was wild and chaotic but somehow she always imagined a pattern beneath its surface. There could be something magnificent in the way she closed the chapters, standing in the kitchen or lounge surveying the broken furniture – because it usually ended like that – and addressing the walls. She never used the words *dear walls*, but she was never speaking to me, they were her audience and her speech ignored most facts, focusing only on how things could never have been any different, how nothing could have altered this jumbled flow or changed this sad story. And I was, of course, a permanent presence, and more difficult to deal with than the men who came and went and banged doors.

She thought my jumbled reactions, my fumbling intentions flowed from a deeper and more sinister purpose. I saw myself as almost devoid of personality. I was nobody and that's why nobody loved me. True, events did seem to confirm that I was provocative, but this was purely accidental. Each time I was taken by surprise. There was nothing like my surprise. There was, at times, nothing more genuine than my surprise, although my mother saw it differently.

"Look at Miss Stubborn. There is no arguing with her."
And her friends nodded, that sad band of conspirators pulling buggies and toddlers and carrying bags of shopping going somewhere they didn't want to go. The only consolation was that I wasn't alone, I wasn't the only one touched by this diabolical wilfulness.

Unable to detach herself and see things in their smallness, she was forever perceiving patterns and motives and summing up events in words that were rock hard in their finality. At four, or thereabout, I told lies and was therefore a liar. I learned how to respond to people's moods and that made me manipulative and sneaky. I told her little, and was suspected of always concealing something. The unfairness and the simplicity of her approach bamboozled and hurt me because I couldn't grasp – what child can – that she didn't like me, and didn't much care, although I hurled it often enough at her in fantastic over-statements: *you hate me and wish me dead*. No she didn't. She really didn't. And the whole thing, our sad confrontations and even sadder misunderstandings were explained by reference to an inevitably crossing of purposes, which neither of us could do anything about.

"Knew it before she was born. Her being Pisces and me Virgo. I knew we wouldn't get on."

We led a queer life my mother and I, tumultuous and misaligned, till finally, all rage spent, I walked out on her with the words, "I'm going." It was about a year later when I saw her again. I don't remember what she said but I remember her face, pretty really and very young. I think I noticed her face for the first time: her hair in need of re-dying and make-up badly applied because she didn't have the confidence or the ability to do it well. Also that cloud of confusion that re-deemed her, inviting something that she didn't want from me.

"We'll have to take Axel with us," said Tina, "or we won't be able to go out."

"Don't you like him?"

"He's all right."

"I like him."

"If you like him, show it and he'll be stupid about you. He's that kind." She pouted touching her breasts pushing them up and inviting comparison with mine.

"Has he had any girl friends?"

"We'll ask him."

And we did. Axel replied thoughtfully that he had had sex with nine girls. He took the question seriously pausing between words as if counting. He was sitting by his desk, a book in front of him, eyes fixed on the wall above us, tantalised by the question.

"Which one was best?"

He blushed.

"The second one."

"Bet there has only been two. And the first one doesn't count because it's a cock up. In all ways. First times always are." She laughed and she seemed too big, too sensual for Axel's small room with its monastic simplicity. There was nothing there except his books, an accumulation of plates and mugs and discarded clothes. He didn't know what to say, and she didn't disturb the silence in which he felt trapped.

She just kept smiling, looking straight at him insolently.

"Did they suck you?"

"All nine of them?"

"Yeah."

"Perhaps only five of them."

"Liar."

Finally, he looked at her, and I could see that he would give anything for her, for this Tina – if only he knew what to do with his shyness which was infecting his voice making him whisper. He began to read his book.

"What are you reading?"

"A book. A book about someone. Someone special."

'What's he called?"

"Stephen. Stephen Dedalus." He said the name very slowly as if it were a piece of magic.

" Stephen Dedalus. That's a funny name. Did he suck girls?"

Confused by her persistence, he looked at her, "Did he what?"

"Suck girls?"

"This is Stephen Dedalus," said Axel and he began reading slowly from the page in front of him without any intonation or feeling. He read of a young man who saw a girl standing alone on a beach. She didn't see him but 'her image had passed into his soul forever and no word had broken the holy silence of his ecstasy.'

"That is Stephen Dedalus," and he closed the book full of expectation. "I like the way he uses words," he added defensively.

"Dad says you have to come with us," explained Tina, "otherwise we can't go out."

"Is that why you want me?"

"That's why we want you."

Resigned, he followed us, waiting patiently for Tina to get dressed, the book in his pocket so that he could take it out and read it if he became bored. He sat on the stairs, and I thought of the stories I had been told about him. He had been born towards the end of the war in Berlin and his father had been much older than his mother, and married. He had spent some time with this father who had other children too, but one day he had come home and his father had told him that he didn't want to see him anymore.

"And I've sold your bike," he said with a finality that a child would understand, and gave him enough money for a train ticket to somewhere, and Axel made his way to London and the Murphys. Why the Murphys? This is something I shall never know, but Julie took him in and cared for him and Martin admired him. As soon as he saw him, he decided that he was all those things we weren't.

"Tell me about Berlin," I asked.

"I grew up in Hamburg. I was born in Berlin but I only stayed there till I was five. Then my dad said he wanted me."

"And your mum?"

"She had died. That's why he said he wanted me, but he didn't really. He didn't like me."

It was impossible to imagine what this quiet child could have done. Even when he smiled he had to overcome his bashfulness.

"He asked you to leave?"

"I came back from a week with the scouts and he said, "You can't live here any more." And, "I have sold your bike.""

Those couldn't quite have been his words, but that was how the story was told and it reminded me of the tales of Grimm where evil is undisguised, uncomplicated and direct. And the story made me feel a special tie with Axel.

"What did he look like?"

"He was very big, and I've got his hair and his nose. Perhaps I look like him," he shrugged his shoulders dismissing the subject, "you should read this book. The words are beautiful and they say that Joyce understands women."

"Do you have many books by people who understand women?"

"Not in English – they're rare. Very rare, but I've some in German, and a few in French. They are better at understanding women." He put his index finger to his lips thoughtfully and he didn't take his eyes off the wall. "You should read Zola."

"Say I love you in German."

"*Ich liebe dich.*"

"Do you love Tina?"

"Everyone loves Tina."

"Why?"

"She has sensuality that stirs the soul."

He spoke very slowly in his strange German accent which made everything he said seem both remote and tangible.

"Shall I read you more of this? It all begins with some cows . . . ."

"Why do you love Tina?" I asked, wanting to know some of the secrets of men.

"She has sensuality that stirs the soul," he repeated without feeling as if it were a fact.

And then *she* appeared on the stairs. Dress arse-length and wearing boots in spite of the heat – she had recently bought them, and therefore *must* wear them. She had lots of make-up on, and her face looked very thin; her eyes were big and dramatic. She had become Tina of the night.

"Are you coming, then?" She said impatiently having made us wait. "Aren't you wearing anything different?"

"I'm staying but don't tell anyone. I'm not feeling well, and I don't want to go home."

That night I persuaded – seduced is the wrong word – that fool of a man, Tina's half-wit father to lie between my legs while Julie watched television downstairs.

"Princess," he whispered, "you are the most beautiful princess."

"Do you think I'm special?"

"Very special."

"More special than Axel?"

"Axel Winter?"

Confused he caressed my legs, pondering the question as if there were no answer.

"You are very beautiful, and you are a princess, a wonderful princess."

4

Max

He couldn't believe what had happened to him, but the child's face haunted him. A small, timid, and insignificant face.

"She's unlucky," he had heard someone say. "Her parents and sisters have such easy charm, and that makes her very attention seeking. Whenever she swallows tablets, she tells someone. Why does she do it? She wants attention."

Similar things had been said by many people. They grabbed hold of the words 'attention seeking' and a Pavlovian response allowed them to brush aside any consideration of *her*, any thought of what she was doing to gain this attention. They didn't consider that she might need help.

He bit his lip. Max hated the easy connections people made between one idea and another. And this child seemed to him worth a lot. She was the daughter of one of his many assistants, women who helped in the dull detail of the running of his empire. At forty Max could not have been more successful; in Tokyo and New York they waited anxiously for his decisions. But he had come from nothing. A tough barrow boy.

★

"Don't you need more details, more fleshing out?" asked Tina.

Tina in the morning, sleep-heavy, a hideous pair of mules on her feet, her hands on the edge of the bed supporting her heavy frame. Tina expecting a child; the child, David. David who will survive us all and to whom I dedicate this book. May it make you understand your mother just a little. Just a little. One generation cannot expect more, or demand more of the other than that.

"I know bugger all about the stock market, but it will all come," I said confidently. "I will find out all I have to; and you and me and the baby will be all right."

"And we will have a swimming pool, like Max. We will live just like Max." Tina kicked one of her mules into the air and it somersaulted across our sad room hitting the curtains and breaking the glass.

"We will live like Max."

"Max," I reminded her, "dies."

"How? A heart attack by the pool caused by a sudden piece of information? His business empire has collapsed?"

"No," I replied thoughtfully and hurt. I was a little precious with my creations, because at the heart of some of the events lay something of the past intensely perceived. My moments of insight, the stuff of memory.

"How could you," she asked suddenly," have sex with my father? He was such an idiot, and not good-looking."

"I can't remember. I was fourteen."

"That's only six years ago."

I finished the first volume of my trilogy two years later and it took a while to get it published. Tina was the one who found my opportunity, my chance and as she had supplied some of the plot, it was published under her new name. Tina Faithful – the Tina who became familiar with the world of money, and who plays quite a part in this story, although not as big as she would have wanted.

*

Max sat pensively by his swimming pool in a comfortable chair. There was not one piece of comfortable furniture in our flat. We called two rooms and a corridor a flat. I used to sit at the only table, which I called my desk. "Don't move any-thing from my desk," I kept reminding Tina. On the table were books, paper, a glass and a bottle of wine. Always a bottle of wine, but I was still in control.

The child was swimming in the pool; she swam with surprising grace. Surprising, because of the medication she took to dispel her peculiar darkness which made her movements less fluent, and her eyes a little glazed.

"You are my princess," he whispered, "my princess."

She climbed out of the pool and was suddenly clumsy. She shook herself proudly.

"I'm a dog," she said displaying her skinny body, standing with her feet far apart.

"My God," he thought, "she could be twelve. What have I done? This could destroy me."

And Max looked at her full of tenderness and regret. No one would understand that he loved her. No one would *believe* that he loved her. She looked at him very quietly in that strange way she had, suspending all thought, all movement.

"Are you taking me to the theatre tonight?" she asked, as if she didn't care; but he knew she did. She was hungry for such things.

"I have to work now," he said," but I'm taking my princess to the theatre."

She kept standing very still, the water dripping off her, holding her head as if it were an object precariously balanced on her long neck. She smiled. He was wondering whether he should say something. It wasn't so much what he had done – he hadn't really done anything – it was her behaviour that was the problem. She was behaving as if he were her lover. She picked up her T-shirt which was lying by his chair and put it on. She hadn't dried herself and it clung to her defining her slender child's body.

"Did you wear that to school?"

"It's own clothes day. You give a pound to charity and you are allowed to wear your own clothes."

"And did you wear that?"

"Yes." She smiled. She had a curious otherworldly way of smiling as if she didn't want to communicate anything, just wanted to be left alone.

"Why did you wear that?"

"None of your business." Now her smile was provocative, and he wished he hadn't asked because she was putting her hand on his thigh. He pushed it away and she saw the fear in his face.

"I was just curious," he said, "because I know you hate the other girls talking about you."

"I don't care. They talk anyway."

"Why wear a shirt that says you are a bitch and a lesbian?"

She didn't answer, but her face looked very closed as she turned her back on him. He knew she was best left alone for a little while.

He sat down in a large leather chair which embraced him with comforting familiarity and stared at his desk. A telephone rang; his mobile played a tune. He knew that he had to do the deal today. Tomorrow might be too late. Still he didn't move, didn't answer either phone. Marooned in insecurity, he had that illusion which he often felt in the early morning that he couldn't move his limbs. He drew a sharp intake of breath.

"Igor," he shouted at the mobile trying to assert control and power, "the deal is on. I'm buying the oil. It'll send the prices rocketing and play havoc with the American presidential election. But who cares. I don't owe the Republicans anything."

"Don't you?" whispered Igor at the other end. Where was the other end? He had forgotten. Was it Moscow? Or Saint Petersburg? Or Khartoum? "I thought you did."

Silence.

Max entered his bedroom – the creation of his latest woman who favoured opulence. The place looked like it had been designed by an architect unfamiliar with any style that might be found outside Las Vegas. She herself lay naked across the bed, the sheets between her legs, her face heavy on the pillows. She was beautiful and petulant. Petulant was the right word. Max had been searching for the right word for a long time. Women don't become any easier if you are one of the richest men in the world. Perhaps they become more difficult, or you become even worse at choosing. It was difficult to know which.

Eva came from Poland, from a village outside Krakow and she was stunningly beautiful. So beautiful in fact that when she came to London she discovered that men would pay a thousand pounds an hour for her time. They didn't pay *her* the thousand pounds; they paid the agency. Strictly speaking, they only paid the agency. Max had asked the agency for three girls one evening, when he was arranging something with some people who needed to relax after they had done all the talking that could be done. Serious talking could do queer things to your brain, even breathing could become difficult. One needed to relax. And there was Eva. The first thing you noticed about her, thought Max, were her legs. Stunningly beautiful. Max was drunk with the sight of her and all the tension of the meeting that had gone before. Girls from the agency drank with you, and then they slept with you, but Eva had been told not to drink. She ordered lavish and expensive fruit cocktails and looked at Max hardly saying a word. At first he thought that she might not speak English, and that her few questions ("you like my breasts, yes") had been taught her. Her voice lacked colour. "Another hopeless whore," thought Max. You wanted people for what they

39

looked like, and then they came with baggage or were simply not good at their job. They muddled through. Eva came with baggage. Next time he phoned the agency, he suggested they send someone else. They sent Eva. This time she drank and talked about Krakow. Her voice was animated and sad. A fine melancholy informed her uninhibited chatter and she forgot about her breasts. She forgot why she was there, but her clothes and her body reminded him and he desired her so fiercely that he wondered how he could still be waiting and listening. And she moved in, because Max was in love. Why was he in love? "There are dark sides to all of us," thought Max.

That winter Max haunted me. I have always found it difficult to sleep and in the early morning my vision of him was particularly clear. He, too, was awake. In the afternoon, after work, I used to stalk his shadow and look for his ghost in streets I didn't know. Once, I stood by a door for so long that someone asked me why I was there. "I'm waiting for Max," I replied.

"Max who?"

"Oh, I just know him as Max. He knows I'm here. He is always a bit late."

Suspiciously the man walked away memorising my appearance, but I was used to that. I was too poor to know Max.

Meanwhile Tina became huge. Her body sailed like a ship through our flat.

"Oh, I'm so sick," she said, "and what will we do with this baby? I don't want this baby."

"Whose baby?"

"I don't know," and she laid her head on her hands overcome with the effort of this new body and its unfamiliar outlines and strange curves which engaged the furniture unexpectedly, "I really don't know. And it doesn't matter, does it, because babies aren't really related to men. Anyhow, this one isn't."

I had never known her like this. Tina, my Tina. Waves of depression hit her, and she would sit very still in the sad landscape of her surroundings.

"What are you thinking?"

"Nothing, I'm thinking nothing."

And I thought of Max. Max moved between his swimming pool, his bedroom, his office, but most of all he walked the streets of London. Max didn't sleep. That winter I kept him company.

"Where are you going?" Tina would ask.

"Nowhere, just walking."

"Just walking," she repeated, her voice dead, as if words didn't matter.

And I walked. I didn't have much money, so when I got tired I would sit on a bench. Sometimes, when it was raining too much, I went to the cinema. Max never followed me there. We walked along the river together, and in the early morning light we heard our footsteps echo in the concrete labyrinth of the South Bank, its crude cascade of shapes flattened by a vast and pale dawn sky. Below, the river hurried past confined by patches of dark mud and unattractive stones. Solitary cars containing people Max knew crossed bridges and made disappearing sounds. The strong light set off the buildings on the north side; tall vitreous shapes responded with signals of cold fire and my eye would fall on the dome of Saint Paul's. A silent panorama pregnant with a new day. Never was the city more beautiful. It was then that my fantastics finally fell asleep, and I could rest.

I rested at work. I sat at a reception in a hotel in Earl's Court answering dull calls efficiently. It was a job you couldn't fail at. I looked very tired, and I compensated for my appearance with vivid make-up which I applied crudely in thick blotches which I failed to notice in the mirror of our dark bathroom. I had dyed my naturally blonde hair black, and my face, thin and pinched, focused hesitatingly on visitors, now with the unnatural and unnerving attention of the insomniac, now with dreamy insouciance. Frequently I fell asleep and was woken by the ringing of a telephone or a light tapping on my shoulders. People treated me kindly and paid me badly. It was a very poor hotel.

Max kept looking at Eva. Dreams played with her face. She sighed. Max put his fingers between her buttocks. Sex was something he understood. "Sex," thought Max, "gets better with age, everything else gets worse."

And, as he kissed her sleeping body, he thought of all the things that get worse, and as he felt his erection coming, he tried to forget all those things: decisions, people, politics, whispering voices. What did he owe the Republicans? Too much. These days that seemed to be the answer lurking behind every question and waiting to be spoken out loud. Too much. One owed everyone too much.

"Max," sighed Eva.

"I don't know what it is with you," said Tina, "but I really need you and all you can think about is Max. The baby will be here in three weeks. What is this with you and fiction? What is this with you and Max? Who cares about Max? He doesn't exist. The baby exists. The baby is right here. Feel. Feel my baby." She put my hand on her hard swollen stomach, and I felt a kick and saw how tired she looked and became aware of the room in which we were sitting: its hastily assembled furniture and ghastly wallpaper, and the window which so failed to provide a view, and which was so difficult to open. People had occupied this space leaving behind the grimy evidence of their bodies, the physical detritus of sweat and dirt. The shapeless sofa with its loud orange flowers on a pale green background was hopelessly marked with large shiny stains.

"No one comes to see me. No one cares. No one cares even a little bit, except Axel Winter. Axel cares. Axel sits and looks at me in a way that drives me mad, and cares. He says he wishes it was his baby."

"Might it be?"

"Does it matter," replied Tina wiping away the tears. "How can that matter? He's a loser anyway."

"He's loyal."

Tina sniffed and didn't reply. Loyalty was something she did without. It made demands on you. Treachery allowed you to be yourself.

The sound of the door made us turn and there he was, Axel Winter with a bunch of red roses.

"I've brought you these," he said, "when is the beautiful baby due?"

"Any time," said Tina.

"I love her," thought Max as Eva slowly woke responding to his familiar body with the reassuring warmth of sleep. Mary was sitting outside by the pool waiting for him, her feet dangling in the water. She had changed and was wearing a black dress which was beautifully cut to accentuate the sensuality of her body. She had been transformed into a child-woman, a creature rich and strange. Gold and silver glitter covered her eyelids and her cheekbones – an intuitive assertion of the child within. And it was the child within who was playing with the unfamiliar cocktail precariously balanced on a mat beside her.

"I must go," said Max, "I'm taking Mary to the theatre."

"Mary who?"

"Phyllis' girl. The typist, you know." Eva didn't know

and Max knew that she didn't know, but he felt that this assumption might help him along.

"Phyllis who?"

"Does it matter?" asked Max crossly. "This typist, anyhow, has a daughter who isn't very well. She has been bullied at school and has had a breakdown. I've let her swim in the pool, and I'm taking her to the theatre. We are seeing Hamlet. We are seeing Hamlet because she is studying it at school."

Eva put a hand between his legs and bit his shoulder but they had finished making love.

"I don't want to be alone," she thought, but she said, "You never tell me what you are doing. I can't live like this." She thought she wanted to cry, but she wasn't sure and she sat up looking in the mirror to see what was expected of her face. It demanded tears, no question about that: those lines, that tiredness were waiting for that.

"She is beautiful," thought Max in whose eyes she was sitting proudly, her back to him, her breasts and face reflected in a large gilt mirror with cupids happily suspended from bows which fell theatrically on either side as if holding back a curtain. The dim light and the age of the glass gave the reflection a painted look. Her breasts and her nipples stood out, pale white and vulnerable; a shadow fell across one side of her face making her seem at once thoughtful and distant. From behind he put his arms round her holding her breasts in his hands.

"You are so beautiful," he whispered. She began to cry.

"Why is she doing this," thought Max. "It's a kind of obstinacy, a female obstinacy, a kind of fear I don't understand."

"You *are* very, very beautiful. And I *think* you are very, very beautiful and I'm very, very rich," said Max hopelessly kissing her nipples, sucking her nipples knowing that life just isn't that simple, even if you are very rich.

"I'm ugly," she said angry at not being listened to. She moved her face and now there was no shadow lending it

44

anything. It was just a face. The face of a not very clever girl who'd taken too many drugs and wasn't good at it.

"I won't be late," said Max.

★

"What will you call the baby." asked Axel.

"Julie if it's a girl, David if it's a boy," said Tina. "We've made a little box for it to lie in. Mum has promised to help out so I can go back to the hotel where Rachel works in the afternoons, if she keeps the job that long. She doesn't sleep."

And they both looked at me, the amazing insomniac.

"You look terrible,' said Axel, putting his hand on my shoulder. I smiled feeling relaxed.

Tina laughed, shaking her body as if it were a large plant, a sturdy responsive thing which has survived both wind and rain. The Tina I had known was back treating us with that dare-devil contempt we loved.

"She doesn't sleep but goes for walks with people who don't exist, but who'll make our fortune."

"People who don't exist? You can't go for walks with people who aren't there."

"Rachel goes for walks with Max. He has a swimming pool. One day it'll be ours."

"And he doesn't exist?" Axel sounded confused.

"Max does exist," I said teasingly, "I know he does."

"And Eva? What about Eva?"

"You know, she lives downstairs."

Eva lived downstairs where she shared the basement with two other girls, except her name wasn't Eva, it was Yvonne – but she too was Polish. She hadn't yet met Max; and, as she worked for a rather downmarket agency, it wasn't likely that she would. In fact, it wasn't likely that she would meet many more people; for anyone could tell that she wasn't, as they say, long for this world. And when you saw her, you realised that for Yvonne every hour of the day was the hour of the wolf.

"What have you done to her," asked Tina, "sprinkled fairy dust?"

"She once told me about Krakow. I'll never forget that."

"There are a lot of things which you say you'll never forget, but you do something to them, Rachel. What did she tell you about Krakow?"

"Nothing much."

"You mean you have forgotten."

"No, I don't."

"Yes, you do."

"Perhaps, but I do remember her face and what it was like listening to her. That's what I'll never forget – what it was like to listen."

"All memory," said Axel seriously, "is reconstruction." He was still holding his roses, too shy to remind us of his gift because he had realised that we didn't have a vase. And *that* I remember: him holding those roses, holding them tightly as if all his thoughts were bunched together into that thorny handful.

"I don't know what I remember," said Tina, "I suppose it depends on my mood." She looked at us and smiled.

That night David was born, three weeks early but strong and healthy. And we put him in a box which said tomatoes on it, Guernsey, First Class.

5

Meeting Ophelia

Four mobile phones located in various parts of his jacket and trousers, Max sat uncomfortably in the theatre. He wished he had told her to change her clothes.

"Are you going like that?" he had said. She had nodded and he had let the matter drift, taking its course; in the way he sometimes did, and liked to do.

'The ineluctable hand of fate,' she had said. Something was the 'ineluctable hand of fate'. Something trivial, something to do with school, he didn't remember what, but the phrase belonged to this evening and in homage to its magic he had let her go to the theatre completely inappropriately dressed. He liked unusual words, if they had a good sound; they graced your existence with their fine texture. They seemed tactile and enveloping. Hearing them was like swimming in a sea with lonely rocks to sit on where evenings came upon you out of a crepuscular vastness and the wind was sudden and raw.

As he was leaving the house, he knew that he ought to say something but the moment had passed. The darkened windows of his car and the face of his chauffeur had increased his uncertainty.

"Men in my position," thought Max, "can lose all sense of what they can get away with and need others to tell them when they are mad."

And that strange word that Mary had used – ineluctable – came back and flooded his consciousness, and he felt very cold; he put her hand on the seat holding it there firmly so that she would understand that they were just going to the theatre, and nothing more. Nothing more. But the strange word ineluctable seemed to be dissolving and losing its firmness, for in this life nothing is inescapable, thought Max. Not if you paid enough. Or killed enough, depending on the situation.

"Will you kiss me?" she said pretending to be grown up.

And as he did, he was immediately surprised by his hunger for this child – never had she seemed more a child than when he touched her breasts and put his hands between her legs.

"My God, I want you now."

"You can have me."

"What is she doing?" he thought. "Why is she doing it?" For she was completely unresponsive. "She must be older than she looks. Must be at least sixteen."

"Did you come?" he asked unnecessarily.

She shook her head and, holding her face very still, she smiled *that* smile, her smile which was different from any other smile that he'd ever seen on a woman's face.

"I love her," he thought, "I really love her and I won't touch her ever again. She's too young, but she's at least sixteen."

Sitting next to her in the theatre, he felt less happy with his self-deception because he could tell that no one would think she was fifteen, which she claimed to be, and someone *could* (though he would be wrong) mistake her for twelve, and he remembered the curious fact (which he wasn't in the habit of forgetting) that a bit of print could be one's undoing.

"Is it long," he whispered, "this play?"

"It's Hamlet," she replied.

And she sat there very stiff, ignoring him, a fine look of concentration on her face.

"Shall I explain the play to you?" she whispered after a few minutes in a voice he could barely hear while two actors were saying something funny very quickly using unfamiliar words, "I know it very well."

"My God," thought Max, "I have no right to do this. She is a complete child."

"Please do," he said, "but later."

"Pass me the popcorn," she said, eating greedily and dropping the husks down her dress. "Are you enjoying the play?"

"I am," he replied bored and mesmerised by strange islands of thought and mangled observations.

'Marry, well said. Very well said. Look you, sir.'

'Inquire me first what Danskers are in Paris.' So said an old man he recognised. Polonius, it said in the programme.

"I will take you," he whispered, "to Rome. It's better than Paris. I shall show you all the fountains of Rome." And he could imagine her late at night having tramped the streets of Rome, astride one of the many strange animals that make up the sculptured waterworks.

The cunning old man on stage wanted his servant to tell lies about his son. Drinking, fencing, swearing, quarrelling, drabbing, he listed as the wanton, wild and usual slips of youth which did not interfere with one's honour, and which the servant therefore could attribute to him. But the servant felt that drabbing was going too far.

"What is drabbing?" he whispered.

"Pursuing loose women says my teacher," she replied laughing, the popcorn cascading down her dress.

"Wanton, wild and usual slips." thought Max. "This play invites them." His brain played havoc with the next few minutes till the old man who was with his daughter now announced:

"Come, go with me. I will seek the King.

This is the very ecstasy of love,

Whose violent property fordoes itself

And leads the will to desperate undertakings"

"That is me," thought Max, "desperate undertakings are me. The old man knows what he is talking about. And leads the will, yes, the will is always being led. But the ecstasy of love? Perhaps, if she would stop eating popcorn . . ." His thoughts were suddenly becalmed. It seemed entirely obvious (what had happened to all those moments before?) that she needed to be taken home where she would be put to bed. Her soul mate there on stage seemed as guileless as she. 'No, my good lord,' she said meekly as Mary would have said those words.

"Isn't she called Ophelia?" He asked.

"Yes," she whispered, "she is called Ophelia, and she drowns herself. Ding, dong, drowns herself."

"Whatever for?" he said horrified. There was a strange reality about this play with its invasive sounds.

"Because that is the thing to do."

And she turned her hands palms up with that strange grace that so became her, and he looked away to avoid seeing that crude criss-crossings which razors had left on her arms and wrists. "And then you float down the river drowning. Ding, dong, drowning."

Silence, and then, "Would you like some popcorn? Don't let me eat it all." Before he had time to answer, as if in a hurried aside, "was I all right in the car?"

"Sh," he whispered too loudly, "we are annoying that couple in front." They turned round and, seeing a father and daughter, smiled.

"It's a long play," one of them said.

"I'm doing it at school," she said laughing as she heard the words, 'You are a fishmonger,' hurled at that rambling old man whose end she knew so well.

"Polonius," remembered Max suddenly, "dies."

In the interval she drank coke.

"Give me lots of ice," she said, and the barman obliged. Max noticed how much her black dress became her.

"I've put glitter on my face," she said. "Do you like it?"

He didn't answer because suddenly he saw the two Russians and the odious American come through one of the entrances to the bar. He had thought that they didn't know each other; he had tried his best to make it so, but the special chaos of his world was becoming increasingly unmanageable, and whom one would meet where, was anyone's guess. Here they were, all three, approaching happily with undisguised familiarity. They were awesome presences.

"Hey Max," they said, eyeing his smallness – why had fate made him small? Fate the ineluctable?

"We have got you a drink," said Dimitri, or was it Boris? He noticed that they were waving bottles of champagne and glasses.

"You know I don't drink," said Max.

"Don't drink?" repeated Jack Colorado, his arms falling sadly by his sides and his handsome face deeply puzzled.

"Don't drink with people like you," said Max. "Drinking is something I do in private. I am a private man."

"Didn't you say, Boris," asked the handsome American peevishly, "didn't you say he drank champagne? Only champagne?"

"That's what he drank with that whore – that shy whore, what's her name? The one who kept crying. Eva – how is Eva, Max?"

"She is well," said Max reluctantly, "I forgot that you had met her."

"Still shy?"

"Sometimes."

"And who is this one?"

"She's called Mary."

"Quite contrary?"

"Yes," thought Max, "quite contrary. Like all my women . . ."

"Why have you come?" he asked

"Ivan," said Boris pouring himself champagne and sipping it, "has something for you that we can talk about later. We will see you later. You must have time to think."

Ivan, lean, red haired and strong featured, smiled and handed him an envelope.

"I'm a former king," thought Max. "This is the way you treat a former king." Obediently he put the envelope inside his jacket.

"I'll speak to you when I want to," said Max, "I'm not going to be hurried." He put his arm round Mary and in his mind she was Eva, or Dolores, or Katie or Nina – he couldn't remember. Women were something you put your arm around and to them, of course, you were somebody with an assertive arm, and in Max's case not much height. Sometimes they were probably wondering whether this was Sam, or Chris, or Boris, and it would be a funny thing if one could only share thoughts.

"We *are* staying for the rest, aren't we?" she asked, putting down her coke and forgetting about it. "Ophelia is good, but I don't think much of Polonius. What do you think of what's his name who plays Hamlet? I have always imagined him different."

"Have you?"

"Are you really important?" she asked throwing away Hamlet, Ophelia and Polonius confining them to a drawer that said, no interest. "Really, really important?"

"People like me," replied Max, "rule the world."

6

Being there

Max knew Rome. He had once spent eight months there. He had been a waiter in a restaurant. There had been lots of young people like him who worked long hours for only enough money to survive. They were reasonably happy, irresponsible and passing through. There was always this wonderful feeling of passing through; of being on the way to somewhere that one didn't quite want to reach. Not yet.

Since then he had returned as Max. He wore Armani suits and had become a wheeler-dealer and power-broker. In unashamed conversations across Europe and Asia, Max discussed ways of changing the shape of this world, moulding its old face like a ball of clay – adding new craters and deep rivers till nothing remained but the strange sum of its features. Max was someone lots of people had to know.

"I've always liked Rome," he said to the senator. "I used to be a waiter in Piazza Navona. We served terrible food to tourists who didn't know any better and didn't care. Even then I had heard of Cittàoscura." Max smiled. "I was no good as a waiter. I was too small. I could only reach the knees of Scandinavians and Germans."

He laughed. Max had charm; his compact gargoyle features and his easy assumptions of common interests and familiarity drew you in. And then there was the fact that he was never quite at ease: he would touch his chin, cradling it in his right hand whenever he was being serious. "It makes them think I'm sincere," thought Max. "Anyway, I can't help doing it. I did it as a kid."

And suddenly – in the middle of the meeting – a strange memory of stairs came to him, hard concrete stairs leading to covered walkways, doors painted in uniform colours and the smell of urine. A waiter filled his glass. This was what money bought you: unobtrusive care offered silently by people whose job it was to notice things about you. Your glass, your coat, your cold, your misplaced items but nothing personal, like your height, or the tiredness in your eyes.

"Only my chauffeur," thought Max, "notices that." Max's chauffeur had known him from schooldays and had followed him like a curious piece of luggage, disliked by his women with the exception of Eva.

"He's the most human thing about you," she would say, mispronouncing human and pausing before the rest of the sentence as if held tantalised by that word. That was her confessed mission: the search for someone, or something human. And then there was her unconfessed self, a less dark creature, somewhat easier to please, who wanted all that money can buy. It was the sad Eva that Max found alluring.

"You are very silent," said the senator. "The waiter will leave as soon as the food has been brought. He is not supposed to stay."

"Sorry, I was dreaming. Sudden memories and unconnected thoughts."

"That happens," replied the senator noticing his eyes, noticing his height.

"How did you start? Wherefrom this mighty empire?" He lifted his right arm above his head spreading his fingers wide.

"Wherefrom this mighty empire?"

Leaning across the table, in a stage whisper, Max told him what he already knew, "blackmail, my brother − different fathers more good-looking than me − ran a gay escort agency. Not much of an agency − mainly himself. He himself was the chief product."

Then he laughed − a laughter that that made you feel included among his special friends although the story was common property, and there were other stories which explained the rise of Max in more complicated and sinister ways. "Don't have a gay affair. There will be rats out to get you."

"And who is the girl?" asked the senator suddenly.

"Which girl?" asked Max, caught off his guard, knowing it was the wrong thing to say but feeling helpless.

"I must have food," he thought, "why can't they bring those four stuffed pastas decorated with whatever on a plate the size of a giant's arse?"

"The girl you are showing Rome to."

Max didn't answer.

"I could do things for you. I know special places – discreet, romantic and alluring. She will never forget Rome."

Memories, this man dealt with them; the unforgettable was his special craft. Memories were what women wanted. The art of dealing with women. Women in Max's experience were strange creatures with a fine sense of detail, often bewitched by visions and ideas in a way that didn't admit compromise. Men and women did not make the same compromises, either with each other, or with life. And their attitude to the great facilitator of human existence, the lie, was strangely emotional.

"I am a liar," thought Max dreamily forking the antipasto which had arrived, brought by a waiter with an apologetic and furtive air. "I knew lies before I knew sex, before I knew money. I am married to lies. And I shall stay married. I have made too many promises to do anything else."

"Stop," he said covering his glass. "Give me mineral water. Sparkling. I only drink in private. I'm a private man."

"I would like to know the private man."

"No chance. He's hidden."

"Deeply hidden?"

"Just hidden."

The antipasto (an arrangement of meats and vegetable with a cubist slant) was replaced by the filled pastas on a black plate decorated with rocket and shavings of parmesan. They were alone.

"I have looked at most of the companies," said Max, "and there are one or two of them that are too obvious. That are, what shall I say, a little lacking in sophistication. It all needs a bit of tweaking. Who thought of the Blue Lagoon? I like that. I like the Blue Lagoon. I am pencilling in Gordon Lewis on the Board of the Blue Lagoon. It is *his* sort of thing."

"Gordon Lewis?"

"You'll hear more of him."

"Does he exist?"

"I hope not. But you never know."

The senator smiled and lifted his glass to his lips. Max looked round the room wondering whether it pleased him or made him uncomfortable, or whether he was too tired to ponder its elegance.

"That desk you're looking at belonged to Queen Christina of Sweden. Hanging above it is her portrait."

"It's a beautiful room," said Max with feeling, returning the queen's sad gaze and seeing the desk for the first time. A Chinese bowl with discreet figures in faded colours seemed to float on its polished surface, its sides reflected in the dark wood.

"I've brought all the papers."

"I'm taking the Blue Lagoon with a few changes."

"Changes?"

The senator looked nervous. With his nails, he began to trace invisible patterns on the tablecloth.

"Of course there must be changes," he sighed, becoming rational and trying to relax. One could never get everything one wanted. Not at once. Slowly does it. He pointed to a briefcase which stood by the queen's desk. "I've brought all the papers."

"What elegant hands," thought Max, seeing them briefly as he bent over his glass of water. As he lifted it, his eye fell on the portrait of the queen. Her eyes were large and sombre, and her nose stood out from her forehead like a fantastic ridge. A tight necklace of large pearls made her throat look fat and bulging. She reminded Max of his first wife. She too had been Swedish.

"Of course there must be changes," continued the senator, "but this meeting is not about the detail. This meeting is about the broad sweep of things. And if you'll forgive me," he added, dropping his voice trying to control his anger, "the devil is in the sweep, in the flood, in the things we are deciding now, in our handshake. Bugger the detail. "

He looked at the floor as if it might be found there: the detail, the names and the pages, the companies and the figures. He saw desks strewn with papers and dead computer screens. He saw a room full of the aftermath of an orgy of corruption. By one of the desks there was a slumped figure: Fabio, a friend from childhood. He had found him and he had told his widow.

"Bugger the detail," he repeated.

"You're upset," said Max letting his large hand rest on his, "I, too, am one for the sweep of things."

"Bugger the detail," said the senator, "I just want to know. Did you kill Fabio Esposito?"

"I don't kill anyone," said Max.

"You killed *him*."

"Claudio, can we return to the plot? I'm taking the Blue Lagoon."

"The Blue Lagoon," sighed the senator, feeling his vision fade, sensing the past disappear with its corpses, its dead, the things that could not be undone. "You can have the Blue Lagoon."

Max lifted his glass. "To the Blue Lagoon."

They shook hands.

7
Tina

"You've done it," said Tina, rising from the bed. "You've done it," said Tina, feeding greedy David. "Oh, you've done it."

"Not yet."

"Not yet? They're publishing it. And you're signing it. Sign it here." And she made room for me and my pen on her bed with its chaos and memories of nights and infants and despair.

"Sign it!"

"I did it for you and David."

"Thank you, Rachel. Thank you for Max."

Nervously I lit another cigarette. Long nights had disfigured me and found me wanting, and the days had not returned me to myself. And this was unbelievable, anyhow, this bundle of papers requiring my signature brought by the morning's post and the consequence of my writing and of Tina's brief encounter (Tina the sensual, Tina of the night) with someone who owned a small publishing house.

"Thank you Rachel."

I signed.

"It says Tina Faithful."

"Our new name. Our new identity."

And so she was born the new Tina, Tina with money, men and time; and, although that was in the future, it was not very far away. I was twenty-one and I knew too much and I looked a little hard. Men didn't like me.

"Hold him. Hold David while I make you a huge breakfast of bacon and eggs."

"I can't eat Tina. I don't eat."

She looked at me sadly, looked at the Rachel who didn't eat and saw her badly dyed hair and her pinched face.

"We are starting a new life," she said. "It's all in front of us, and glamorous."

From her dressing-gown she extracted the remains of a tissue paper, blowing her nose, while I held David waiting for the neighbour's voice. "Get that fuckin' baby to shut up." Immediately, the voice was there, inexorably, while Tina, on the way to fame, was making wings out of her eyebrows, her feet wide apart and her dressing-gown open so that the mirror reflected her breasts heavy with milk and the fierce concentration on her face.

"What happens to Max?" she asked as she plucked, moving closer to the mirror, putting all her weight on one foot and steadying herself on the sink.

" What happens to Max?"

"Have you forgotten? He dies."

The death of Max. While Tina finished seeing to her beauty, I savoured the death of Max, Max the magnificent. He was going to die, but not yet, not yet a while.

In the mirror, Tina admired her face and enjoyed her reflection, trying to see herself as others saw her.

"I want a man, Rachel. I need a man."

Tina the hungry. Man-hungry and getting ready to go out rubbing cream into her cheeks.

"Don't kill Max yet. I like him. I really like him but he's too short. "

She turned round and looked at me and David, pleased with herself. She hadn't written the book, but she didn't doubt that she had got it published. She frowned, and I knew what she was thinking, what to do with David? On the bed behind me lay the contract with my signature, Tina Faithful, and she had her eyes fixed on it.

"When we get the advance will you give me half? Half for David?"

I nodded, and later I gave her the first of many bundles of notes.

"How does he die? How does Max die?"

"Mysteriously."

"Like Axel?"

"No. Not like Axel."

Did I shout? Did I sound angry? I have a better memory for what people looked like than my own feelings: Tina in a dirty dressing-gown sleep heavy and triumphant, her eyes on the contract.

"Do you think Axel *did*?" Tina had wonderful a way with the dead and the living. Neither could escape her.

"Do you think he *did*?"

"*Did* what?"

"Kill himself stupid. You know what I mean."

"No."

"Why not?"

"I just don't think so."

"Why don't you think so?" The question hung sadly in the air and she seemed suddenly aggressive.

"And you *do* think so, really. You just don't want to say so. Sometimes people just don't want to live anymore. I had an aunt who did it. Paracetamol. I wouldn't do it like that. Would you?"

Tina in the land of possibilities. With an answer. Always with an answer.

"I think he did."

"And I think he didn't."

"Oh, Rachel you are always frightened of the truth. Except in books, and what kind of truth is that? The truth of books."

Tina, the same old Tina. The Tina who had told me all those lies about her father, and his killer hands.

"I don't understand the truth of books and I don't care

about it either, but I hope that lots of people will want to read about Max. Do you like the way I've done my eyebrows?"

There were hardly any left. She took a pencil and drew a firm line just above where they had been. Her face looked thinner and more refined, but colder, like something sculpted in ice.

"Should I have told him that David might have been his?" she asked adding rouge clumsily. Tina wasn't very good at make-up, but not as crude as I was.

"He always seemed to think he was."

"And I should have seen him more often, should have given him more of a place." She looked suddenly at David remembering her duties and forgetting the shadow of Axel. Axel the mysterious, Axel the dead; Axel who had had this in him, this crossing of boundaries.

"I'll feed him before we go. Yvonne will look after him."

"Yvonne? She might die before we return. She is a phantom. She is only just here, Tina."

"Okay, we'll take him with us. I'll take my little angel with us."

We went to the park and drank wine and ate crisps

"I'm in love," said Tina." I'm in love with that poet we met at your publisher's. The one who is as thin as a scarecrow. I don't know what is happening to me."

8

Understanding love

Max knew all about love. He had been learning about love since he was knee high to a grasshopper, and it was, as far as he could see, not a pretty thing, except for moments in the here and now. Like so much in life, the parts were much finer than the whole. They contained all that was beguiling and mysterious, like Eva naked on the bed with her face cupped in her hand talking about Krakow. What a hopeless whore. And now this child who was sitting opposite him in Piazza Navona drinking a crazy cocktail containing a bowl of fruit and some green leaves.

"I love Rome," she said, picking at the fruit," I really love Rome." She took one of the leaves, held it with her finger tips and let it drop. "I'm so glad you brought me here."

"I will take you anywhere," said Max, "anywhere where they serve crazy cocktails. I will take you anywhere, princess."

"Will you?" she asked, playing with the question mark and holding it out to tantalise him. "Will you?"

"Yes," he replied drifting away, drifting into his own thoughts," I will take you anywhere."

Max thought of the senator and of the Blue Lagoon. These Italians were so wonderfully corrupt and they took it all so naturally. The senator had reminded him of his brother Jason, except for a certain timidity, a timidity which descended and seemed to catch people unawares when they were in the presence of Max. It was as if they could never prepare themselves for what was *him*; for this hobgoblin of a man, for his curious appearance as if he had been modelled and shaped out of another material than flesh and blood. One could almost *see* someone making him. A sculptor with sense of humour had arranged his features, his fleshy nose, his sensual lips, and his small lively eyes in the mountainous landscape of his craggy face and left it all so exposed to his changing moods that one experienced a sense of intimacy which was both alluring and false. He reminded Mary of a strange little figure with blue hair which she had once been given. A Norwegian troll.

"Did you sell that man something?"

"Which man?" asked Max rearranging his thoughts.

"The one who told me about cocktails and about the walk at night we must do listening to fountains."

"Oh, that man . . . I sold him lots of things. Lots and lots of things . . ."

"Like what?"

"Wigs and false beards and birds in cages, and he told me where to buy crazy cocktails."

"How old are you?" she asked suddenly.

"Thirty-eight," he said thoughtfully.

She became very quiet and still. She had lost interest in her drink. Stillness became her. Max thought of his brother Jason who had been very handsome but was now too fat. As a teenager he had had charm. He had had a lively expressive face and a quick sense of humour, but he knew how to suppress his charm and become hard. His hardness was something he slipped into all too easily and could sustain relentlessly. His gay escort agency had been run very efficiently, and, unlike Max, he rarely fell in love.

"I'm still learning about love," thought Max.

"Shall we go now," she asked finishing her drink," I want to see all those fountains. I want to see a world of fountains and water cascading, and I want to listen to water till the dawn comes and gets rid of the moon." She stood up; just a little unsteady but very determined.

"Do you like my shoes?" she asked.

"Haven't you got anything but cheese?" comes the voice

from the bed, from him among the sheets whose name I don't know. Tricky that. I, too, have my ragged pride. And while I'm searching for his name, my brain is hell-bent on seeing whether there are any images of my attackers lurking in its cavernous depth. Who were they? Who did this to my poor nose? Somewhere among all those misplaced memories something might be found that could tell me who did this to me. It was down by the river. Battersea Park I think.

"You don't like cheese?"

"I said, don't you have anything else? Yes, I do like cheese."

"There is some bread and a mango."

"Shit ? no wonder you're so thin. Look at you."

I feel his eyes on my body, and I'm mortified as if I were fifteen. I wish I knew his name.

"You, you . . ." I try, hoping that he will help me.

"I never told you my name," he says sharply. "You didn't even ask."

"Sorry. I'm asking now."

"It's too late now, but I'll tell you anyway. I'm called Mo."

"Mine is Rachel."

"You've told me that. You've told me most of your fuckin' life story."

"I'm sorry."

"No hard feelings, I enjoyed it."

"Are you sure?" I have a finger in my mouth, like a little girl; but I know that I look like a witch. Time has done that to me. Time and alcohol.

"Yeah, I'm sure. I also liked the bits you read from your book. I liked hearing about Max and I liked the way you read it. How did you invent Max?"

How did I invent Max? In what part of my brain was he born? Where did I dig out his tissue, in what furnace was he made, where do I breed my fantastics?"

"I didn't invent him. He's real. I've even met him."

"You have?"

"Yes," I say firmly putting an end to any more questions. "I met him once walking down Oxford Street. He said, "I'm Max, pleased to meet you," or something like that. He didn't look quite as I had imagined, but his manner was exactly as I've described in my book, or books. He was with a girl who was quite a bit older than Mary, *my* Mary, but that isn't important."

"How old are you."

"Forty," I reply thoughtfully, hoping that I've chosen a number that adequately sums up these lines, this thin worn body. Emaciated is, I think, the word but I'm not good at words that describe me.

"You're sure?"

What a raucous laughter echoes round the room, reverberates in my head, my poor wounded head. "Forty! Forgive me, I thought you were more than that. I thought I was making love to my grandmother. Well, almost. No hard feelings."

No hard feelings. Of course, no hard feelings. I don't do hard feelings. I'm Rachel and I'm thirty-eight, and, like Max, I lie about my age. Like Max I need to be touched; like Max I need sex, but here the resemblance ends.

"You should eat more," he says tenderly and I nod. I'm always accepting this strange gift, the tenderness of strangers. "Do you really want me to stay?"

"Of course. Just make yourself at home. There is even a flat upstairs which is empty. The crazy student who used to live there has left. I own the building."

"You own the building?" He's impressed. Impressed by this nondescript Edwardian creation, this towering lot of decaying architecture with its bricks of several colours, and tasteless pilasters.

"The shop is mine too," I boast. "It's all that is left from the money I made."

"Is that really all? How did that happen? Where has it

gone?" He looks round as if searching for clues. There is not much to see. Some African masks and a huge, framed photograph of Venice with a younger Rachel dressed in black emerging out of an arched window, and caught, as if by chance, by a candid camera. Hair very short and badly cut, urchin like. In those days I looked too young.

"Where has it *all* gone?"

"Men. I'm a bad picker of men. And a few women too, but mainly men. This is all I have left."

"I hope I won't disappoint you too." He looks as if he means it and his humility betrays his innocence. Only the young know how to be really humble, although it is us, the old bastards, who should have some humility.

"Do you mind if I go and fetch something to eat?"

"No."

"Give me some money then."

In his hand I put a crumpled note. He takes it and leaves the room. There is lightness in his step.

I'm a bad picker of men. There is something about the first tentative moments of intimacy that overwhelm me; maybe because I tend to fasten on aspects of people's character that are either not there at all, or less so than I think. Whatever the reasons the result is a bad picker of men. Take Mo, what fool would invite a man of around twenty to live in her flat on the strength of a sympathetic face and a lovely voice? And, of course, that hint of a sense of irony lurking in the tilt of his head. It is that, above all else, that has secured him a place to stay till he decides to take his bags and move on. Actually, he does not even seem to have any bags. He has come out of the mystery of the night, just himself – like a character in a book.

9

Rome

Childhood is something we ought to leave behind us. What use are these crumpled half understood memories with their odd moments of clarity? At two o'clock in the morning Max found that he could not sleep. The bedroom with its closed shutters was too dark. Max pushed back the shutters and opened the window. Leaning on the cool marble window sill, he gazed at the building opposite with its wonderful textures of ancient bricks and stone arches. Via Giulia was empty. Max took a piece of paper and tore it. He tried to absorb himself in watching it fall. Looking at these too solid buildings, this too solid street, he felt uncomfortable. The room was better with its darkness and shadows and Mary asleep; her body like that of a doll, very pale in this light. She was lying on her front, the sheet covering her legs, and by her side of the bed lay her clothes. Where had she found those silly shoes and that even sillier hat? The mystery of women.

The mystery of men and women; faith and betrayal. These were things one learnt gradually. The child asleep on the bed had hardly any of this adult knowledge. She curled and she uncurled; dreaming no doubt. She moved her legs further apart like a pair of scissors and put a finger in her mouth. Even asleep, she looked thoughtful. She had taught him so many new words. Where did she get them from? Must be books. Max took another piece of paper and watched it tumble into the silence of the street, feeling the cool air on his body. The tensions of yesterday's events wouldn't leave him alone.

"I must," he thought, "speak to the fuckin' president. I can't stand all these old buildings. There are too many old buildings in Rome. Pity the Germans didn't blow them all up." Max sighed.

"There is something wrong with me," thought Max. "Yesterday I wanted fountains and the Colosseum. Perhaps it's all better when they are all fakes. They have got this lovely fake stuff in the US with burger bars and cocktail cabinets where you least expect it. I wish I hadn't told the Republicans that I would help them win the next election. Does it matter who is president of the US? Does anyone care? I'm tired of power, and I don't know where it's all going. I don't know where my power is going. I don't know where my power's *gone*," he corrected himself truthfully. "The higher up you are, the more there is something you don't know. You don't even know *what* you should know. And you learn the meaning of the word *deceit*." Max sighed and said the word out loud, *deceit,* as if it had been invented by someone he didn't know, and smuggled into his life with the many turns and chances a person takes on his labyrinthine journey to wherever. A room somewhere. A person somewhere. The present night.

He didn't like this night, this room, and this darkness. What had the senator asked him? "Did you kill Fabio Esposito?" Who the hell was Fabio Esposito? Max found it strangely unnerving that he didn't know. He took his mobile out of his trouser pocket and pressed some buttons. The screen lit up responsively. Max sighed.

"Who the hell, Trevor, is Fabio Esposito? Someone mentioned his name. Have you heard of him?" Silence. He should have thrown in a few friendly words. "Sorry for bothering you," he added apologetically, "I just wanted to know. I think it might be important. I have to know things. I mustn't look stupid. Trevor, are you there? Are you there, Trevor?"

"Sure, I am here. It's three o'clock in the morning. What's this about Fabio Esposito? Does he matter, or are you losing your cool?"

"Bit of both, Trevor, old friend. Bit of both. But I think he might be important. This senator, this guy has some special relationships with him and you can't ignore the personal, if you know what I mean. It can cut across other things and become dangerous. It can linger in the blood and before you know . . ." Max gesticulated, one hand above the other waving the mobile away from his ear, as he felt he must do whenever that phrase hit him, *before you know,* with its sinister meaning and memories.

Memories. He had so many memories of *before you know,* particularly with women. And always the sense that he should *have known,* should have anticipated these unspoken layers of complexity, this trembling and fear when they were washed up on the shore of Max's wealth and found themselves, well, alone. Alone and difficult, because Max didn't *know* and didn't *understand.* With men there was a different kind of *before you know,* a more dangerous territory, not so much a blind alley as an open desolate landscape where people wanted to do each other real and lasting harm. A land of scorching sun and no return, because one *should have known.*

"It's three in the morning," repeated Trevor. "It's three in the morning, but I shall see what I can do," he added, as Max knew he would. Trevor was his faithful, his one true friend, and he had known him since he was a teenager. He had met him because his brother Jason used to sell him. At fourteen Trevor had run away from his home in Newcastle, arriving in London with nothing; nothing but himself. At fourteen he looked twelve. Jason had found this vulnerable kid at King's Cross where he used to lurk waiting for boys like Trevor. There were plenty of them.

"Are you still having difficulty sleeping?"

"You know I don't sleep."

"Where should I be looking for this Fabio Esposito?"

"The Roman bank deal. I think he's in the Roman bank deal. *Was* in the Roman bank deal. He's dead, and that has

81

upset the senator. I need to know before I speak to him again."

"He's probably a nobody."

"I must keep track of nobodies. I always keep track of nobodies. If you don't, *before you know*," he whispered. Trevor knew what he meant. Like a true friend, he knew the meaning of phrases, and like a true friend he stood by you.

"I understand," said Trevor.

"I must have the knowledge, Trevor. I need the knowledge."

"What's wrong Max? You're not yourself."

"Of course I'm not myself. When was I last myself? Don't be stupid."

"Have you taken your pills?"

"What pills? For fuck's sake I take so many pills. Too many pills."

Max looked out towards the window which let in the sultry night air. A big black hole opening onto the street. He wondered whether he should tell Trevor about his heart, about the pains he felt in his chest.

"Sorry for waking you," he said kindly, thinking of his heart, "that Fabio Esposito is probably not important, but I must be on top of things."

"I've completely lost the thread," thought Max, "I felt it happening a few weeks ago. There are times when I cannot trust myself. This is one of those times. I know it because I'm making too many decisions and behaving too much like God and then panic hits me like ice. One minute I'm God and the next it's all gone, all certainty gone and I know I can't trust myself. I'm not *indeboondable*. Not even with Prozac."

Indeboondable was Jason's word. Jason was too practical to be good with words, but he had handed Max this word, *inde-*

boondable, one morning sullen over breakfast. Good-looking, hard, and only seventeen years old.

"I tell you what I'm going to be. I'm going to be *indeboondable*. No one is going to get the better of me. Ever."

"Good luck," Max had said. "Good luck being indeboondable."

Jason hadn't replied but had looked at him full of the contempt which, at seventeen, the beautiful have for the ugly.

"Good luck," Max had said without meaning it, but Jason had flourished.

"I think," whispered Trevor, "one of the Russians has your mobile. It's been tracked," he added with ice-cold certainty, and now Max knew why he hadn't been able to sleep. It was the mobile, of course; thoughts about that mobile lurking deep in his brain had made him light-headed sending him on this crazy journey, with this kid, this child, for God's sake. Finding oneself on a precipice, one is moved to do strange things. But why dance, you might ask. Why dance? Because it's the thing people do, because it's the thing *to do*. Some-where, somehow it makes perfect sense and the feet follow the tune, hear the music and dance along. How much would he give for sex with a child? Not much, in different circum-stances but a lot yesterday. He had even put her on display as if he wanted to *create* danger. He had kissed her by every foun-tain in the awesome loneliness of the night. A loneliness that was only theoretical because Max had bodyguards lurking where Mary couldn't see them. He didn't travel anywhere without bodyguards, and he didn't travel anywhere without spies. The loneliness of the night was just a fiction for Mary. One of Max's many creations, but as he had lifted her and placed her on the lip of a fountain to kiss her breasts he had pretended to himself that he didn't care about what was fact and what was fiction. She was so beautiful. So desirable.

"I shall always love you," he had said.

"It's been tracked," said Trevor, "to Saint Petersburg. To Potemskaya number 20, or thereabouts. Does that mean anything to you?"

"Yes," whispered Max, "yes it does. Good night Trevor," he added slowly full of a sudden awareness of every bit of furniture in the room, its heaviness and its sombreness. Old oak. "Good night Trevor."

10
Memories of Leningrad

Did he remember Potemskaya number 20? What a question! He remembered being there too well – the drabness. The peculiar Russian drabness of that interior: a room, a kitchen, a toilet and furniture that was barely functional, but which had been much used and had accumulated grime in that sad Russian way, because improving upon it wasn't worth the effort. Everything needed replacing, but nothing would ever be replaced. Life would remain the same however much you hit out at it. Such was the room, and there were many like it. He had himself been in dozens, and he only remembered this one because of its pictures. Enormous abstract paintings with strange vibrant shapes arranged in violent compositions. Through the dirty window, you could, if you pushed aside the curtains which had lost their pattern and colour, catch a small view of the mighty river at the end of the street.

There had been a curious mismatch between the room and its people, who were young, animated, and treated the furniture as if it couldn't break. One of them had done the paintings and was explaining their meanings to Max. They were about sex, death, and violence. Max agreed that they communicated their subject in a wonderful way, and, before he knew it, he had bought them and the artist had begun to take them off their boards (they had only been loosely nailed) and roll them up.

"Art doesn't imitate life. It *is* life. Don't you agree?" Max agreed. He had agreed with most things said that evening, and was to agree with many more.

"Suffering," said the artist, "is something Russians really understand. Do you know how many died at the siege of Leningrad? Does anyone know? Can anyone count the

Russian dead? People produce figures, but they are meaningless, and no one is interested in them anyway. One million, two million – it is meaningless. But try to imagine a landscape of snow – a landscape stretching as far as the eye can see, yet you know that it goes much further. You know that however many steps you take, that snow landscape will just continue. A tree here, a hill there, but relentlessly the same, and empty. That is the Russian dead. That landscape is the Russian dead. Silent and empty."

As he finished speaking there had been, Max thought, a sudden silence in the room as if the place itself conspired to remember the Russian dead, and he had to step carefully across the rolled up paintings as if they were corpses lying there in their white stiffness.

"You don't have to buy all of them," said Boris who was, he learnt, the painter's brother, and who lived in the flat. "You don't have to buy all of them. I know Peter is very convincing."

"Why shouldn't he want all of them? They go together."

"I want all of them," said Max. "I think they *do* go together. And I've got lots of dollars."

Out of his pocket he took lots of dollars and started counting with no end figure in mind. His dollars were a Russian landscape. Endless. Peter sat down and helped him count.

He had never regretted buying those paintings, and, as he sat there, blood-brother with Peter, far gone on vodka, he knew that he wouldn't. A little tiny bit of him had remained sober; the bit that knew that he wanted these paintings. Many years later they were to hang in his main living-room; a room on three levels, each level wider than the previous leading down white marble steps to where you could sit in comfort and look out over the garden. But when he bought them he had had nowhere to put them. He had not yet become Max. Max the indeboondable. He had been nothing but a small crook. A small crook with a fistful of dollars.

"Boris must have my mobile," thought Max, "Boris the rat."

Time had taken Boris and changed him, or revealed him as he really was: a rat. A very clever, manipulative rat.

With age, thought Max, everyone you knew became simpler and more complex. There was people's greed, and their vanity. Greed was simple, vanity complex. Vanity had deep roots in the past. People's vanity defined them as individuals, while their greed made them human. And always you had to deal with those two things, greed and vanity, the one simple, the other complex. Max sighed.

He loved those paintings with their crude shapes, coarse textures and crass compositions which communicated the simple message that the world was violent and unstable. To others it seemed odd that he should hang them in a room carefully designed to avoid obvious symmetries and hard angles: the steps leading from one level to another followed an s shape as if it were not a room but a garden, and the marble had been carefully integrated with deep red mahogany cut in different shapes with no pattern, no regularity.

"You are a git," said Jason who understood beauty intuitively, but spoke simply.

"You could hang a Picasso on that wall and leave all the other walls bare, and this room would hit you, hit you with the force of MOMA, the Museum of Modern Art," he added for Max's information. "And what do you hang? Four huge paintings, four gargantuan, humongous pieces of crap by a peasant whose simplistic view of the psyche would make even Sigmund Freud turn in his grave. Why don't you buy a Picasso or a little bit of Matisse?"

"I've got a Picasso," said Max,. "It's hanging in my bedroom. The shapes are better I admit, but these paintings, these pieces of crap by a peasant, they haunt me. That yellow box about to fall off the triangle onto the face below which lies trapped in the mud and snow – well I don't know about art."

"But you know what you like."

"Yes, I know what I like."

"And you've hung a Picasso in your bedroom. Does Eva like it?"

"I don't think," said Max thoughtfully, "that she has noticed it."

Nietzsche once said that there is no one you are less related to than your father or your sibling, and that certainly was true in Max's case when it came to Jason, his brother; this hard, polished middle-aged man who seemed entirely to have left his past, his background behind him except for the occasional phrase and a timid interest in football. He still lived off men, his gay escort agency, but it was kept at a distance, almost forgotten in everyday life. Max kept his past around him. It littered his present. It lay dormant, expectant; ready to strike.

Looking out on via Giulia, leaning out as far as he could to see a crescent moon hanging at the end of the street, Max thought of Russia and that cold room in Saint Petersburg where his mobile could now be found, where Boris would be poring over entries and numbers. How many would he make sense of?

"I love you," he whispered to Mary, kissing her legs, "I love you." She was deep in sleep and unresponsive, relaxed like an infant.

"What was that word that she taught me?" thought Max tired. "That's it – 'ineluctable'. It's a good word and it's real; not like *indeboondable.* I wish I could remember quite what it means, though I'm not sure I care, and perhaps it doesn't matter. This *was* the very ecstasy of love, but now I can't sleep and it's a long time since I *did* sleep. It's all fucking ineluctable. Whatever you do, there you are: ineluctable. Ineluctable, my princess. You never know what is happening in Saint Petersburg, in some room, in some place. There is always some room, some place and bugger all you can do about it and you can whisper 'yes' and you can whisper 'no' and there aren't any words in between, my princess. Not in this quagmire. Not in this world, there aren't. Not in my experience." And it seemed to Max that what made up his experience was palpable and present like the heavy air in the room, and ineluctable.

Max kissed her forehead. "I'm in love," he thought, "I'm in love. I'll do anything for this kid."

"I like Max," says Mo. "I like your Max. Have you been to Saint Petersburg?"

Have I been to Saint Petersburg!

"Yes, but when it was Leningrad. I was there for a few weeks in October of, let me see – 1985. Yes, 1985 and the Neva was full of ice but not solid. No, the banks were frozen but the river was still fighting, churning up mud and ice, and it was very cold. I had an English coat that was completely useless but very pretty, dark red like wine with black buttons. The wind would go right through it, and I cut up a blanket to wear round my neck. Every day I used to stand on one of the bridges and watch the river fighting with the ice. I stayed in Potemskaya, a street by the river. I was living with a boy called Peter who was tall, clever, an artist, and probably my best lover. We shared the flat with his sister who was frighteningly intelligent and didn't say much. She was jealous of me because I had so much make-up. I have always worn a lot of make-up, although many people have told me that it doesn't suit me. Peter's sister was a teacher. Very beautiful, very serious, always marking books sitting very up-right on one of those uncomfortable chairs, but she could laugh, and she was one of those people you felt you knew when she laughed. I don't know what she thought of me and Peter. I suppose it was awkward with only two rooms. I was mesmerised by his paintings and his talk; his talk of suffering and how it became a yellow triangle poised on a box about to drop on something lying below. When he traced the shapes with his hand he was very convincing – it was all there. Everything he wanted was there."

11

Mary's dream

Mary dreamt the old man kissed her, the old man with the face of a gargoyle. She dreamt he kissed her, starting with her toes, then her legs, and finally her breasts. All the time he was laughing and telling silly jokes. There was one about an ant-eater. He looked very old and she laughed to keep him happy. His hands were big, mottled and dark-veined and out of proportion to his size; he waved them about like oars as if he were in a boat making its way through a choppy sea.

She had noticed how clumsy he was immediately when she first met him. He had asked her mother whether he could take her to the theatre, suggesting that maybe he could help her. Help her with his pool, his enormous house, his money and his certainty. He knew just the right psychiatrist, the right treatment. Like all rich people with power, he thought he had a handle on life; and he had the audacity and bad manners to communicate to others that he could potentially do *anything*. But his hands denied him; they waved about betraying him, and he couldn't stop them. He couldn't stop touching his face, his nose, his lips and his chin. Mary had felt a little afraid, because she sensed what he wanted. Sensed it while he was still talking about help, and how her life could be ironed out, and she could become like any other teenager. When she had looked at her mother, she had seen that she was thinking the same thoughts. She had a face that said, "I refuse to think of the consequences. Don't ask *me* about the consequences. Haven't I had enough problems with the past and the present? The future is your problem."

His hands had reassured her, made him human and made her feel a warm pity; the sort of pity she felt for small animals;

animals that needed holding tight, and perhaps even taking to bed. Like Hammy, the hamster. And Max had responded in the right way, because he remembered this tactile age, this age which hadn't outgrown the child's tendency of dividing the world into things that were good to touch and those that filled you with disgust.

"I'm a little Norwegian troll," he'd said, "I am a little Norwegian troll and I can do lots of magic. I know I'm very, very ugly."

Lying on the bed in a room with the highest ceiling she had ever seen, Mary dreamt about Max. His body became lean and tall and his arms dangled from his shoulders as if they were only loosely attached. His feet and hands were huge. He was followed by a tiny dachshund which she tried to pick up, but it bit her. Then Max began to shrink. He shrank till he was the size he was in real life and they were back in the theatre, but the play was a wild confusion, a cacophony of words and events competing for one's attention. The dachshund had joined the actors and was an important part of the play. It needed affection; it needed love; it needed Mary, and Polonius jumped off the stage and gave it to her.

"I told him you wanted it," said Max, "I'll give you anything and I can get you anything. I'm fabulously rich. I could buy the whole world if I wanted to, but I don't. It's too much trouble."

"Too much trouble," repeated Mary's mother who was sitting behind Max and who had been asleep but had woken up when she heard the word *trouble* which was one of her special words; one of her anchors which she would throw out mooring everyone and everything around her.

"You can't be doing with *that*."

"Doing with *what*?"

"The world."

"What are you talking about?"

"You could be doing without that," said Mary's mother stubbornly. "Doing without the world. I've tried it; I could have done without it. I really could. Did me no good at all, it did." She looked very hard at Max and Mary, and Mary felt drawn to her face; drawn into it, as if she could become part of that big nose, those thin lips, those weathered cheeks and disappear entirely.

Max smiled and patted the dachshund. He was on Mary's side. The dachshund was asleep. It lay heavy and happy on her lap while she watched the play and Max ate popcorn. She felt her mother's presence behind her, and didn't turn round.

"That's not his daughter," said a woman fiercely. She was sitting in front, but she had turned round and was staring at them. Mary knew that she was in disguise. She was a man in drag; she had the face of one of those silent men Mary had seen while sitting by one of the fountains. She pretended not to notice her, as she had when she had seen those strange men as she walked round Rome with Max; but it was very difficult – much more difficult in the dream than it had been in real life.

"That's not his daughter."

"It is," said Max, "you just don't understand. You don't understand about love. I can tell you all about it. I can tell you all about the thing called love."

"Tell me then."

"Well . . ." said Max.

"Thought so, you don't have anything to say, do you?" She turned round angrily shaking a mane of hair that looked like a blonde wig.

On stage someone said, "This time Polonius won't die, but only by special arrangement. Don't expect *that* to happen again. This is a special performance for a girl called Mary. Ophelia will give her some flowers. Give her the flowers Ophelia."

"I know all about love," Max was saying, "I've known about it since I was knee high to a grasshopper. It's not always a pretty thing, but you *can* improve upon it. You can make something of it, if you want. You Mary," he said turning towards her and saying things she had heard him say before, in the way she'd often heard him speak, "you, Mary, can do whatever you want. You just have to want it and you can do it, because you're special. You've got what it takes. Most people haven't got that. They haven't got anything. You want to write books, you'll write books. You want to paint paintings, you'll paint paintings; because you've got what it takes."

His words had a strange weight. On her lap the dachshund felt warm and soft.

Mary smiled and kept her head very still because everyone was looking at her, as they do in dreams.

Many years later when people asked Mary about Max she would say simply, "he wasn't really very clever." Then she would smile as if searching for more words, but she never said much more than that. She was always very quiet and would leave people to think this and that, as they would do, because they knew she had lots of his money; and the story of Max had become well known, and was told in various ways, but in none of them was he summed up with such candid simplicity.

12

People and places

Boris, the rat, held the mobile in his hand. He cradled it fondly. He had given a lot for this mobile; and he was going to enjoy decoding its secrets.

"He's thinking of me now," thought Boris with easy telepathy. "He's in via Giulia, in that baroque pile he always stays in, with some whore he's picked up, some lonely whore. The world is full of lonely whores, and Max picks them up. Women are a strange country, stranger than men."

Boris imagined Max in via Giulia. He saw the room with its dark walnut furniture. He saw it well because he had dealt in furniture. He saw it better than Max who just saw sombre shapes occupying large spaces they'd probably been allotted centuries ago. There was something threatening, Max felt, about the way this place proclaimed time. Mary moved in her sleep, mouthing something; her little body announced her part of time. "Almost fourteen," she'd said, but sleep made her look even younger.

"But she is clever," thought Max, "and knows a lot of words. More words than I knew at her age." He paused uneasily wondering where next to turn his thoughts which were hovering and wheeling above a landscape which felt too empty and well travelled.

" I hate the stuff in this room," he tried. "Give me modern, or give me something Las Vegas style. Call it vulgar, but it feels good. Yes, it feels good." He thought fondly of Eva who would at this moment be lying in their bed in her silk teddy bear pyjamas. The teddy bears' picnic. He'd brought them back from his last trip to Italy.

"If you go down to the woods today," his thoughts picked up, but the song had become menacing, "the woods today," continued his thoughts, "the teddy bears will be having their picnic. Picnic time for teddy bears."

The woods were very dark and the bears were very big. They were real bears. They were eating something and it wasn't a picnic. It was human. There was snow in the woods and there were big spaces beyond the woods; spaces without roads or habitation. It was all very still, and the bears were very quiet but relentless, as happens in dreams. The landscape reminded him of one of the paintings that hung in his living room and of the conversation he'd had years ago with the painter. Something about Russia. Something about suffering and snow.

Far away in Saint Petersburg, Boris saw the room. He had stayed at that hotel several times, once with Max. He saw the eighteenth century walnut furniture with its delicate inlay. There was probably a large wardrobe, an elegant chest of drawers and a discreet writing desk. Each room was individually furnished.

"French," he whispered, "and very good too."

He saw Max asleep, but he didn't see Mary. He saw the legs of a very tall girl with beautiful breasts lying on her side.

"The bastard. But it will only be a lonely whore. One of those lonely whores Max knows how to pick up. Like Eva. Who would want Eva?"

He flicked through the numbers and pressed a button.

"Hello cunt," whispered Boris, "remember me?"

Eva remembered Boris. It wasn't a good memory. She had a lot of memories like that. Memories of men. The only good thing about her memories was that most of them were hazy, insubstantial; they vanished as you pondered them, making room for other memories, other thoughts. Veil upon veil till you drowned, or felt that you might be drowning. Life, thought Eva, was best not remembered.

"No," she said, "I don't remember you."

"Of course you do. Of course you remember Boris."

For a moment his face appeared: strong features, green eyes and a lick of brown hair. A nasty piece of work – that she knew for certain. One of those men with dull certainty and no regrets. Someone who used you, and didn't care, if you minded. Eva searched his face for information and remembered a room somewhere and Boris with a towel drying his legs. One leg on the bed while rubbing the other.

"I like to wash when I make love, all the time when I'm making love. I like to be very clean." He put talcum on his legs. "Now I'm ready," he said, "for more."

"Dirty bastard," thought Eva, unable to recall why she hated Boris. There was more, much more than a room and some talcum powder, but she couldn't remember what.

Boris looked at the mobile, seeing Eva – or rather her reflection – in the mirror. The mirror came from Russia and he had given it to Max. He had told him that it came from the Tsar's palace. Anyhow, it was valuable. Louis quatorze. He saw Eva's face and her body and that confused look; that haunted look, as if she didn't know what questions to ask, and wouldn't pick the right ones, even if you gave her more time. Eva always wanted more time. What was it about women and time?

"Goodnight. Sleep tight. Do you know where Max is?" he added mischievously.

Silence. She wasn't going to betray him.

"He's in Rome," continued Boris, "in Rome in his usual hotel; his hotel in via Giulia, with his minders and a woman. That dwarf has always got a woman. He pays and he gets. Gets what he wants."

Eva moved on the bed. She sat up and thought of Max. "He doesn't get what he wants," she thought angrily, "he doesn't know what he wants." She threw the book she had been reading at one of the cherubim, breaking its trumpet. "He doesn't fuckin' know what he wants."

"He hasn't got a woman," shouted Eva, "he hasn't got a woman at all. He's in that stupid place with a child. She's twelve." Silence. "But what's that to you," she whispered, knowing she had betrayed Max, "what's that to you? That's none of your stupid business."

"Sleep tight," repeated Boris closing his eyes, contemplating the opulence of Max's bedroom: the heavy curtains tied back with tassels, the enormous bed with its wrought iron, the mirror with its cherubim looking at you, fixing their gaze beyond their trumpets, the inlaid dressing-table on which Eva scattered her scents, her bottles and her make-up, the Chinese chest of drawers with its inlaid dragons, mountains and pagodas, the figurehead of a mermaid from a defunct vessel on which Max used to hang his dressing-gown, and finally in a corner above an uncomfortable chair which had been reupholstered, a small painting of angry lines and sharp angles, which any fool could see was a Picasso. Any fool, except the fools who inhabited that bedroom. Max, of course, knew because he had paid for it; but he didn't know in any other sense, in any worthwhile sense.

The mobile lay in his hand inviting him to forget about that bedroom in London, that bedroom in Rome. He scrolled through the names: Nexus one, two and three, Venus, Jupiter, Mars, Athena, R47, Steve, RM14. There were hundreds: names, numbers and letters, and combinations of all three. With time, he would make use of them. A grey day was dawning over Saint Petersburg, and Boris followed the dawn, followed its tentative progress across the Neva while he waited for the city to wake.

Eva couldn't sleep and she didn't want to read. Her book lay on the floor where it had fallen after hitting the frame of the mirror. Eva read thick paperbacks about people like herself and Max (rich powerful men, and women who were mostly bitches). She enjoyed reading about these strong men and women who had no scruples; who were almost as bad as the real people she knew but twice as good with words. She picked up the book and let it drop, knowing that she couldn't concentrate.

Something inside Eva was gathering strength, making itself felt, directing her thoughts towards something specific: the specific was Max. Was Max for lack of anyone better. The feeling was a strong one: the urge which children have to please, that urge which will always be asserting itself in some people in spite of experience, in spite of everything because it gives them something to hold on to.

"Hullo Max," she whispered.

"Oh God," thought Max, "not Eva. Why did I leave that mobile on?"

"Hullo Max. I've spoken to Boris. I told him about Mary. It was a mistake Max. It was a mistake; please believe me. Just be careful. Be careful no one sees you with Mary. I am sorry. I am really, really sorry."

"Yes," said Max. "Yes."

"There was a lot in that 'yes'," interrupted Mo, suddenly sliding his legs out of the bed and throwing on a few clothes. "A lot in that 'yes'."

"There was everything in it. His tiredness, the balmy air, via Giulia, his fear, and the creatures of his fear. It was getting light and suddenly he felt too tired; but of course he couldn't sleep. He had to be ready for the day."

"He always has to be ready."

"He doesn't feel at all sure of himself. He doesn't feel sure of *anything*. He doesn't think that anything he does is right, but he knows he has to get rid of Boris. He lies down next to Mary and puts his hands heavily on her shoulders. He is thinking of Saint Petersburg and he sees the Neva with its slurry of ice."

"He is thinking of that as he makes love."

"Yes, he is thinking of it and he sees it very clearly, as they say you do when you are drowning. The room, the icy flow of the river, and those streets."

We both thought of Max.

"Tell me about Tina. Tell me about you and Tina, and – and that death. Death by the pool," whispered Mo a little shyly as if ashamed of the way in which he remembered our life in headlines, as it had appeared on the front of pages of various tabloids. Death by the pool, or in the pool; I can't remember which.

"Tell me about Tina."

"There is a lot to tell about Tina, and it ends by the pool on an autumn day, but I'll tell you the story as long as you stay. I have such a hunger for company." I looked round the room as if to measure my hunger by its white walls, by its emptiness. My companion, the hardly known stranger, dug into his Chinese takeaway which he had got as if by magic. I had barely noticed him leaving the room.

"Will you tell me about Tina?" he asked throwing his head back full of youthful impatience and easy promises.

13

Tina goes out

"Yes, she was Tina in the morning. Tina half awake shaking the night out of her hair, ready for the day. She was Tina in the morning feeding baby David attached to her breast, drinking greedily. There we were. Rachel the thin and Tina the opulent. Rachel eating nothing, and Tina eating everything; sardines out of tins, dripping oil on the bedclothes, sausages and beans, fried fish and chips, spaghetti and toast.

She was Tina thinking and pondering and reaching conclusions which were there, all wrapped up and needing nothing doing to them. She seemed to know what she wanted. She *was* what she wanted. Her desires shaped her, gave her personality, made her lovable. She didn't just laugh, she *wanted* to laugh. Her every action seemed the result of a pin-prick of desire.

"He's beautiful," she said looking at baby David, "he really is beautiful, but I don't know what to do with him when he cries."

David had an urge for tears. Tears were his day, and shaped his night. He was a bundle of unknown wishes and disappointments. He was only content when he was feeding. We were young of course, and didn't know what to do with him. He had come and brought something larger than himself with him; and there we were in that small prison consisting of two rooms and a cooker. Tina the opulent beside Rachel the ghostly. Black hair, black eyes and taut skin; not so much white as corpselike, transparent. I'm really not exaggerating. I looked terrible and all I had as my offering to the world, my excuse for this act of self destruction, was my fantastics, my phantasmagoria, my castles in the air."

"And then they bought it."

"Yes, and then they bought it."

109

"Prometheus Press."

"How clever of you to remember."

"I bought your first book. The first in the trilogy. I didn't finish it, but I saw the film. I loved it. I was madly in love with Tina, Tina Faithful. Look!"

And there it was just above his left buttock: Tina on Max's bed waiting for him to return from Rome, and next to the bed the lavish wooden mermaid on which Max used to hang his dressing-gown.

"Good isn't it?"

"Wonderful. I'm surprised I didn't notice."

"Lots of people don't, but it's a cool surprise when they do. Then I explain: it's Eva waiting for Max and that's his mermaid. The guy who did that tattoo was a real artist."

"I'm sure lots of people have admired it," I said continuing with the story of Tina, the story of Tina and love, the story of Tina and men.

"I hadn't really thought much about Tina. Not in the sense of thinking about who she was. To me she was just Tina, a perfect presence, a solid presence; and then of course this baby came along and upset the apple-cart of my understanding. I still ask myself sometimes, "who is Tina, what is Tina?", but I can't say that I'm much interested in the answer. There are dark forces in everyone, and what you learn about yourself and others certainly isn't what you expected, or wanted to know. She wasn't Tina Faithful, and she wasn't Tina Murphy and she certainly wasn't Tina the actress. She couldn't act at all, and no one would have given her any part, if I hadn't insisted that she play Eva, but she made that part her own and she appeared in every glossy magazine that she wanted: Playboy, Vogue, Cosmopolitan, and a few, not so savoury; the big tits brigade. Then there was television. Television shaped her and gave her the self she wanted until . . ."

"Not yet," whispers Mo, "let's have no *until*, just yet. I

need the story first. Do it properly – like that woman with the funny name who told the story of Ali Baba. I always liked that story. I could really imagine him hiding among all those thieves."

"Scheherazade."

"Yes, that's right," he says quickly, "she was called something like that."

"And you will stay then for a thousand and one nights?"

"That's a long time, " sighs Mo touching his tattoo. "That's a very long time."

"Let me start by giving the atmosphere, the backdrop, if you will, of us marooned in that bed-sit with that baby, that child, David. David of sorrows, David of tears, David of no return, David the human child who couldn't be left with anyone, because everyone in our life was so unreliable, particularly Yvonne the addict, Yvonne the whore; Yvonne whose fine blonde hair enclosed that too thin face like something already dead. Of course we *did* leave him with her, and I would come home to find Yvonne asleep, or passed out, and the baby playing happily among the needles. The child was a mystery. Sometimes happy, sometimes not; and I can't pretend that I understand him now that he is grown and brings what is his own with him, his own kind of silence. He sits in the chair in which you are now, and listens to me, if he feels he has the time; more out of pity than curiosity I suspect, but he never asks about his mother, about Tina.

At first, she hung out with the count, the count who was also a poet and who had been published by Prometheus Press. It was thanks to him that I sent my book to Prometheus Press. He was Jules le Comte de Braband and liked to wear yellow. I seem to remember that the first time I met him he was completely in yellow, and arrived with a bottle of whisky making a bulge in his jacket pocket. The rich colour of the liquid seemed to drain his suit and made one suspect that he had probably dyed it himself. He was a complete fraud and had the inimitable charm that sometimes comes with real dishonesty, and Tina drank in that charm and it swelled her and gave her confidence. I hadn't noticed that she had been in any way lacking in that respect because I had been too pre-occupied with myself, but now I saw Tina of the morning and Tina of the night stepping out into the day and embracing it as a new conquest. The morning had always been hers: Tina preparing, Tina of the bottles and lotions. And the night, of course: she had always been Tina of the night. With the count, the day became hers, and there were suddenly things that she had to do, and places she had to go. New and strange events which she treated with a touching and naive familiarity ballooned and floated on a fresh horizon, which drew her and needed her; and it wasn't really surprising that the child was abandoned, or forgotten, in this carousel of events.

She went to poetry readings and book launches The count dressed her, he insisted on that. She was used to dressing too vulgarly, too provocatively but she had no idea of that, and the first time he criticised her she was taken by surprise. She was only used to admiration. Remember what Axel used to say of her, "she has sensuality that stirs the soul." The poor boy never got beyond being stirred, never got beyond standing in the doorway except very briefly, for a week or so, and then he had that transparent calm that comes with real happiness. He had the same cow-like look when he held baby David, and Tina pretended not to notice. She wouldn't allow that it might be his. She regretted that when he slipped away, vanished, departed this life, or whatever words you want to use for someone who takes too many drugs at a party with whatever intent.

The count was not stirred by the cheap boots which didn't really fit and the terrible clothes; sequins sewn onto cheap material with slits here and there which were supposed to be daring and alluring, but were really just crude.

"My God," said le Comte de Braband, "you are not wearing *that*." His eyes took in *that* very eloquently, too eloquently.

"I fuckin' well am, you cunt," said Tina. "Why isn't it good enough for your poetry friends? Who are they?"

"People who wouldn't want to know someone like you, unless I dress you. Let me dress you." He bent down and took out of a bag a black skirt, and a brown and black jumper with queer flowers on it. It looked very Japanese, but it was Italian. It had a deep neckline and an unusual cut. She looked very beautiful.

"Do I," she asked, "looking at herself in the mirror, "have a sensuality that stirs the soul?"

"Who told you that?"

"A German I once knew. He used to say, 'you have a sensuality that stirs the soul,' in a very slow German accent."

"All women can stir the soul," replied the Comte de Braband as if drawing on wells of experience. "All women can stir the soul, in the right time, at the right place." He put his arm round her waist and she kissed him.

He always dressed her after that, and she never complained. In the morning she would sometimes wait for him to come and choose her clothes. She would lie on the bed in some enchanting negligee he'd given her and wait for him to come and make love to her and decide which clothes she should wear. He didn't often stay because he didn't like the flat and it took us sometime to get out of it; a year or so. When we moved to our flat in Chelsea, the count stayed. Our living room was just right for poetry, he said; and his friends gathered inside and out. They sat in the tiny walled garden, drinking white wine and eating food he had cooked or bought from a delicatessen. She tried poetry, but only briefly.

She became an actress and an artist; something that needed quite a bit of money. The child, of course, needed looking after. The child had become morose, or had always been so.

"Teach him to smile, Tina," said the count, "teach him to smile."

The child looked at him with that unnerving hostility peculiar to children, as if they knew something about you that you didn't know yourself. A hostility that makes you feel that you are innocent and a loser, because no effort can overcome that invisible boundary. I felt sorry for him. He really did try. He bought presents and made faces while Tina became more and more distant. She would buy clothes and sing nursery rhymes and throw herself into symbolic occasions: birthday parties, Santa, the first day at nursery. There were waves of motherhood and, I suspect, seas of indifference, and the count was not unlike her, appearing unexpectedly with smart tricycles which David would ride very solemnly, having thanked him with a kiss on the cheek.

14
David

"He is," said Jules, "a devil on a tricycle. A right little devil."

David rode very slowly surrounded by attention, feeling its warmth and security. Yes, a devil, a strong mighty devil. He might not yet be there, but another little push would complete the miracle. Meanwhile he would drink in these words, and, as he forced down the pedal, he felt closer, closer to being a devil, a miracle on a tricycle.

"A devil, *un diable*."

"*Un diable*," repeated David to those two on the sofa, those mountainous beings on the sofa. His back to them, he pedalled furiously while his mother laughed. He knew then that she was in a good mood and would pick him up and kiss him. Jules would put his warm face close to his and whisper in his ear.

"*Un diable*," he would say holding him in those familiar arms, those strong hairy arms, his large face hovering over him, staring at him closely so that their noses almost touched. A huge face and small lively brown eyes; the usual bigness of adults, though in this case it wasn't true. He knew it wasn't true because Tina had said so. He was a dwarf. Well, not quite a dwarf. Not really, just very small.

But when he bent over David and picked him up he was big. Not as big as Tina, but much bigger than Rachel, aunty Rachel, and his warmth was strong, welcoming and frightening. David closed his fists, pushing hard on Jules' chest trying to make him go away.

"What a small devil. The devil has shrunk. Take him off the trike and he's a small boy, but on it, he's a devil."

Small boy, devil or *diable*, as Jules called him in that strange language called French which they spoke where Jules came

117

from. Jules had lived in their house for as long as he could remember, but before David was born he lived somewhere else. Perhaps France where people knew him as le Comte de Braband, even if it was true that one of Tina's friends had looked him up in a book which contained the names of all the counts in the world, and hadn't found his there. David didn't care, because he knew he was le Comte de Braband in that special way you can know things that Tina couldn't understand. Tina was his mother and she had a way of talking and laughing that made him want to be very close. He had a memory of this, of how much she really meant to him. A memory that did more than stay with him, and, unlike the tricycle memory, it told him things he didn't want to know.

He was at a fancy-dress party and the party was Rachel's because her book was going to be a film – and Tina, he had always called her that – was going to become famous because she was an actress: an actress and an artist. Her art was on their walls and now she was going to be in a film, a film about someone called Max who loved women, money and power – and who died. His memories at this point were conflated, because the film was being made at the party and his grandfather was there; although, by the time they had all become very famous and films were made, he was already dead. His grandfather had killer hands, and David was very lucky that he was gentle and old because he had been in the habit of using those hands before David was born. At this point his memory played a strange trick because his grandfather interrupted the shooting of the film, and told everyone about his brother. He had flown in the war, the war against the Germans and had, according to everyone, been very brave *but*; grandpa took hold of that *but* with his ageing killer hands, full of the raw indignation of someone who knew that no one was listening: *but* he didn't amount to much. In fact, he was a right bastard and there had been better people on the ground getting killed where those bombs fell or were falling. For it seemed to David that, as grandpa spoke, the bombs were still falling and he and grandpa were in a curious twilight between past and present while everyone else was simply hearing a story they'd heard before.

And look at him now, look at brother Mike now, the hero pilot: running a successful business with his son, but no one in their right mind would work for them because they were so hard. Mike was a hero and in his son's veins was the blood of heroes, as everyone would agree. Wouldn't they? Grandpa's monologues needed audience participation and assent, and if he didn't get it, he only spoke for longer; begging, cajoling, and forcing people to agree that he was right. David knew the pauses and supplied the answers wondering why he needed them since everyone knew where he was going, like an old path through a wood. By twist and turns you would end up in the same clearing, with the same gnarled certainties.

"Jesus," said Tina. "Someone get him to shut up. We are busy shooting. Scene one. Take two."

"But look at Axel," continued grandpa.

"He's dead," shouted Tina, "and we are busy shooting."

"Look at Axel," whispered the old man ignoring the distinction between the living and the dead, the boundary between now and shadowland. "Look at Axel. His dad supported the National Socialists before they'd even got into power, before every fool, every Tom, Dick and Harry went around saying Heil Hitler. But look at his son: a real human being. Look at Mike's son: a right bastard, even if he has been and got himself a degree and runs a business." Grandpa's voice rose as it always did when he reached the end, as if he were waiting for applause when the truth of what he was saying struck home, which it never did. It remained a damp squib, but there was always fresh hope in the telling.

"Take two," shouted a voice. He could hear the clapping of boards and he could see his mother, his beautiful mother lying on a couch being Eva, the lady from Rachel's book; the one who probably, like her, had sensuality that stirred the soul. Tina lay on the couch, remote as if dreaming, while grandpa talked, but now no one was listening because all eyes were on her. Nevertheless, all you could hear was the sound of his voice, an old man's voice, insisting on old truths. Everyone had always admired Mike, but was he a real person? Who was on the ground all those years ago when the bombs fell? Had Mike ever given that much thought? You had to know who was there, when your bombs fell. David knew that, understood that. Grandpa marvelled at the way he understood, appealed to him across the generation that had failed him and held him in his killer hands. "I'm leaving all I have to you," he said, cupping the boy's ears in his hands trying unsuccessfully to block out his mother's voice itemising the sad list of grandpa's possessions.

"You're Axel's son," said grandpa, "and the only bloody human being in this family."

In from the garden came people (Tina's and Rachel's friends) wearing the most wonderful fancy-dress. They were meant to be characters from the history of England, but David found it almost impossible to recognize them. They bent down, whispering in his ear who they were. He kept laughing in amazement. The filming was over and grandpa had gone. David couldn't believe what he saw and he wanted to show Tina who was sitting by the window with a glass of wine.

"Look," he kept saying bringing them to her, taking them by the hand, insisting that these fairy-tale kings and queens show themselves to his mother. "Look," but Tina didn't look. She was talking to le Comte de Braband who was very serious, very humble and kept saying, "please Tina."

Such were his memories, as he told them. We had lots of parties and there certainly was a fancy-dress party when I sold the film rights, and the count lost his self-control because Tina had made him jealous with some poet or other. She had drunk in his charm and finished with him. He had taught her how to dress and told her to become an artist, and she did that. Did both to perfection."

"And meanwhile?" Asks Mo surveying the debris of my life, surveying me, Rachel of the shadows. I haven't come out of it too well, not on the surface anyhow, and the surface is all he'll ever see, being so young and me so old. That's the way it is between the generations.

"And meanwhile," he repeats smiling, knowing that I won't resist.

"Meanwhile I finished the trilogy about Max and I discovered that I don't understand men. I know what you are thinking; and, yes, it is true I was drinking too much even then, but I'm not going to tell you about myself. You know enough already. Like Max, I'm a private person. Let me tell you about Tina."

"Tina became known as an artist. She's even got something in the Tate Modern. Conceptions. The Tate bought Conceptions; a creation of plaster and glass. Meanwhile the count was discarded; and she made him realise that she had seen through him, though it had taken her a few years.

"You're a fake and a liar," said Tina, "everything you told me was a tissue of lies."

"What does that mean?" shouted the unhappy count, "a

tissue of lies? And you are a cliche-loving chameleon. I've never seen such a chameleon. You can stuff Conceptions up your arse."

"You're just jealous," whispered Tina, her hand resting on the cardboard tower which was Conceptions, "just jealous. It's been nominated for the Turner Prize."

The child kept looking at him. He was standing very still looking at him, a book in his hand. He had given up tricycles long ago, but he was still serious, very tall and serious. He seemed to walk round the house like a ghost, or someone who didn't really live there, and was only there because he was lost, or didn't have anywhere else to go. The count had long stopped trying to please him, but he did love him. He showed it in the way he relaxed in his company and in the tone of his voice. David accepted him as he accepted no one else. He referred to him as 'le comte' without a trace of irony, and with a quiet obstinacy as if he were putting the world to right.

"Are you going to kill her, Jules?" he asked without any expression on his face, completely deadpan. "I would. I would kill her and get rid of her damned sensuality. The sensuality that stirs the soul." Then he turned round, very slowly, very theatrically and threw his laughter at us as he closed the door.

"You are a bitch Tina," said the Le Comte de Braband. "Nothing but a bitch and a fuckin' chameleon."

15

Fame

David was wrong when he thought that the count had lived with us since he was an infant. He was just such a frequent visitor that it almost seemed so; his absences being unexpected and announced in sudden asides. Cities or countries demanded his presence and he would mention names, as if they were the names of people whose whims had to be indulged.

"I *must* go to Baghdad, *you know.*"

We nodded showing that we knew and asked no questions about when he would be back. Evidence of various aliases lay scattered around the house: he was a count, then a marquis and sometimes just Mr Smith or Mr Jones. We didn't look into it, and we didn't ask. It seemed small-minded to bother someone with details who was so clearly a poseur. I have always assumed that if people tell you lies, they have a need to be believed, and that one has an obligation to do just that or at least to pretend to be doing it.

I missed him when he wasn't there. I missed him in the way one misses people one really cares about, and whenever he returned, I felt that I was rediscovering the familiar shape of his presence: Jules eating; the food in his large hands, his elbows on the table while he was busy unwrapping a story. He unwrapped stories, peeled them apart, and invited us to join him in his amazement as he lorded it over his kingdom. A deadly kingdom of intrigues, contradictions and lies where nobody was quite who they seemed. His stories were all the more interesting because he couldn't tell us everything and had to leave key questions hanging in the air. He had to leave his own presence somewhat unexplained and names couldn't always be included. He had the gift of the gab and the gift of intimacy, in the way of hollow men, and I'll accept intimacy from anyone, hollow or not.

When he first met us he had belonged to a circle of poets. I paid for various poetry magazines, and set up a press which he ran. It didn't amount to a lot of money, but I should have been suspicious because of the quality of the books. I mean quality in the literal sense: the paper was awful and the binding so crude that our little volumes fell apart. The poems had something about them: Jules had had an eye for the real thing. He was good at picking out other people who were in the business of the real thing, and the result was a curious mixture of humbug and quality. All in all, I suppose I lost a hundred thousand pounds on that venture, which didn't seem like a lot of money at the time, but certainly is now when I'm living on cheese and Chinese takeaways, and don't know where the next bottle is coming from . . .

After a couple of years he lost interest in poetry. I discovered later that being an editor had not been his only occupation at the time. Meanwhile, Tina had fallen in love with one of the poets and become a successful artist. Conceptions became quite famous, although she was, of course, already famous as Tina Faithful, the author of the Max trilogy and an actress. She was Eva, the melancholy whore, a role that really suited her, and probably the only role she could ever play convincingly. Rachel stayed in the background. Stayed in the background and wrote, and without my writing there wouldn't have been anything. No one would have taken any notice of Conceptions, and the poets would have put their poems back in the drawers from which they had come . . .

It had happened like that because, at the time, it seemed to me better to put her name on the cover. Fame was something she wanted, and something she knew about. Knowing about fame and famous people had been her business since she had taken her first tentative steps in the adult kingdom, as it is for a certain type of woman. I never anticipated, of course, that the Max trilogy would become really famous, but she was the right choice. I didn't look good on television.

Tired of poets, Jules returned to the world of politics, money and arms. Sometimes he would hint that his role was small, and that he had just been allowed a view of a vast and surreal panorama, but his stories amounted to something more than that. His presence in world affairs was too ubiquitous. He knew the truth behind whatever dark story was in the news, and he handed it to you with a gloved hand leaving you to draw conclusions. He knew – or had personally organised – those who had left God's banker to dangle under Blackfriars Bridge. He was a liar, of course, but a clever one. He never became entangled in his lies, and we were too bemused to sort out fact from fiction, which was a waste of time anyway, because there was a strange truth in the whole. His stories, as the phrase goes, rang true. They were of the right metal, and when I later borrowed some of them for the final volume of Max, I began to receive sinister phone calls and even had several men turning up who said they *were* Max, and how dare I? By then Tina had left with her pot of gold, and le Comte de Braband had more or less emptied my bank account, or rather accounts. By then Paul, the poet, had died by the pool, and nothing seemed to matter quite so much anymore. Max too had died, but as he died in a book, his death was very different, although fact and fiction are no longer so easy to disentangle. What remains clearly in my mind, like something lying, say, at a station long after a traveller has left, is the image of Paul's cocktail on the table and his body – but here my memory plays tricks, I know, because I don't think I ever had a clear view of his body . . .

Fame caught us unawares, and we never got used to it. My second book was suddenly something everyone had heard of. The first one had done very well, buying us a mews house in Chelsea and paying for a nanny for David. But it was the second one which suddenly included us in a world which Tina found easier than me, because she had been waiting for it. She had been waiting for people to take her photograph and interview her. She had been waiting to take part in shows. She was very lucky. Most people wait all their lives and only see it happening to someone else.

Paul the poet came and stayed. The count took his possessions, put them in an overnight bag and slung it in an empty bedroom which became his. He didn't own much: a few suits, a trouser press (he liked to dress well), some personal papers in a black case, a gold watch and a pair of cuff links. That was the first time I really noticed his smallness. I found him sitting on his case, eyes fixed on his trouser press as if its size and solid presence gave him some kind of stake in the place.

"That bitch," he said, "has fallen for Paul. He's a complete idiot, and she's a twit – but I could kill both of them. Can you explain that? I could kill whoever fucks her. Pure jealousy of course. But why ? I mean, I knew she'd find someone else. She already had behind my back. So why does it matter? But it does. I can tell you it does." He looked at me very carefully as if he expected me to deny some part of what he'd said, but I didn't. I had long ago lost interest in Tina and I just waited for him to continue as I knew he must. He couldn't bear silence.

"I'm on my way to Rome. Do you mind if I leave a few things here? I have to meet a senator. He wants to talk to me about a Blue Lagoon. The Catholic Church has invested in the Blue Lagoon and so have a host of other, even less savoury organisations, and I must sort it all out. Little me. The church gargoyle, the dwarf, call me what you will, Rachel, call me what you will, but they need me." He paused. He had a talent for the right pause which at first seemed impressive, but later cheap and contrived, though I loved him for it. I have a weakness for hollow men.

"Call me what you will, Rachel."

I didn't call him anything. He put his hand on his Rolex watch, that curious symbol of so much in modern life; in his case, I think, power. Certainly not money. Not that he didn't have money. He had other people's money in sudden splurges, but he never made any attempt to make an attribute of it. There wasn't anything permanent about Jules' ability to pay for anything. Money took him by surprise and he expected his friends to feel the same way; as if an open wallet, or ready cash, were the consequences of a conjuring trick. About power he felt differently. Here he implied that he had *knowledge*.

"Call me what you will, Rachel."

I sat silently thinking about whatever was occupying me at the time, something very trivial and visual I suspect, while I let his airs and graces run their familiar gamut. There is something very pleasing in the ritual of listening. I was looking at his hands. Such delicate hands, and so at odds with the coarse persona he was dramatically laying claim to.

"You're looking at my watch. Well, the Vatican paid for that, and, as for the cuff links, they're a family heirloom. I don't owe you anything."

"But you would like to stay? "

"I would like to stay."

He got up from sitting on that sad travelling case and took my hand. "Of course, Rachel, I would like to stay. I want to stay even if it means seeing that bitch with Paul the poet. He isn't even a poet, you know. No one but us would publish him. We used to publish mainly good stuff. No one should knock the

Well of Arethusa as a publishing house. What is it that the Guardian called us?"

"A brave maverick publisher."

"That's right. But sometimes we were a little short, and I have accepted a few who used us as moonshine and who paid the costs."

"And Paul was one of them. Who else?"

"Oh, I can't remember. But she thinks he's the real thing, and she wants the real thing does Tina; and I could kill her because she's got that fuckin' sensuality that stirs the soul. One of the few real things around here, but meanwhile I must go to Rome. I have promises to keep and miles and miles to go before I sleep. Will you come with me Rachel? Will you come with me to Rome? I know a hotel in via Giulia where history comes and goes, where the night is full of shadows, and all those things that do one a world of good, because one can't forget them in a hurry."

"Perhaps."

"No perhaps, Rachel. Sometimes one has a longing for the baroque. There never was a better antidote to failed love than fountains, curlicues, seraphim and obelisks. In that order. Or any order you want. Just don't leave out the obelisks, and, before we forget, the Theatre of Marcellus, which you come upon unexpected, and the Tiber . . ."

"Also unexpected?"

"No, Rachel, no. Don't be silly Rachel. Don't be so stiff and silly. You need to relax. You should come to Rome. You sit here like a statue. You walk round the house like a statue, mad with some unhappiness, though you pretend it's not so. Tina is right: you spend too much time with books, too much time with your fantastics."

"I'm a very private person."

"You just share your bed with people and walk away. That's no way to live."

"I do what I want."

"People who say that hardly ever know what they want, and certainly never get it. Come to Rome and stay with me in via Giulia. You'll love it and you might need it for Max. A man like Max has to see Rome."

So I went to Rome and I did love it. Max, of course, hated it but then his circumstances were very different. He saw it in a moment of crisis, but for me there was no crisis; just a vague sense of apprehension and boredom. I wanted Jules to show me Rome, and I wanted to meet the senator whom he'd mentioned in an ill-judged aside, because his vanity was always being tempted.

We had dinner together; we were the only people in a vast room with high ceilings, chandeliers and graceful furniture. The only ones, except for Jules' minder who sat very bored on an uncomfortable chair beneath a picture of Queen Christina of Sweden. He was solemn and solid, and, because he seemed so at ease, there was nothing menacing about him. Like a lot of calm people, he was whatever you wanted him to be, and to say he created a false impression would be wrong. He made no impression at all really. Since then I've discovered that killing people didn't bother him, provided he'd been told to do it, but I didn't know that at the time. The senator was clearly better informed, or perhaps he didn't like what Jules told him, for he stammered and spluttered. I saw a real look of fear in his eyes; like the fear I have since experienced myself, when, overcome with drink, sitting on a bench, I have seen figures coming towards me. Figures looming out of a strange reality that I can't any longer control or understand; but which I know will take me by surprise, because it is fast, while I'm slow; and it has a *purpose,* in the queer way things do. Why did those young people hit me down by the river? Because they did; because they wanted to. Why is Mo sitting here on my bed drinking coffee listening to my weathered self telling a rambling tale? Because he wants to. Because the coffee tastes good and he is in the mood for listening, and occasionally a rambling tale is what you most want and nothing else can satisfy you, because you've done with shape and structure.

The minder was called George and he came from Liverpool. He had a sympathetic enough face, and what he himself called a professional attitude; this meant that he never voiced an opinion about whoever employed him. Jules didn't know him well, but he knew his type. He enjoyed showing him off and explaining what a professional attitude means in a bodyguard. It means exactly what you'd expect, what you have read in books, and there is a certain dullness in that because there isn't much the mind can do with unquestioning loyalty, but accept it as a fact.

After we had dined with the senator, Jules and I walked for hours through the streets of Rome. It was a warm summer's evening. I love cities at night, and Rome is one of the finest for a night walk. George followed us at a discreet distance. Although I barely noticed him, I didn't like his presence. He stayed in the hotel and ate breakfast by himself, drinking his coffee very slowly and thoughtfully like a man used to being on his own and enjoying his private ritual of dunking a dry slice of cake into a cup in the absent-minded way of really lonely people. I can't say I liked him, though I know that I am describing him as if I did. I saw something in him as he sat there that morning with his back to one of those clumsy engravings of the Colosseum which you see in most Roman hotels. He looked like he belonged in the engraving himself, dressed as a gladiator or a soldier. *That* would have been altogether more appropriate than sitting at his separate table in his elegant casual clothes which made one aware of the size of his hands, shoulders and neck. He was already there when we came down and had almost finished his breakfast. As he left, he whispered something to Jules.

"He's going to see someone he calls a lady friend for an hour or two. It looks like he's got some kind of private life, and I can't deny him that."

Within a few minutes George was back. He returned to his seat and began to read an Italian paper in a very slow and unconvincing way while tearing a paper napkin into strips which he rolled into little balls which he chewed and spat out.

"He's certainly got killer hands."

"People like him need them. He's an excellent body-guard."

"You talk as if you had always had one."

"Not always, Rachel, but sometimes. Sometimes we all need bodyguards. The world is *that* nasty and I'm mixing quite frankly with the *wrong* kind of people, but you always discover that when it's too late, and you've done too many people too many favours. They gave me George to look out for me."

"It looks more like he's keeping an eye on *you*."

"Do you think so? Do you really think so?" asked the count anxiously. "I wouldn't say so. I really wouldn't. What makes you say that?"

"Intuition, Jules, only intuition. Intuition and the fact that I know how unreliable you are."

"Am I? How can you call anyone who has been Tina's lover for almost a dozen years unreliable? I'm brim full of reliability."

"I suppose that is one way of looking at it."

"It's the only way, and you should employ George. You need a bodyguard now that you've got fame. You and Tina don't understand fame. It's not just a pain in the arse. It can be downright dangerous."

George continued tearing up paper napkins but he seemed calmer and had begun to arrange them in neat piles as if they were toy cannonballs. Suddenly he looked at his watch, got up and placed an envelope by Jules' long finished cup of coffee.

"For the flowers. That is for the flowers."

Jules rose immediately.

"We must go Rachel. He wants us to go. I'm buying flowers for his lady friend." Jules smiled, put the envelope in his pocket. "I wonder which flowers I should choose?" He began to hum. "Flowers can be very special, don't you think?"

There was something in the art of lying which held him spellbound so that he could never leave well alone: "a dozen white lilies, the symbol of purity. Or should I go for red roses? Should I tell him you need a bodyguard? You can't do without one in our new house in the country. Five acres and a pool. They'll be lurking in the bushes to catch a sight of you and Tina after you have immortalized her as Eva the melancholy whore."

He was right there of course, and George did become our bodyguard and I got used to his silent and solid presence. I never liked the man, but I never asked myself what he might be thinking of me, though I'd seen evidence that morning that he could be affected by the personal. I never saw him again so taken by the unexpected, so put out that he didn't care what other people might be thinking. He sat arranging balls of paper completely absorbed in his thoughts, even helping himself to more napkins from the table next to him where they were piled high, as if it was being used for spare odds and ends. When I next saw him unnerved, there was, by comparison, only a flicker, a slight adjustment of the surface: he stammered and couldn't get his tongue round the words, "I made a mistake, Rachel."

"So he became your bodyguard," said Mo thoughtfully, "because you needed one in that vast mansion . . ."

"Residence. We called it our residence. We liked that word because we'd grown up nowhere and that word belonged to somewhere; to the world of fame."

"I've seen pictures of it. I saw it in something called, "Beyond the Walls", about a day in the lives of celebrities. You were Tina's friend and sometimes the camera lingered on you sitting silently in a large chair. You used to sit in a huge red armchair."

There was always an armchair. Something huge into which I could disappear. And then there was Tina smiling at the camera; Tina glowing and exuberant.

"You couldn't forget her. She had a way of talking and laughing and hitting back at the interviewer. She said that fame wasn't everything and that she believed in the paranormal. Then she explained what that meant. It meant that she could communicate with other people's souls because she had a special gift, and the special gift was worth more than fame. The special gift was in people everywhere, but it had to be awakened by Chinese philosophy, and something or somebody from Japan. She sat on the edge of the pool talking about her special gift. Paul sat next to her. They both dived in and came up holding hands, and ran across the lawn. Tina answered the happiness question and Paul was asked what it felt like being the lover of Tina Faithful, the novelist and actress.

Paul was tanned and very good-looking. I suppose I'm jealous, but he looked an empty sort of guy and a bit arrogant. Anyhow, he said, "Yes it can be difficult being an item with Tina when you are a poet, and she writes such tripe." I don't understand how anyone could use that word of the Max trilogy, but that's the word he used – *tripe*. Tina just smiled, and now that I know that she didn't write it, I can understand why she didn't have hurt feelings. He talked about how poetry is very special and not coarse like prose. I don't read poetry, so it didn't mean anything to me. He explained that poetry is very difficult and you have a very special relationship with language. It is the medium you use, but it has also got a life of its own. It's multi-layered and multi-surfaced. Every word has a bottomless pit of meanings because every reader is unique, and consequently every reading is the only one of its kind. Tina said, "Yes, darling." And, "he's taught me so much."

Then she put her chin on his shoulder, her hand on his wet thighs. She looked really beautiful. I think you were sitting by the pool and I understood that you were Tina's friend. You were wearing huge sunglasses and looked thin, particularly next to Tina. I don't remember you saying anything."

"You don't really remember me at all. Admit it. I did say something. They interviewed me as well because Tina explained that I had inspired her and helped her with some of the writing. They kept cutting what I said, till there wasn't much left. They much preferred Tina."

"Why should they want to interview a clever old cow?" shouted Mo, laughing, putting his arms round my shoulders. "Who should want to interview you?"

So it was probably cow he had said all along, cow and not cunt. I'll accept cow.

"Please continue your story," he whispered, "please continue. I want to know what happens next. You are all in that residence, as you call it. And there are God knows how many bedrooms . . ."

"Bedrooms coming out of your arse . . ."

"And a pool . . ."

"And a pool . . .."

"And a minder . . ."

"And things happening behind the scenes that I didn't know about – that I never found out about – that I don't know even now. For in all stories there is darkness. Darkness and light, and the questions you should have asked, and the answers you should have known so that if on a winter's night . . . "

"Like tonight."

"Like tonight. If on a winter's night, like tonight, two people should meet, or someone should be reading this book, to listen to the story of Max, Tina and Paul, then what they will hear will be a mixture of silence and sound and what they make of it, will be their own business . . ."

16

A party for Paul

"David spent most of his time in his room, but sometime you would find him in the garden; on one of the benches in the meadow, or in the orchard which lay beyond the garden and which was surrounded by a low dry stone wall. Very refined, very silent, that was David. We left him to lead his own life, accepting his presence when he offered it, and asking as few questions as possible. As he never wanted to be found, we didn't look for him. It was enough to stumble across him somewhere among the woods and hills I had purchased. He preferred distance, and we were a little in awe of the person he had become.

It angered Tina that he should keep himself so to himself. She had no patience with silence. He said very little when she was there, and she saw it as his way of showing contempt. I think there may have been something in that, although there wasn't much in his contempt, or his silence, except a little bit of pride: I think she had hurt him too many times. He couldn't entirely avoid fame, but the journalists didn't get much out of him, except that he didn't think much of Conceptions; and no, it didn't surprise him that it had been short-listed for the Turner prize. Yes, of course his mother did take her art very seriously, but he took it, and her, rather less seriously; and, no, he didn't think much of Max. He preferred philosophy to fiction. I remember him saying that; very primly, looking out beyond the camera as if he were reading the words off a prompter on some distant hill. He was about sixteen years old then. He's much less stiff now, much more assured. He's got a droll sense of humour. It's difficult to imagine that he's the same person who said, "I prefer philosophy to fiction," in that very dry and colourless way he used to speak, as if he didn't care what you thought.

Tina had become a new Tina. The count was right when he called her a chameleon, though there was always that which remained: the Tina who made you welcome in her company, who shared the moment and what it contained, a glass of wine, a bowl of olives, a seat on the sofa. But she had also become an artist. She spoke about painting and of different types of texture and techniques, and of formal possibilities pushed to their limits. Her hands had become tools of creation, and she would sometimes look at them pleased and surprised, definitely taken by surprise by her talents, but not in doubt, although not arrogant. There was no arrogance in Tina, just a grain of complacency that was skin deep and innocent. She was older, a little rounder and more attractive, fuller of the sensuality that, as Axel said, stirs the soul, and her certainty was beguiling. She could talk about art, and she did."

"And Paul?"

"Paul listened. He was good at listening. When he got bored, he would get up and leave without any warning. You would be in mid-sentence, and he would disappear down the garden and return with a flower or a vegetable which he would chew thoughtfully, sitting down on some piece of garden furniture or a stone, as if you didn't exist. He seemed to be making a point of there being an inner life of a finer sort from which the rest of us were excluded. There were lots of people living in my house, including Paul's many poet friends whose works were published by the Well of Arethusa which had been created to make up for the vulgarity of Max and fame. Paul loved being a publisher. He had taken over the publishing house as Jules would have nothing to do with the Well anymore. He just lived in the house, lived with me in an absent-minded way, as if I had drifted into his life with all my money, land and the house, our residence, which wasn't a house at all but a Georgian mansion with outbuildings intended for horses and separate wings for servants, which were full of poets, and one or two painters. One of them painted that thing over there, above the bookcase. Grey and orange in mighty swirls that you might call dynamic. It needs more space, more light but I can't give it either; and I suspect that it isn't very good but it reminds me of fame, and the sunny days of fame."

"What is it called?"

"Unless; it's called that, and you mustn't ask, unless what? I learnt not to ask questions but to look tantalised as if I were waiting for everyone around me to do something, become someone, hatch some new idea or attitude; meanwhile no questions asked, all bills paid. I can say that I enjoyed that: spending money and waiting. What would the Well of Arethusa publish next? I'm good at waiting; it's my strongest attribute and if I had had less of a presence, if I had been less pinched, less intense, then perhaps people would have noticed that and said, thank you. Thank you Rachel. Thank you for waiting for the wind in my sails, the change of mind and opinion, the dredging of so many seas, the miracle of mermaids. Thank you. Meanwhile, I was a bit of an alcoholic, a nuisance. No one was comfortable with Max, no one *appreciated* Max, and I had become filthy rich. Much too rich. Jules lay in my bed thinking of Tina, and Paul thought about poetry, or seemed to be thinking about poetry. People came and went thinking very carefully about who they were. I enjoyed this drifting of souls so much more than my inner self that it took me some time to notice that I was being a bit naive; that because I enjoyed it, it didn't follow that everyone else did.

"You should," I said to Tina, "be a little more patient with Jules and David."

"What do you mean? That I should sleep with Jules?"

"Well, you could. It would do no harm."

"And what if I already do? Of course I do. Don't tell me you don't know."

I didn't. I've always had a tendency to see the surface of people, the polished surface with all the grains nicely showing.

"I can't bear that innocent bit of you which is all pretence, all bollocks. You *know* he sometimes fucks me, but that isn't enough. He's jealous, he's obsessed. Why does everyone take me so seriously? Why does everyone take me so seriously, not as *me*, but as the Tina *they* know, or the Tina they think they know, the Tina they want, their fantasy Tina, their fantastic? Why doesn't the count pack up his lies and take them somewhere else? And Paul – Paul is becoming too serious, too inward."

"Inward? I thought that was what he and you wanted: a pose."

"God, can't you see? He wants *success*. He knows you don't respect him, and he's not happy with the chorus of poets who shred his poems behind his back and flatter him insanely to his face. I suppose I'm unfaithful too, but you know what it is about sex. It can give you such peace of mind, and I sometimes wonder whether it is the only thing left that gives you perfect peace of mind, except of course art."

She was sitting on the swing, swinging back and forth looking very happy and relaxed as she analysed the male world around her. She slipped in her reference to art as if it were the most natural thing to mention next so that you couldn't possibly dispute it. Smiling she outlined her personal claim: sculpting and painting gave her a feeling of peace, like reading Confucius.

"But you are all very jealous of me. It was better when I only did sex."

In out, in out, her legs cut through the rush of air as if she were having sex with all creation. With her taut body and her smile, she was so much the old Tina, the Tina of our fantasies, that I was momentarily transported back, back to that hideous house with its smells and faded colours and Tina standing on the stairs proudly in her cheap boots while Axel explained that only European novelists really understood the secrets of women. "Only they understand their inner souls."

"David is a teenager and he hates me because I'm a wicked woman of a thousand compromises and no principles, and the only important thing that I say I am, he doesn't believe. He doesn't believe I'm an artist, and he doesn't think anything of my acting. He hates the way men crowd around me – even if I ignore most of them. I don't have time for most of the poets."

She kept swinging higher and higher lifting her legs stiffly into the air pointing them towards the pool where a crowd was arranging itself as if for a purpose, and I remembered that it was Paul's birthday because I had seen him decanting wine. Paul decanted wine carefully. He had taught Tina the art of wine. Jules had taught her the art of dressing, but he'd never taught her the art of wine. Maybe he felt that this couldn't be communicated so easily, or maybe he just enjoyed her ignorance. Jules enjoyed ignorance almost as much as he enjoyed style, and Tina so charmingly combined both, and she knew it, of course.

Paul was too serious for ignorance. He enjoyed the rusty colour of good claret, and would hold his glass up to the light having carefully ensured that the sediment remained in the bottle. By the time Tina had learnt all about wine, she had given up on ignorance. Ignorance belonged to her younger self, her vulgar self and it wasn't something that Paul valued because he'd spent too much time fighting it in himself, too much time crudely cutting it back, reading great swathes of poetry with the intensity that comes of determination, and that achieves no more than that, no more than the goal.

"Are you coming to Paul's birthday?"

Of course I'm coming. It's my bloody house. Those were the words I didn't say, because suddenly I wasn't sure that I *did* want to go. Why should I be there because it was my house, my residence, my park, my pool? Did I care? Ownership didn't make people notice me, so why my presence? Did I want all of this, this endlessness of space, these horizons of nature, this presence of hills, trees and wind? The wind, perhaps. The wind was always good. The rest could go to hell.

"*I'm* coming," said George very quietly as if the words had some kind of special importance which he expected us to understand.

As he had come from the woods, we hadn't seen him, and he was next to me quite suddenly.

"I'm coming," he repeated. "But I don't think you should go."

"Do you mean me or Tina?"

"Well, Tina, of course, has to be there. It would look a little strange if she wasn't." He looked very relaxed, if a little thoughtful. Thoughtful in the way of people willing you to share something with them, or trying to remind you of something that you shouldn't have forgotten.

"It would look a little strange, wouldn't it? But why should you be there? You could go for one of your many walks in the wood. Yes, I think that would be a good idea."

George smiled. He was, as usual, too well dressed, or perhaps what I mean is too carefully dressed. He was always going around the place as if his presence had a specific purpose, which of course it had; he was a minder. I only wished he could have acted as if he belonged. Tina disliked him and had been nagging me to get rid of him.

"He pops out of nowhere."

"Just ignore him. He's useful. We need someone. We really

do. There are always people sneaking into this place, and sooner or latter someone . . ."

"Why should someone want to harm you? Why should anyone want to shoot you like they shot John Lennon?"

"There have already been two prowlers. Two that we know about. And I heard someone outside my window the other night. I didn't see anyone, but I definitely heard someone. We need George."

"Do we? We need someone. But why George?"

This was a question I couldn't answer, because the answer was simply that we had George, that he had drifted into our lives like everyone else, and that there was as much reason for his being there as any one of the poets, including Paul who was running the Well of Arethusa. Life *is* chance.

That afternoon he seemed his usual awkward self, and Tina wasn't going to hide her irritation.

"What are you after?" she asked throwing her head back and letting her legs cut through the wind pushing the swing to new heights,. "What are you after? Are you staging something? I hope it's something grand. It bloody well better be after all this blather, this talk and silence. It's about time you *did* something, do you understand what I mean, you old cunt? Don't you agree Rachel? It's time George *did* something."

"They are going to be serving drinks," said George, ignoring her in a way that was bound to infuriate.

"What is wrong with that wanker," whispered Tina angrily. "What about the drinks?"

"I'm going to help them with them, *and* I have promised to serve the snacks. Large prawns wrapped in something; filo pastry, I think. You must come with me, Miss Tina. Paul has been asking for you."

That made her jump out of the swing and follow him. Their backs were turned to me, but I knew that she would be

147

making faces, and that he would have his usual inscrutable smile that made her so angry.

From the raised voices coming from the pool, I could tell that Paul had welcomed them. George stopped before he had reached the happy crowd, but she joined them and there was the usual closeness and touching that there always is with Tina. I saw her put her arms round one of the poets, while Paul was standing apart, busy with a bottle of champagne.

"Still the same sensuality that stirs the soul," said David loudly watching the swing that she had recently abandoned move back and forth before catching it with his hand and holding it hard, "still the same old thing. Paul doesn't seem to know as much about champagne as he does about wine. I wonder why? Perhaps he's fake in that respect too, as in everything else. Why don't you tell him to fuck off, Rachel? I think we should rid this place of some poets. George doesn't like them either, you know. He can't stand poets. Where did you find *him*? Where did you find George? He's a dangerous idiot, if I ever saw one. Don't ask me why, but I *know*."

He let go of the swing and looked at me very still, very determined as if his little speech had been a moment of truth. Very adolescent, but I was struck by it as if by a revelation. It wasn't anything he had said, but a sudden sense of the atmosphere.

The atmosphere of the place was petty and poisonous, and I had allowed myself to think of it differently. I had mangled and twisted reality to see what I wanted to see. What was in front of me was not a pretty thing, but you can improve upon it, as Max had said of love. Yes, you can improve on petty, small-minded people, if you refuse to see their small-mindedness; because it's the one thing that can destroy you, if you take a proper measure of it, if you dare to see it in all its dreary detail. What I saw by the pool that evening (the sun was just setting and you could really hear the birds) was a measure of smallness that fairly took your breath away, if you wanted to care about it, and at that moment I *did*. I really did, and I wondered whatever it was I had ever seen in the physicality of Tina, or the aspirations of Paul, or the various individuals who made up the crowd which was wishing Paul happy birthday. The count was standing a little further away from the rest waving to me conspiratorially.

"He's all right," said David, "Jules is all right."

"You've always liked him."

"He's less of a fraud than the others. Less of a liar."

It seemed an odd thing to say.

Jules was walking in our direction waving his glass and a bottle. The others made a separate and compact group round the pool. George was coming out of the house with a tray which he was holding high in the air, as if he were playing at being a waiter. Paul was beginning to make a speech and there was a modified silence which allowed me to hear a few words.

"Thank you. Thank you so much, all of you. It's really good of you. We are all here because it's my birthday and, of course, because of Rachel. I would like to thank her for all her support and her friendship. Rachel you *are* a friend. A special friend to all of us helping us fulfil ourselves." He paused and they all drank; then he repeated the phrase 'fulfil ourselves' but quietly, as if he had just discovered some new irony; and he looked round as if savouring it. When he continued, they didn't listen to him so quietly, or perhaps he didn't speak so loudly after he'd finished talking about his gratitude, and what we had all achieved.

Jules had stopped to finish his glass, but he was still waving his bottle to show us that he was coming.

"Yes, he's all right. He's real."

I wanted to ask him what he meant by that, but he said it with such conviction that I just nodded. I wanted David to like me; the others could disappear. I wished the earth would swallow them up, and that I could start all over again.

"Yes, he's real," I repeated. Real what?

"You love him, don't you?"

"Yes," I replied because I knew I did. Of course I loved the count. I loved him, because I knew that I would miss him.

"Could you love me?" he stood very silently waiting for an answer, his face very tense and determined, showing that he meant it. He was very drunk.

"David I am too old."

"I have watched you through the window. You never draw the curtains. Why should you? Your bedroom faces the garden and the darkness. You are beautiful." He spoke very quickly as if to get it over with, this prepared little speech.

"I know I'm very drunk. Very, very drunk, but you don't mind, do you Rachel?" Suddenly he fell out of the darkness, his hands clutching me as he slid down towards the grass.

"Kiss me Rachel." His hands tugged at the grass throwing tufts of it into the air. He turned his head to one side and closed his eyes. Jules had finished his drink and I waved to him to come over. By the pool they were opening the doors and going inside. The music was becoming louder. George was standing with his back to us talking to Paul who was shaking his head like a puppet. Perhaps he'd already had quite a bit to drink. Alcohol didn't become him; it brought out a sourness he didn't know what to do with, a dull awareness that the world didn't appreciate him or his poems.

I sat down in the grass by David and Jules next to me, his face turned towards the house. There was something he wanted to say and he seemed to be addressing the hub of light across the lawn beyond the trees. The land rose slightly towards the house. We were hidden in the shadow of the incline. The light was distant and we seemed a long way away, in a private night.

"Has Paul been telling you anything?"

"No."

"You mean that Rachel, you really do?"

"Yes."

"He hasn't been talking about money?"

"He always talks about money. I'm throwing more money at Arethusa. Tina has agreed to be in reality TV. The third volume isn't doing so well, but Tina will make up for it. She can be a celebrity. She is good at that."

I could see Tina standing in the huge window in the hallway upstairs. I had chosen the house because of its windows and its wonderful Georgian symmetries, its great plates of glass letting in the light. I had been brought up in the crepuscular darkness of the London Edwardian terrace with its curious excesses, bay windows, pilasters and motley coloured bricks and I loved this simplicity; all these clear lines. She was wearing a short black dress and very long earrings. Everyone was inside now. David was fast asleep, and Jules had begun to whisper and stumble, making a hash of what he wanted to say. It was something about money but linked to something else; and it was the something else he wanted to talk about, but didn't know how.

"You do *trust* me, don't you Rachel. All the lies apart, you *do* trust me. I mean there are things I do, and things I don't do. There are things I don't do."

"I know that. There are things you don't do," I replied firmly wondering what they might be, the boundaries seemed to have been moved so often.

"I didn't think Paul could tell such lies. I really can't believe it." He looked wretched.

"He goes around saying the most extraordinary things. Really hurtful things."

Other people's lies, they always take you by surprise; and with the wind suddenly out of your sails, you are left with a jaundiced sense of being misbegotten, not rightly equipped for this planet with its shimmering shadows and deceptive moons.

Jules moved out of the light toward the woods.

"Promise me," he said, "that you just won't believe him. Whatever he says, you won't believe him."

"I promise."

"It's important. Very important. He's even been talking about the police – about bringing in the police."

"He's got some nerve. What business is it of his? Doesn't he use me, too? Can't I decide who uses me?"

"Rachel, please." He knelt down beside me, his small familiar body next to mine. "Don't talk like that. Me, use you? How can you say that?"

I laughed because it suddenly occurred to me that I hadn't recently looked at any of my bank accounts – like most rich people I had more accounts than I could keep track of – and I had given Jules access to most of them. Why? Because they're dark sides to all of us, as Max would say; strange things that we feel impelled to do.

"Shall we wake the boy?" I asked changing the subject because I didn't want to ask any questions, "we can't leave him like this."

"It's a warm summer evening."

I took his hand and we were about to go. We had our backs to the house and neither of us saw anything; we just heard a splash. We couldn't have seen anything – but later we both *thought* we had. We both thought we saw Paul slip into the pool. Memory is a curious thing. With hindsight we heard shouting, but at the time we were sitting with our backs to the house holding hands. We didn't turn round till we had whispered several things to one another, and it was all over.

152

Apparently, George jumped in immediately and pulled him out. There was no one else there, but he reacted quickly and precisely with all his knowledge of saving lives, but he didn't save Paul.

"Death by the pool."

"Yes, that's what they called it. Death by the pool."

"There was a lot of talk about it. Talk about money, arguments, and drugs."

"There wasn't much in the way of drugs. Tina and I didn't read the papers, but we couldn't move for journalists and I can't remember what anyone said, except that there was a lot of aggression. No one would leave us alone."

"Death by the pool."

"Jules and I were walking towards the house where suddenly there was noise and lights. I heard Tina shouting. George was standing by Paul's body. I walked into the house while everyone else streamed out through the doors and formed a circle round the doctor who'd arrived. I don't know where Jules went, but I stood alone in the room we called the library with my back to the door staring through the window out onto the drive. An ambulance had arrived. I felt someone behind me. I knew it was George because of the way he moved. He said, "I got your message, Rachel. I got your message." He put his hand on my shoulder but I didn't turn round. "I got your message and I did what you asked me to do in a very quiet and professional way. The best way." I turned round and looked at him in the way you do when in a state of shock.

"Don't worry," he whispered and smiled, "everything is all right."

"What is all right, George? I don't know what you are talking about and, whatever it is, we can talk about it later. What's all right? Don't you understand what's happened? Can't you see: Paul's dead? You can tell me another time what's all right." I spoke softly, as if he were an idiot, I wanted to humour. I was thinking very slowly. I kept looking at the ambulance as if to check that what I knew had happened, really *had*. Through the haze I noticed that something was all wrong. George was thinking too quickly, responding to something unexpected, something that had just taken him by surprise.

"I mmmade a mistake, Rachel," he stammered, "I made a mis-take."

"You made a mistake?"

I knew exactly what he meant. Not for a moment did I have any doubt. They say that the brain knows what signals you are going to send before you know it, that you rationalise afterwards. You think you will move your leg when movement is already an established fact. I knew before either of us had spoken what we would both say.

"I'm sorry Rachel. I should have checked. I really should have checked. I just wanted to show you that you could rely on me. Yes, I should have checked. I should have checked the message. I should have asked, but I didn't. I made a mistake."

"Whose message? Who told you?"

He looked at me very thoughtfully. "I'm not saying Rachel. No, I'm not saying. I'm not going to tell you or anyone. I'm not going to get that person into trouble. After all, I should have checked. I thought it was quite explicit, but looking back perhaps I misunderstood. Yes, I should have checked. I should have asked you whether that was what you wanted." He wiped his brow with his hand and I noticed perspiration. He put his hands on my shoulders.

"I love you Rachel. I wanted to show you that. Can't you see? It was a crazy thing to do. I'm not saying that I haven't killed a man before, but at a party with everyone there? And I've got a way with it. I've got away with it. It's a beautiful piece of work – no one will ever suspect. I made it look perfectly natural. I'm good at my job, but I'm not good with my feelings; I'm quite a shy man."

Then he began to talk and he couldn't stop. He kept talking, in an impossible hushed whisper and I caught this word and that. "I don't tell people what I feel. Why should I? Does anyone do that? I don't have much respect for people who do, I can tell you. I'm a shy person, and I can tell that you are too. The way you get undressed and kneel in front of that dwarf, Le Comte. I hope you won't mind that I call him a dwarf, because he is just that. No disrespect, but he doesn't deserve you. The way you take off your clothes and kneel in front of him. It's the shyest way of making love I've ever seen, but it's very beautiful. You don't mind that I say that do you? I suppose I shouldn't have told you that I've been watching you. I should have kept it to myself that I've been among the trees outside your window. You didn't see me among the shadows. You are beautiful Rachel. Please let me hold you."

He didn't wait for an answer. He just put his arms around me and I imagined him and David outside our window in that friendly darkness marked by strong, tactile shadows cast by trees and bushes, the home of owls, foxes and all those scampering creatures who like the dark.

"Did you see anyone else in the bushes?"

"Anyone else? What are you talking about? I think I would have broken anyone else's neck. No, there wasn't anyone else."

"And you stood there watching me. Watching us."

"Watching you do it to him was almost a religious experience."

"Really?"

"You had made it seem like a ritual."

"That doesn't sound very exciting."

"Well, it was." After a moment's silence, he coughed.

"You can laugh at that, can't you? A man has a wank and pilgrimage. I liked the way you did it, though I sometimes wanted to crush him. I wish you'd asked me to kill Jules. Yes, that would have been altogether better, killing Jules." He laughed

"I didn't ask you to kill anyone."

"Sorry, my mistake. I hadn't forgotten. I just got carried away, carried away with my imaginings." From outside came the sound of voices and I could hear words and phrases relating to the dead man, and already what had happened seemed inevitable. Someone called my name, but George held my shoulders firmly with one hand and placed the other over my mouth; his hands, his killer hands and for a moment I was back with Tina aged five saying, my dad has killer hands.

"You are very beautiful. I hope you don't mind my saying. Everyone here has eyes for Tina. I don't understand that. She is cheap compared to you. She's just sex. You are more than sex – much more if you can understand a man saying that. The way you kiss that dwarf and kneel in front of him."

"Who gave you that message? Who told you I wanted this to happen?"

"I'm not telling. No, I'm not telling. I made a mistake. I can't even remember the words now, if I'm honest, and it wouldn't be a professional thing to do. It would be like shifting the blame, and I'm not in to doing that, whatever other people may do. I should have checked; yes, I should have checked. I should have come and asked you to make sure that I'd heard right, but I was so keen to do the right thing, what you wanted. Also, a shyness comes over me sometimes when I see you. I can't explain that, and you'll have to take it on trust, this shyness thing. I can't change anything now, but nothing is going to happen to you or to anyone here. He was a right bastard the way he cheated you, all wrapped up in himself and not a poet at all. He just had you pouring money into the Well of Arethusa and his big head. I know I shouldn't have an opinion about poetry, but I do read some sometimes, now and then. I have a good ear for sound and he wasn't a poet, whatever Tina says; and it seems funny that she should be so certain of it. Sometimes I thought that that was the only thing she was sure of in the world, that he was a poet. A funny thing to be so sure of, but that is the way some women are, and you'll have to hand it to them, because it *is* something, although they shouldn't be so stubborn when they get it wrong. They are mad for the idea of a man and they'll hang their life round an idea, however inappropriate. And he cheated you asking for all that money; and he didn't use all of it on Arethusa. Oh, no. He's bought himself a car, or two, and watches and jewellery for Tina. Don't you ever look at your bank statements? You'll get a shock when you do. He and Jules have fleeced you. Did you know *he* used to have women in Rome? *Any* woman he could pick up, or that I could pick up for him. That was part of my job, to pick up women for Jules."

I'd never heard him say so much.

Outside two people were approaching the ambulance carrying a stretcher between them.

"Kiss me Rachel, kiss me," he whispered. "Please kiss me."

"And did you?" asked Mo, rising suddenly from the bed heading for the fridge and returning with a lump of cheese. The only thing left, I suspect. It's amazing what young people can eat.

"Did you?"

"Did I what?"

"Kiss him?"

"Kiss him? I don't remember. I might have. Not long after I sold everything. I had to. He was right. They had fleeced me. With what little I had left I bought this palace, my new residence and I have lived here ever since. Mostly on my own. But if you will stay a little longer," I added reaching for his hand because suddenly I didn't want to be just me; me alone in this house of unkempt memories and sad passions, "if you stay a little longer, I'll tell you the rest of the story of Max. The bit they didn't make into a film. The bit you won't know."

"I'm not in a hurry," he replied. "Not at the moment, anyhow. Will I discover who made George kill Paul?"

"Maybe. You never know."

17

Breakfast in via Giulia

"What are you thinking about when you kiss me?" asked Mary leaning on the pillows drinking orange juice and looking greedily at the breakfast tray: croissants, cakes, fresh fruit, coffee and juice.

"When?"

"Just now."

"Just now I thought about the river Neva, Saint Petersburg, and the ice in the river Neva. In winter the Neva is a slurry of ice and mud. I dreamt about that ice. It was a bad night. A very bad night."

"And before?"

"Before? Before I thought of lots of women," replied Max truthfully. "I thought of lots of women and the feel of lots of women – I thought that memory is a funny thing because I couldn't really remember the lots of women, except perhaps Eva. You know Eva. She is very stupid and wouldn't hurt a fly. I tried very hard to think of women, but I couldn't – I thought of you."

"But you thought of lots of women first?"

"Tried to. Tried to, but couldn't." Max yawned. Things were not really working out: he felt tired, too tired. Among the pillows he felt something hard, his mobile. "Fuck my dick," thought Max, "it's a flaccid thing. The only hard thing in this bed is this machine, though Eva could do it. Yes, Eva could do it. She can work miracles with my dick. Her laughter in that bed. Her reflection in the mirror surrounded by cherubim. Christ, young people are too serious."

"A real rat phoned me," he explained his sad humour, loss of words, lack of lust and the disappearance of whatever had been, "a real rat called Boris. You wouldn't like to meet him. You wouldn't like to meet Boris."

"Perhaps . . ." whispered Mary, instinctively sensual as if the night had done something to her.

"What is it with women?" thought Max, "She was half asleep. It was a failure, even by my standards. My standards sometimes," he corrected himself, "sometimes. I *can* do good sex. Very good sex. But I can't when I'm thinking about Boris, not when I'm thinking about Boris and my mobile, and the whole hell-hole of things, the sea of events, the cacophony of experience, the triumph of the enemy – my enemies. Yes, my enemies. All of them on the march. A host of deadly rats."

"Perhaps what, my princess?" asked Max pouring himself a cup of coffee remembering all the things he used to feel when he called her a princess, but not quite feeling them.

"Perhaps I could talk to him?" she laughed, playing with the mobile.

"Talk to Boris? You must be mad. No one can talk to that rat. No one can talk to Boris." But drinking coffee he dialled, "Hullo Boris. Hullo Boris, the rat. *My* rat. Every man has his own rat. His own personal rat. How is the Neva? How is the old Neva, old rat? Remember how we used to drown people in the Neva? Well not people, just one person. A person. Not much of a person. Not by *our* reckoning, anyhow. Happy days, eh Boris? Those were happy days. Now Mary wants to say hullo. Say hullo Mary."

"Hullo Boris."

"You have to say more than that. Hullo Boris, that's no conversation."

"How are you?" asked Mary very shy, very prim, all her courage gone. "How are you?"

Stretching out her legs, she knocked over the coffee pot and she began to giggle. "How are you? I've just knocked over the coffee. We are having breakfast in bed, in the biggest bed in the world. And it's in Rome. The room is full of really old things. It's like a fairy tale. And I wish you were having breakfast with us because there is lots and lots. Cakes and everything. I love cakes."

"I wish I were," replied Boris, "I wish I were with you instead of in Saint Petersburg, but I don't like cakes. But you could save me a kiss. Just a little kiss, Max won't miss that. How old are you Mary?"

"Fourteen. Fourteen very soon."

"Oh," said Boris and was silent.

"You shouldn't have said that," said Max feeling the weight of the furniture in the room and the absence of Boris which could be worse than his presence, or at least as bad. His absence made you see him, smell him, feel him. Max saw the room in Saint Petersburg and Boris lying on the chaise longue. The flat had undergone many changes since he had first visited it long ago, before the fall of the Soviet Union. A curious opulence had invaded the small set of rooms since Boris had begun to deal in furniture. A chair here, a couple of chest of drawers and writing tables there, and in the larger of the rooms, from which you could see the Neva, an elegant chaise longue upholstered in yellow with a design depicting flowers and birds in a vaguely oriental landscape. By the window, a huge ornamental Chinese vase with dried flowers and a Pembroke table.

With closed eyes Max tried to recall the detail, the feel and grain of the wood; the birds, were they mythological or real? Was there only one, or several Chinese vases? Was there an enormous grandfather clock in the kitchen which had still retained its old-fashioned large white sink, and fifties gas cooker standing full square out from the wall as if embedded in the linoleum?

Boris didn't care for comfort, didn't have a mania for re-decorating, or display anything for effect, and was almost the opposite of Eva who touchingly filled her rooms with anything that was soft, opulent or sentimental. Anything that gleamed, swung or curled took her fancy, and Max would buy it for her: bears and cherubim, things that cost nothing and things that cost more than she could ever imagine, or understand. She never asked about the price, but she knew how to admire and desire, when in the mood.

"My mother would have loved that. My friend Hannah would have killed for that." Some of the things Hannah would have killed for were cheap and tawdry and made even Max feel a little ashamed, while others came from *that auction*. A chance catalogue had alerted Eva to *that auction* and made her fall in love with a doll's house, an intricate and realistic creation with a chest of drawers that opened, carved beds and chandeliers. It had been a surprise long ago, in the olden days, Max explained, for princess Alice, the youngest child of a frumpy old queen. Eva didn't understand history, didn't like history, and had a strange animosity for the subject as if it might go away, if sufficiently ignored, like so much in life. Like most things in fact, with the exception, of course, of men. Men didn't go away, they just came and went. Individually they disappeared, but their betrayals remained, a steady flow of them. Their betrayals came and went. Max found it strange that someone as uncerebral as Eva should have reduced all her men, her many lovers, to an abstract noun. Betrayal. Men meant betrayal.

Otherwise, Eva didn't generalise about anything, couldn't understand anything except in the mad riot of particulars. Her days were full of attention to useless detail. She was drawn to facials, hairdressers and shopping arcades. Yet this same Eva could, when the mood took her, discuss *angst* with an intensity worthy of whoever had first coined that word. And this Eva, the Eva of angst, would sit in the middle of Max's huge bed, naked in the lotus position crying her eyes out, or stiff as a statue, talking endlessly or saying nothing. She was inconsolable and she would make quite clear to Max that there was nothing he could do, nothing at all except listen and wait. He was good at listening and waiting. He knew that when Eva was in the grip of angst, she wouldn't accept that he might understand. He couldn't make her feel that he was standing next to her, sharing her view of the abyss. He was helpless and he knew that none of his offerings would be accepted. Not even Goering's bear. He'd tried that, the much coveted bear from *that* catalogue, but she'd hurled the catalogue at the mirror when he'd reminded her that he had bought it and that it would be arriving soon, in time for her birthday.

"I don't want that stupid bear. I don't want it any more. Bet Soothby, your friend Soothby gave it to you as a frisbee because you buy so much."

"Freebee. And it's Sotheby's, but who cares."

He knew she didn't mean it, that she would welcome the bear. Her eyes were already on the picture in the catalogue which lay open on the floor. Her mood was changing. She no longer sounded so convinced although he was still hearing the same old phrases between the sobs: nothing, nobody, when would she meet a real human being, someone to talk to?

What was it with women, wondered Max, that they so needed to share their thoughts and feelings? It was the sort of stuff best reserved for the privacy of books. Or, if you were on a lesser scale, like Max himself, you did it with dignity, in the common way, and went to Mass. Max had been to Mass in every capital in Europe, but Eva wasn't a Catholic. She didn't understand much, and she didn't believe in anything.

"Boris," said Max suddenly and for no reason because he didn't think so, "Boris understands women."

"I am not," said Mary with the uncompromising clarity of an adolescent, "a woman."

"What are you then?"

"I'm a child."

"Stuff and nonsense," shouted Max grabbing a croissant and touching Mary's face. What a beautiful face, the most beautiful face. Yes, the most beautiful face. She was beautiful like a statue or a painting is beautiful.

"Stuff and nonsense," he said. "There was an adult lurking in you the moment you were born, the moment you clapped eyes on the world. I bet you lay in the womb whispering difficult words. Ineluctable. You were lying in the womb thinking about ineluctable and you sat there in your high chair smearing breakfast all over the chair and your face, just like now but thinking things no one could guess. There is croissant in your hair, and marmalade on your lips, and your breasts and your legs are covered in crumbs. Why there is coffee on your toes! How did you do it? This old gargoyle could lick the marmalade off your lips and suck the coffee off your toes while you are seeing things that he doesn't, and never will do, although he's very old and knows things about the world that you won't ever, because there is an adult lurking in you somewhere, a dead scary adult."

"As scary as Boris?"

No, scarier than Boris. Sometimes. Only sometimes, because Boris can be the scariest thing in the world when he's whispering that it's curtains, that it's curtains for Max. Now tell me, tell me: would you like a facial *or* Goering's bear?"

"What?"

"There you are, the only answer, the only adult answer: what? But Eva has a different answer. Yes, she would like a facial *and* Goering's bear, but not the bear now. Oh, no the bear has to wait till she's in the mood. In Goering's bear mood. Everything must wait for her mood. The earth moves around the sun, but only when she's in the mood. She's got infallibility like the pope."

Mary laughed. She couldn't stop laughing. Max looked so funny sucking her toes and she enjoyed listening to him talk.

Laughing, she looked round the room. There was the bed with its breakfast things spread all over it, the huge window with the curtains a little parted, the shutters drawn, letting in a wonderful light, and the sound of bells. So this was what it meant to be an adult. The old man was a fool and harmless.

Many years later, she thought differently. Long after the-last-person-he'd-expected-would-do-it had put a bullet in Max's brain, she thought differently. She had by then become a very quiet person and journalists found her difficult and a little annoying. Mary thought for a long time before she gave very short answers. She was a thin, spinsterish woman whom most people thought dressed oddly, and she seemed to take every-thing you said very seriously. She failed to understand that no one wanted any answers to their questions, but just a bit of gossip because Max had made her a very rich woman. He'd made sure of that before the bullet got lodged in his brain, but Mary didn't pretend to understand why that was so. Many found her immature, naive, a child almost. She didn't seem to get that her age at the time made her story interesting, as well as the fact that there hadn't been any men since. There had only been Max.

"Do you think he destroyed your sexuality? "

"I don't know. I haven't really considered that. But he was, in his way," she offered as an explanation, a timid explanation, "a little charismatic and he could be funny, in an anarchic sort of way which appealed to me then. I suppose it appeals to me now too, but he wasn't nearly as complicated as I thought. No, in some ways he was very simple, and it was his apparent complexity which drew me, but it's all such a long time ago. I thought he was very old – but of course he wasn't. He can only have been in his early forties when he died. When I met him he'd only just discovered that he wasn't what he called *indeboondable* and that gave him another dimension which lent him something. " The journalists didn't think that was much of an answer. Was he depraved? Mary didn't know. They suspected she didn't care.

Eva was much more communicative. Older, plumper and wiser she enjoyed interviews and wrote a book called *Being a Gangster's Moll, My Story by Eva*. "He gave me everything I wanted. He just adored me. "Eva," he used to say, "you *are* love. I *need* you." He had a great need for love, for affection. I suppose he was insecure and that's why he loved power, but he needed *me*. I'm not saying he was faithful. I don't think he really understood the meaning of that word, though he would have argued that he was, basically, in his way. I don't know about Mary – he only spent a few days with her. In Rome I think. Of course, he liked schoolgirls. All men do. I have no idea why he left her all that money. Makes no sense, no sense at all, except as a last minute thought, just before he died. He was full of last minute thoughts and sudden splurges. But he treated me like a goddess: he would buy me *anything* and get me anything I asked for if I told him that I *really* wanted it. He once bought me diamond earrings and a matching necklace with ruby hearts; another time, a doll's house that had belonged to a princess, and Judy Garland's pyjamas. Just before he died, he bought me a bear that had belonged to Mussolini, or someone-or-other. Someone who was really famous and bad. I can't remember who. It was someone really, really wicked, but I liked it because it was missing one eye. When I saw it in the catalogue I thought, "I really want that bear with only one eye because it's like me, it's been hurt and damaged like me. Men don't see that, they only look at my tits and my arse. Arse and tits. They don't see my one eye. No one sees my one eye." So, as soon as I saw it, I wanted it. I didn't tell him why. He wouldn't have understood. And he like, "Eva you can have *anything*, I will buy you *anything* . . ."

But all that was many years later.

18

Afternoon

Later in the day, one of Max's minders took Mary to the airport. She was wearing a large hat that Max had bought her and a very elegant red dress. In her hand she held a thick book full of photographs of Rome. Deferentially, the minder carried what luggage she had, as well as a present for Mary's mother. On the plane she read her book, closing her eyes now and then to see their midnight walk, and their room in via Giulia. She saw fountains, Piazza Navona full of people, narrow streets with moonlight and Max's cragged face. She wondered whether sex would be very different when she did it properly, with someone her own age. She wasn't going to discover this, because there was only going to be Max, but she wasn't to know that. She didn't think about Boris or the senator, and she tried her very best to ignore the large, square man who was sitting behind and who paid for everything. And for the first time in her life she realised that she was beautiful. She looked in the mirror which she took out of the elegant handbag Max had bought her, and she saw that she was beautiful. If she had been able to see the future, she would have seen that she would remain beautiful: very elegant, although a little wistful perhaps. She would become a famous photographer and would never really need Max's money, but he wasn't to know that. When she arrived at Heathrow journalists appeared from nowhere and took photographs. They asked questions she didn't want to understand, and even less to answer.

Meanwhile Max walked around Rome, his body heavy with the debris of the night and lack of sleep. He was walking aimlessly but his minders imposed a sort of purpose and shape to his wandering by asking him where he was going. He didn't know, but from time to time he muttered the names of streets or buildings, and they slipped in around him forming a protective shield, guiding his steps to places he didn't really want to go. There were three of them: one in front, one behind and one not quite by his side but close; too close. "I don't know," thought Max, "what they mean by the loneliness of power. A fiction that. A big lie. There is no fuckin' loneliness, and no fuckin' being alone."

"Let's all have a drink," he announced in a hasty whisper and they looked at him surprised; Max didn't drink, but they didn't say a word. "I know a bar by the Colosseum. It's a crap place, and I can't stand the Colosseum, but I used to work there once. Long ago when I was a waiter. It's got good memories even if I don't like the view."

Memories: life dealt in them. Italians dealt in them – sold them to you by the lorry load, and before you knew it you were back there with them, back with your memories older, unhinged and unfocused perhaps, but back there reliving or trying to relive something. And the *something* always took you by surprise: it had more to offer than you had suspected, long forgotten smells, voices, faces and unnecessary details which you had thankfully forgotten. "The past," thought Max, "I hate it." Standing by the bar waiting for the drinks he'd ordered, and which seemed to take an eternity – that is the problem with alcohol, once you decide you want it, you want it *now*, you even want the *next* drink now and the one after that – he thought about the past, the distant past, Max the waiter. It had all been rather drab really working here, and the young man who threw the drinks on the table and told him that he came from Sweden, didn't look too happy either. "The owner is a real bugger." Well, things hadn't changed.

"You're sure you want that?" whispered George politely. George had been with Max for several years and he was perfect for the job, but Max didn't trust him, and he therefore felt annoyed.

"Sometimes I drink."

"No, you don't. You don't drink Max and, if you don't mind my saying so, that's very wise of you. A man in your position can't afford to drink."

"A man in my position does what the fuck he likes."

"If you don't mind my saying . . ."

"I do. I do mind you saying. Just shut up and have your drink and enjoy the view of the Colosseum."

They sat down at a table by the window and Max fixed his eyes on a horse and carriage full of sightseers. The horse was wearing a bright red plume and one of the children, dressed as a gladiator, was waving his sword at another gladiator, a fat Roman dressed up with a sign in front of him inviting the passers-by to be photographed with him. A Japanese family arranged themselves around him and had their photograph taken. He looked triumphant. A middle-aged woman entered dressed as a gypsy, dressed too perfectly to be anything but a fraud. She was selling roses by the stem wrapped in silver foil and offering to tell people's fortune. A very lean and melancholy greyhound was following her closely; it showed a persistent interest in the bottoms of Max's trousers. Thoughtfully Max finished his whisky, patted the dog and ordered another.

"I used to do the dogs. Dogs and horses when I was young. Particularly dogs; I was always putting money on dogs. I'm a born gambler and my granddad had dogs, four greyhounds, vicious beasts but great runners. So I knew about dogs and I was always betting on dogs. One of my happiest days was winning a hundred and fifty quid on a dog called More Simple Simon. They gave them crazy names. The people who owned the dogs, understood nothing but dogs. Dogs and football." Max smiled drinking less slowly. The gypsy, who was as much a gypsy as her friend by the Colosseum was a gladiator, placed a red rose by Max's glass and held out her hand. "Pay her," he whispered to his minders addressing them as a crowd. "More Simple Simon did me proud, odds of fifteen to one and I watched him coming in, knowing he would come in, and feeling that I was at the beginning of something. And I was. More Simple Simon launched me in to my peculiar life with a hundred and fifty quid, sent me on my way. Even Jason, my brother was impressed. And it wasn't easy to impress my brother, with his escort agency and his style. Jason always had style, knew how to dress, and how to speak. You've been with me to his house in Hampstead. You wouldn't believe he came from a council estate; or that he was my brother. He's a prick and a dick-head, but he's got style and he's got height. He isn't exactly tall, but he *is* normal. He walks around Hampstead talking art and his partner is a sculptor. He's famous and has exhibited everywhere. I think Eva made better things when she went to evening classes run by a retired art teacher in Lewisham. Anyhow, no one nominated Eva for any prizes, and she didn't call anything she made Conceptions or If. They were called Frog or Dog, and the most abstract was a piece of two people called Happiness."

George leant over, placing his hand on Max's arm, but Max asked the waiter for another drink and continued. The two other minders sat in silence, each with a glass of wine. In the centre of the table was a plate with a small pizza cut into four slices. Max helped himself.

"Do you mind if I just phone Eva? Hullo Eva. No, don't worry about Boris. Don't worry about anything. I'll be back soon. I'm just seeing a few people in Rome and then I'm back. I'm sitting here in front of the Colosseum and it's fucking big. I've bought you a rose."

Eva put the telephone in its cradle and tried to imagine Max in front of the Colosseum. She had been to Rome and had seen the Colosseum. She had sat by that very window, and she guessed that was where Max was. She knew whom he would be with: George, Martin and Rory. A silent wall of muscle to protect Max. A wall of muscle who gave her the creeps. She had seen them in action once when someone had attempted to burgle their house. Slowly Eva rose from her chair, looked out of the window and decided that the pool was inviting. Sitting by the edge she dangled her toes in the water thoughtfully, wondering why Max had let himself become so drunk. It was unlike him. In her hand her mobile moved.

"Heya, Eva." She didn't answer.

"Heya Eva, you cunt, I've been trying to get hold of Trevor. I need the special number you've got for him. I know you've got it, so give it me. Understand?" Eva switched her mobile off. She had talked enough to Boris. Boris was a rat. Where was Trevor? Where was Trevor the chauffeur, the most human thing about Max? The only human thing about Max? Eva looked at her feet and felt a sudden certainty. "I knew," she was to say later, "I knew that he wouldn't return. I sat by the pool crying because I knew he wouldn't return. That it was the last time I would ever speak to him. Suddenly I knew he wouldn't return, and I also knew how much he meant to me."

In Rome, Max helped himself to a second slice of pizza and decided what he wanted to do: he wanted to see Leonardo, his old friend Leonardo who had a jewellery shop not far from the Colosseum. Leonardo whom he had known since he was young, who had watched and assisted Max's ascent. Leonardo the money-launderer, the jeweller, the friend. Good for a laugh.

"I must go to the loo," said Max.

A few minutes later he dashed through the familiar kitchen and out into the street. Down a few roads, away from the Colosseum, down via Capo d'Africa with its dull buildings, and then into Leonardo's shop. It had a small but impressive display of very expensive jewellery and Max had to press a bell to enter.

"*Sono un amico di Leonardo.*"

From the back, from a room which Max knew so well, came Leonardo's voice, "*entra.*"

Max sighed. Everything was going to be all right. No one like Leonardo for building your confidence. Max opened the door slowly hoping to find what he did: Leonardo behind a small desk covered by a piece of red material, a pair of tweezers in one huge hand, his elbow resting on the silk. In the other hand he held a special contraption to decide the worth of each stone. Leonardo concentrating on his fine craft, his special talent: assessing the carat of diamonds. Three tiny heaps in front of him. Slowly he lowered the tweezers and gave Max that welcoming smile he knew so well.

"Max!"

He hadn't changed, except as Max had expected him to change. Age had done exactly what you would have expected it to do: it had enhanced his nose which had always been one of his strong features, drawn a few rivers towards his mouth and made that a little fleshier, thicker lipped. Age, in Max's experience, took most people to a foreign land, but with Leonardo it seemed a natural continuation. Had he been sitting at this table for all these years, twenty at least, scrutinising diamonds and making deals?

"What brings you here?"

Max sat down, picked up some of the diamonds and let them fall through his hand back into their heap, their little mountain.

"Still diamonds?"

"Of course, but you know that. Still the same contacts in old Antwerp, but you know that. Remember your trips to Vestingstraat with diamonds in your pocket?"

Leonardo smiled and Max saw behind that smile the same feelings, the same animation that he had known more than twenty years earlier: the youth who had introduced him to the diamond trade. He had gone to Antwerp for Leonardo, old Antwerp as they call the district of diamond dealers, and from there to various shops in Hatton Gardens.

"You know my business. The same as ever. Leonardo's business. The same clients. Different names, same clients. The more things change, the more they remain the same. But you know that; all old men know that. I'm still looking at diamonds; the world is still looking at diamonds."

"Yes."

"And I have been following you. News and gossip reach Leonardo. They tell me you are a rotten apple Max."

"They've always said that. Some people have rotten apple written on them from birth, and others haven't."

"Still jealous Max? Still jealous of Jason?"

"Jason? I forgot you met him."

"I did. He came to Rome and I looked him up in London. I even used his agency once, but I was disappointed." Leonardo laughed.

" People are wrong," thought Max. "People are wrong when they say that all that sustains one is hope. I've given up on hope years ago. Hope is a dead thing." "Finally," continued Max wondering why his thoughts were returning to Eva; after all, he'd left Eva, he'd long left Eva, "finally I will be able to tell Eva when she is in search for *the human*, as she calls it, when she asks what *is* human about me , what *is* human about me apart from Trevor, apart from Trevor my chauffeur – though his *human* is a fat lot less impressive than she thinks, a fat lot less impressive. I'll place my bottom dollar on that, on him being the crap we're all made of. But laughter, there you've got it. There you've got the human, as Eva calls it. Leonardo's laughter. Leonardo the old swine, wheeler-dealer, diamond–monger, and blackmailer. Yes, his laughter. His laughter in the dark."

Carefully with his tweezers Leonardo picked up another diamond. "You know what they mean when they say a rotten apple." He put down the diamond. He sighed. His laughter was all gone. "You know what they mean, Max."

"Yes, I do."

"They mean a dead man. They mean a dead man walking. Why are you a dead man, Max? I want to know. I want to help you."

"It's a long story."

"It always is. Tell Leonardo."

"There is no point. I don't even know it myself."

"One never does. Never completely, but tell me what you can. Tell me what you want." A diamond fell carefully discarded into its heap.

"I just lost control. I don't know when. I'm not even sure *where*. Did I lose control in New York? Or did it happen in London, Saint Petersburg, Antwerp or Buenos Aires? Where did it first happen? Where? It hasn't happened yet in Rome. In Rome they still think . . . ."

"They suspect, Max. They suspect. And what is this?" Leonardo pointed to an Italian paper folded up on the floor and Mary's face. She was in Piazza Navona drinking her cocktail and next to her Max, a tired Max. "What is this? She looks twelve."

"Almost fourteen. Next week. Fourteen next week."

"Max – what made you take her to Piazza Navona?"

"And what made them take pictures? They wouldn't have a few years ago."

"But they will now. And it will be all over the English papers."

"I know Leonardo. I know now, but some times someone like me needs people to tell them what they can get away with and what they can't. Because one loses sight. Yes, one loses sight." And Max thought back to the evening, only a few days ago, when he'd taken Mary to the theatre, and he remembered thinking just that, that he, Max, needed someone to tell him what he could and couldn't get away with, and of course Trevor had tried to tell him that as he made love to her in the car.

"It's ridiculous," whispered Max in a flat voice. "It really is ridiculous."

"Yeah, you can drown people in the Tiber or the Neva . . ."

"You know about the Neva?"

"A guess Max, a lucky guess. I thought it would be you. When he disappeared, I thought it would be you."

"That's a long time ago, a very long time ago."

"But it's still true: you can make people disappear into the Tiber or the Neva, but there are other things you can't do. Much more common things that you can't do."

"And all of that is a long time ago."

"But this is today. This is what is in the Italian papers today, and tomorrow it'll be in the English papers." He shook his head, "She *looks* twelve but *really* she is fourteen. Next week. Fourteen *next week*. You look fifty. Fifty this week. And you'll look worse next week. What is wrong with you Max?"

"What is wrong with me? With *me* . . ."

Leonardo laughed, "Stop it Max. Just stop it Max."

Max didn't answer. He knew that Leonardo was right: people like him had forfeited indignation a long time ago. A very long time ago.

"So it'll be all over the papers, but I'll handle it. It'll disappear from the papers. I'll make it disappear. You make things disappear. It's easy."

"Is it?"

"You know it is . . ."

"Sometimes."

"You'll see."

"Why are you here alone Max? You shouldn't travel alone. You *don't* travel alone. And you *don't* drink."

"I still don't drink."

"You are drunk Max. You're drunk and alone. Why?"

Suddenly Max did the unexpected, and the unexpected, when it happened, seemed something entirely natural; even Leonardo did not look surprised. Max cried. Steadying himself on the desk with his short sturdy arms and big hands, Max cried. He wondered whether his tears were due to drink or whether crying was the thing to do, the thing you had to do because of fate, fate the *ineluctable*. It didn't matter much.

"Be careful Max. You shouldn't have come here alone."

"I don't need George and his gang. Not right now."

"Get them to come here. Get them to come here and pick you up."

"I don't want them, Leonardo. I want to be on my own, I don't want George. I can't stand George."

Leonardo opened the safe behind him and put away his diamonds.

"You need someone Max. You can't walk the streets of Rome alone."

"I can't walk the streets anywhere alone."

"Do any of us do that? Come on Max."

Max sighed. Fate the ineluctable. It was time to meet fate the ineluctable. Leonardo didn't understand. No one understood.

"I'm going, Leonardo. Good to see you again after all those years. Good to see you still at your diamonds. I would stay for longer, but I have to go." He got up slowly steadying himself. Had he drunk more than he thought? Why was he so drunk? He must have forgotten to eat, but he remembered having had breakfast. Croissants with Mary. He could hear her laughter

180

and he could see her lying in the bed dropping flakes of pastry everywhere and overturning cups, saucers and finally the coffee pot. What a wonderful mess, what a fantastic mess, what a God-given mess, even her toes covered in coffee and jam, and the light streaming in through the window which she had opened, and he had let her. A bit careless that. From outside, the sound of bells which had kept him awake all night, but which sent Mary into some sort of ecstasy. It awakened something in her, and she jumped off the bed and did an energetic dance with a doily, which she had found on the breakfast tray, on her head. "There is nowhere as beautiful as Rome. I'm mad about Rome. Shall we come again? Will you take me again?"

"Definitely," Max replied stretching his legs, resting his tired body amongst the chaos of the bed. "Anywhere else you would like to go?"

"New York, Paris, Moscow and Cardiff." She lay down on the floor throwing the doily at him and lifted her legs into the air folding them behind her neck so that her feet stuck out on either side of her head like comic ears. "My trick. Very few people can do that. Bet you never could." She laughed unselfconsciously.

"No," said Max, "my body was always the wrong shape. Legs and arms too short."

"A dwarf."

"You could say that."

She laughed and undid her legs.

"I could eat more breakfast. Lots and lots more. Ring for more."

He did. And she ate it all, down to the last drop of apricot jam . . . She must be in London by now. Eyes closed, still seeing Mary and hearing her laughter, Max continued to steady himself, preparing to leave.

"I must go," he repeated.

"Suit yourself, Max, suit yourself," replied Leonardo

stretching his arms out wide and turning his palms up to make clear to Max that he wasn't stopping him.

"You can stay as long as you like, and you can go when you like."

"I'm going," said Max.

"I would ask someone to come with you," said Leonardo, but Max had already closed the door.

In London Eva got out of the swimming pool and wrapped herself in a large soft towel. Then she took out her mobile.

"Hullo Max," whispered Eva, "I've heard from Boris, and I was wondering . . ."

But it was George who answered. "Shut up Eva," said George.

"What are you doing with Max's mobile?"

He didn't answer and Eva knew that there was something very wrong, and she began to suspect with hideous clarity that the worst that could happen was already happening. *Was already happening* – yes, she had always known that one day it was going to be like that: one day *already happening* would hit you like a wave and you'd be drowning, and the day was *today*. Eva sat down very carefully steadying herself like Max far away in Leonardo's room. She didn't cry, but sitting very still she did her statue trick.

"Sorry to disturb," said a young man. So many people worked for Max that Eva didn't quite recognise him. Robert she thought his name might be. "I'm sorry, but there is some-one here. Someone from Sotheby's. They are delivering something. They say it's a bear."

"Tell them to bring it in. I'm coming."

"I can tell them to take it away again," said the young man eager to please noticing her flat voice, "I can tell them it's not convenient. That it's the wrong time."

The wrong time. Eva closed her eyes. She was in a church, it must have been for a funeral – Eva didn't go to church.

Someone was saying that there was a right time for everything. A right time to sow and a right time to reap. There was
a long list of right times. And the length made it sound good,
but in Eva's experience life hardly ever dealt in right times, it
was almost always the *wrong time*.

"No, tell them to bring it in. It's a special bear. It belonged
to some Hun. Attilla, I think, but I'm not sure."

"Attilla?"

"Probably, but no one is sure. It's not the sort of thing you
are ever sure about."

They unwrapped it very carefully and placed it on a table.
With its one eye the bear looked at Eva.

Max stepped out into the street. He felt in his pocket for his
mobile and noticed that it wasn't there. He felt again to make
quite sure, and, when he had, he looked straight ahead, the
way you do when you realise that you know everything there
is to know.

19

Evening

He decided that he wanted to walk towards the Pantheon. He didn't quite know why he wanted this bit of purpose. He remembered evenings spent in the square of the Pantheon with its dome, grand inscription and huge Roman bronze doors still in their place. He remembered sitting on the lip of the fountain in front of the Pantheon smoking cigarettes and scooping up water with the hollow of his hand to cool his head on warm summer evenings.

Facing the fountain was a large old-fashioned hotel and he knew the owner. Fondly, he remembered how well he knew him. Perhaps he could stay the night? Perhaps? No, he was sure he would be able to stay. It wouldn't be a problem. Things were only a problem if you thought they were. He didn't have a mobile. Why was that a problem? He must have dropped it. Perhaps Boris had snatched it! Perhaps he had flown over and snatched it from Max's pocket. He imagined Boris flying through the air and laughed.

Avoiding the grand main street, via dei Fori Imperiali, with its views of the Roman remains – squares, triumphal arches, columns, and extraordinary edifices erected by mad emperors hungry for glory – Max stepped cautiously into side streets. He moved slowly: there was no need for hurry now. He needed time to think, but he wasn't sure what he should be thinking about. He would go to the Pantheon, and Roberto would let him stay at the Abruzzi and then he would contact Trevor. There was nothing more to think about except Rome itself. Rome with its emperors and popes, its power-mad emperors and popes and their fountains and obelisks. Everywhere there was a hunger for glory. The city was infected by it. With a sudden surge of confidence he crossed via Cavour with its traffic and dipped into the labyrinth of smaller streets.

"It won't take long," thought Max. "I know all the side streets. I know . . ."

A car came up from behind, unexpected, as Max knew it would do, one day. Someone was standing in front of him and someone behind.

"Get into the car, Max."

Carefully ensuring that his belt would not get trapped in the door, Max got in. Careful does it. As long as something remains of whatever you were, you are still in the game. A very old rule that, and it has sustained people as long as there have been people. Cave men clung to it, the Christian martyrs clung to it, Galileo knew it, and lesser people, absolute rats like Max, scum like Max, they know it, too. Galileo whispered the truth, Max removed his belt. I am *me*, as long as I am *me*.

Someone was already on the back seat, and the someone was looking straight ahead in front of him and wouldn't look at Max. And the someone was Trevor.

"What are you doing here?"

"I'm sorry Max. I really am sorry."

"Sorry?"

"Of course I'm sorry. But you must understand. You must *understand* Max. I am so sorry. I didn't want this to happen I really didn't want this to happen. But what could I do? I mean, what could I do?"

"Try to make sense Trevor? What are you doing? Where are you taking me?"

"To the river, Max. We are taking you to the river. And I never thought . . . No, I never even dreamt. Why I have known you Max, I have known you . . ."

"Since childhood," supplied Max. "Since my lucky break on More Simple Simon. Since I was knee high to a grasshopper. You have known me as long as a man can know a man."

"Yes," sighed Trevor, "I have known you for all that time. I have known you as long as one can know a man and longer."

"Not longer Trevor, not longer," whispered Max, "but long enough. Quite long enough."

And Trevor did what was expected: he cried. Betrayal isn't easy. It isn't easy, but one does it; one does it because one is human. Betrayal *is* human. And somewhere in his head, but not quite in words, Trevor came to the conclusion that betrayal is *the human*. Tears covered his face, and he sobbed loudly.

"And what are we going to do by the river?" asked Max. "What are you going to do by the river?"

"You know," sobbed Trevor, "you *know* what we are going to do by the river, that fuckin' river, what its name?"

"Tiber, it's called the Tiber. *Tevere* in Italian."

"You *know* what we are going to do."

"I do. I know what you are going to do. I just wanted to hear you say it, Trevor. I just wanted to hear you say it." And then, "Are you sure you are going to do it, Trevor? Quite sure?"

Trevor didn't reply. He was quite sure. He knew he was sure because so much had happened, because Boris had the mobile, because Max had forgotten what he owed the Republicans, the President, and what he could and couldn't do. Christ, what had made him think he could openly have an affair with someone under age? Trevor didn't know the word ineluctable, didn't understand what Mary had been saying in the car about *fate the ineluctable,* but he knew, what he knew.

"I knew," he explained later to Eva, "that Max had to die because there was nothing else *for it*. And I'm the last one who wanted it to happen, the very last one, but why did he do all those things? All those crazy things? Why, what did he expect to happen?"

"He didn't," replied Eva firmly without doubt or hesitation, "expect *you* to kill him." "What else could have happened?" shouted Trevor waving his arms about, angered more by the firmness of her answer than by what she had said. Why wouldn't her pea-brain make any allowances, why wouldn't it make the same leaps his had? The leaps that ignored the one thing he hadn't told Eva, that Boris had told him to do it, to organise the doing of it *or else*.

They drove down the Corso Vittorio Emanuele with its busy evening traffic, down towards the river. They passed crowds of people walking towards Piazza Navona where the night before he had sat with Mary drinking a crazy cocktail with George discreetly a few tables away.

"Where *is* George and his gang?" asked Max.

"They have left you," replied Trevor. "They have left you Max. What else could they do? You thought you were escaping from them saying you needed the john, but they let you go. They let you go for us to pick you up. You didn't really think they fell for *that*, did you? George fall for, I need a toilet? George is clever, has much more brains than me. *I* wouldn't fall for that."

"Shut up," thought Max, "just shut up Trevor." But Trevor wanted to talk. Trevor couldn't stop talking. He talked, his face fixed on the windscreen, as if he were speaking to someone outside.

"Why did you suddenly want to see Leonardo? Why did you want to see that old guy still fencing his diamonds?"

"Because I did. Because he was a friend and because he knows how to laugh. I wanted to see his face and hear his laughter. Yes, that's all I wanted to do: to hear his laughter."

And suddenly life seemed to Max to be nothing but a long

journey to hear Leonardo's laughter. Everything else had been removed, picked off, discarded, everything but Leonardo's laughter.

"You two old has-beens," whispered Trevor to the windscreen, "you two has-beens getting together."

"I'm not *a has-been* yet. I'm not *a has-been*, Trevor, till you make me one. Not till you put that bullet in my head."

"Shut up," said Trevor, "shut up Max."

They were by the river now and there was less traffic and fewer people. Just past the island in the Tiber, they crossed to continue on the other bank. Everywhere became less busy; the green patches wider, the banks of the river darker.

"We are getting out now," said Trevor as the car slowed down. "We are getting out and walking down to the bank of the river."

There were only three of them. As they moved away from the path and crossed a sad patch of bushes full of discarded bottles and various debris, Max thought he recognised the other man. He thought it might be Ivan, one of Boris's friends who had given him an envelope during the interval of Hamlet. He hadn't opened the envelope and it was still in his pocket. It amused him to think that didn't matter any more.

"Hey Ivan, you know that envelope?"

"Yes?"

So it was Ivan. Young, red haired and strong. He had offered him and Mary champagne during the interval and Max had told him that he didn't drink. He still felt a little drunk. He must have drunk a hell of a lot. Thank God for that. Thank God for small mercies, as his mother used to say. Small mercies come at the end, at the very end. It amazed Max how you went on, how you continued till the very end, this babble of thoughts till the very end. He seemed to be stumbling over a phrase Mary had read to him: something or other till the last syllable of recorded time. Or was it *my* recorded time. Personal or impersonal? Max thought it was personal: till the last syllable of my recorded time. "*My* recorded time, you son of a bitch."

"Hey, Ivan," he shouted slipping amongst the bushes, "you know I never opened that envelope. Should I do so now? Want me to open the envelope?" He laughed trying to sound like Leonardo.

"Shut up," whispered Ivan. "Be quiet. There is nothing to talk about now. I have had enough listening to Trevor. I'm not listening to *you*."

"But I am talking," said Max, "I am talking and you can't shoot me here. You can't do it *yet*. And you'll have to listen."

"Tell us what you have got to say," whispered Trevor his voice full of emotion, full of those tears he had cried at the windscreen. "Tell us, Max."

"I want you to give something to that girl. To Mary."

"And Eva?"

"Let her keep the house, but make sure Mary gets something. She can have one of the Swiss bank accounts. Make sure she gets a Swiss bank account."

"Why do you care, Max? Why do you care what happens to Mary? Why you don't really *know* her. And you have had so many women. God, for a man your size you've had a lot of women."

"Thank you, Trevor."

"I don't get it, Max. Who cares about Mary?"

"I do. I don't know why but I do. I didn't two days ago, but I do now. Make sure she gets a Swiss bank account. The numbers are in the safe. You know where they are. You know where everything is. I trusted you, Trevor. I trusted *you*. Make sure she gets the one that ends with 78, Trevor. Make sure of that."

"Why do you care? Why does it matter? Nothing matters

anymore Max," shouted Trevor, angry with him for prolonging the interlude, for insisting that there *was* an interlude between being dead and about to die.

"It matters. It *does* matter. It matters till the end of my recorded . . ."

"You are not," said Ivan fiercely turning round suddenly, "recording *anything*."

"Not anything," repeated Trevor, "we are not having you recording anything."

They stopped. In front of them the river flowed darkly and the lights of the towpaths seemed far away, and although distant voices could be heard, one couldn't make out what anyone was saying.

"Time," whispered Max, "I was only recording time. *My* time. The last syllable of *my* time. My fuckin' time."

"Kneel," said Ivan.

"Oh, Max," whispered Trevor. "Oh, Max."

20
Epilogue

"And that," says Mo, "is how he died. That is how Max died. Did they find his body?"

"I don't know. I only know how he died. They'll have put him in the Tiber of course, so probably his body was found."

"And so all that's left of him is my tattoo. My tattoo of him and Eva, what did you call her? The melancholy whore?"

"That's what Max called her."

"Well here she is, and here he is, and there is his mermaid." He displays his buttock proudly pointing to each item. "I got a real artist to do it. Good isn't it."

"Beautiful. Had I known that what I wrote would become a tattoo . . ."

"You would have been flattered?"

"I would have been gobsmacked. Did it hurt?"

"Not much. They all hurt a little. All those needles, all those tiny pricking needles going into your skin. The first tattoo you ever have done is agony. Like childbirth. Then you get addicted."

"It's beautiful. I can't take my eyes off Max's mermaid with his dressing-gown slung over it, and there is Eva in her bed."

"Stop staring. Stop staring at my body, old bird. You look like an old bird. An old bird, like a heron; an old heron standing in a pool of water thinking of the past, reminiscing. A reminiscing bird carefully feeling its way down the river with a little bit of elegance still in its beak, still in its feathers, its walk, its curious eyes. Elegance clinging to it. But you shouldn't stare."

"I am sorry."

"Don't worry. It's time to get up anyway. Time to get up and go."

He lifts himself out of the bed and goes purposefully to his bundle of clothes lying on the floor. For the first time I notice how worn they are. Jeans, trainers, a top and his little rucksack for his personal possessions: a packet of cigarettes, a lighter and a wallet.

"I could do with a shower." Then, without waiting for an answer, he picks up his clothes; already his mind is changed.

"What did you say your name was?"

"Scheherazade."

"No, your real name."

"Rachel."

"And what did you say you were?"

"A bad picker of men."

"Yes, that was it: a bad picker of men. I thought that's what you said. Funny, some women are. Got any money? I mean just a little bit, just something you could spare. Enough for a couple of packets of fags. Whatever you want to give. As a friend, of course."

He's put his clothes on and stands in the middle of the room leaning on a bookcase.

"You never told me about all the photographs, but I suppose that can wait to another time." He is implying that the future is full of time. But I'm not fooled.

"You are going?"

"Suppose so. But I'll be back." Unembarrassed, his eyes search the possible places where I might have hidden my crumpled notes. My secret stores. "Scheherazade, what a name. How many stories did she tell?"

"A thousand and one; nine hundred and ninety nine more than me. And I have only got twenty pounds." I go to the obvious place, my purse, but a timid knock interrupts my action. And there, coming straight in, not waiting for an answer, is David. He's carrying a similar rucksack and has almost identical clothes, but he looks refreshed. Refreshed and happy.

"Aunty Rachel!" He takes off his rucksack and drops a

newspaper he's been carrying on the floor. "Aunty Rachel, you know I'm off to uni?" He barely breathes between words and I need only nod at questions. Yes, I know. David is off to study philosophy at Edinburgh. Of course I know. The student coming to say his goodbye. He ignores Mo, his sad double who picks up the paper and reads the front page.

"I'm off to uni, and well, I was well hoping . . ." Smiling he kisses me on the cheek.

"How's your mother?"

"Oh, I don't know. By the way do you ever hear from George?"

"George who?"

"George the crazy minder. *Your* crazy minder. Your minder from the days when you were rich." He lifts me up and hurls me round the room. What a dance!

"Ever hear from him?"

"No, why?"

"Why? Because there is something I must tell you. Something I've wanted to tell you: he was a complete maniac. Did you know that? A maniac. And dangerous. I mean *dangerous*. Really dangerous. Why he would take anything you said seriously. Anything. Why I once said something just as a joke you know, just as a joke. But perhaps I should tell you another time."

"Yes, another time."

But Mo isn't listening. Mo hasn't heard a word. His eyes are on the headline and the story: Tina Faithful has been evicted from the Big Brother house. There she is, legs apart, hair flying, all anger spent. Yes, there is a big smile on her face. She was Tina in the morning legs dangling, all those mornings ago, and she is Tina now. "I had a good time while it lasted," she says. Like Max, she forfeited indignation a long time ago. "I had a good time, and I don't regret it for a moment, though there were some real bitches in that house. Some real bitches."

Behind some books I find a bundle of notes. Amazing what I have hidden in these nooks and crannies for a rainy day. David stuffs them in his pocket pausing only just before heading for the door which he slams shut not looking back. And why should he? Behind the closed door is a middle-aged woman, her eyes still on his exit, listening to his footsteps tumbling down the stairs and the front door opening and shutting. Now he is outside, now on his way, now gone. Gone. Yes, gone.

Recommended Reading

If you enjoyed reading *The Dream Maker* there are other books on our list, which should appeal to you. If you like books with stories within stories and literary game playing, we recommend the following books:

Music, in a Foreign Language – *Andrew Crumey*
Pfitz – *Andrew Crumey*
D'Alembert's Principle – *Andrew Crumey*
The Arabian Nightmare – *Robert Irwin*
The Limits of Vision – *Robert Irwin*
Exquisite Corpse – *Robert Irwin*
Satan Wants Me – *Robert Irwin*
A Box of Dreams – *David Madsen*
The Double Life of Daniel Glick – *Maurice Caldera*
The Angel of the West Window – Gustav Meyrink
Stephanie – *Herbert Rosendorfer*

If you enjoy atmospheric thrillers we recommend:

Gabriel's Bureau – *Mikka Haugaard*
The Mysteries of Algiers – *Robert Irwin*
Zaire – *Harry Smart*
Enigma – *Rezvani*
Dragon's Eye – *Andy Oakes*
Citizen One – *Andy Oakes*

These can be bought from your local bookshop or online from amazon.co.uk or direct from Dedalus, either online or by post. Please write to **Cash Sales, Dedalus Limited, 24–26, St Judith's Lane, Sawtry, Cambs, PE28 5XE**. For further details of the Dedalus list please go to our website www.dedalusbooks.com or write to us for a catalogue

Contemporary English Language Fiction from Dedalus

Dedalus first list on 30 November 1983 consisted of three first novels and we remain committed to finding new authors and developing our contemporary English Language fiction list.

Titles available include:

When the Whistle Blows – *Allen*	£8.99
The Double Life of Daniel Glick – *Caldera*	£7.99
D'Alembert's Principle – *Crumey*	£7.99
Music, in a Foreign Language – *Crumey*	£7.99
Pfitz – *Crumey*	£7.99
The Acts of the Apostates – *Farrington*	£6.99
The Revenants – *Farrington*	£7.99
The Cat – *Gray*	£6.99
Pleading Guilty – *Genney*	£9.99
The Political Map of the Heart – *Gray*	£7.99
False Ambassadors – *Harris*	£8.99
Memoirs of a Byzantine Eunuch – *Harris*	£8.99
The Dream Maker – *Haugaard*	£8.99
Gabriel's Bureau – *Haugaard*	£7.99
The Arabian Nightmare – *Irwin*	£6.99
Exquisite Corpse – *Irwin*	£6.99
The Limits of Vision – *Irwin*	£5.99
The Mysteries of Algiers – *Irwin*	£6.99
Prayer-Cushions of the Flesh – *Irwin*	£6.99
Satan Wants Me – *Irwin*	£7.99
Primordial Soup – *Leunens*	£7.99
Faster Than Light – *Lucas*	£8.99
A Box of Dreams – *Madsen*	£8.99
Memoirs of a Gnostic Dwarf – *Madsen*	£8.99
The Confessions of a Flesh-Eater – *Madsen*	£7.99
A Bit of a Marriage – *Mellinger*	£9.99
Defying Reality – *Mellinger*	£9.99
Citizen One – *Oakes*	£9.99
Dragon's Eye – *Oakes*	£9.99
Zaire – *Smart*	£8.99
Bad to the Bone – *Waddington*	£7.99

Contemporary European Fiction from Dedalus

Dedalus began its European Classics List in 1984 with the D. H. Lawrence's translations of 2 books by Giovanni Verga. In 1992 to celebrate the Single Market of the European Union as a cultural event Dedalus began translating contemporary European fiction.

Titles available include:

The Land of Darkness – *Arsand*	£8.99
Helena – *Ayesta*	£6.99
The Experience of the Night – *Béalu*	£8.99
The Prussian Bride – *Buida*	£9.99
The Zero Train – *Buida*	£6.99
An Afternoon with Rock Hudson – *Deambrosis*	£6.99
Milagrosa – *Deambrosis*	£8.99
Androids from Milk – *Egner*	£7.99
Alfanhui – *Ferlosio*	£8.99
The River – *Ferlosio*	£9.99
The Man in Flames – *Filippini*	£10.99
The Book of Nights – *Germain*	£8.99
The Book of Tobias – *Germain*	£7.99
Infinite Possibilities – *Germain*	£8.99
Invitation to a Journey – *Germain*	£7.99
Magnus – *Germain*	£9.99
The Medusa Child – *Germain*	£8.99
Night of Amber – *Germain*	£8.99
The Song of False Lovers – *Germain*	£8.99
The Black Cauldron – *Heinesen*	£8.99
The Lost Musicians – *Heinesen*	£9.99
Alice, the Sausage – *Jabès*	£6.99
The Great Bagarozy – *Krausser*	£7.99
Lobster – *Lecasble*	£6.99
Portrait of Englishman in his Chateau – *Mandiargues*	£7.99
Mr Dick or The Tenth Book – *Ohl*	£9.99
The Staff Room – *Orths*	£6.99
On the Run – *Prinz*	£6.99
Enigma – *Rezvani*	£8.99
Letters Back to Ancient China – *Rosendorfer*	£6.99

Gabriel's Bureau – *Mikka Haugaard*

"A deliciously twisted tale of darkness, espionage and murder. A gripping read, with an edginess so often hard to find in a debut novel."

BJ in *Buzz Magazine*

"As much as you'd think being a spy would have its perks, *Gabriel's Bureau* illustrates the all consuming pressure of the job and the danger that follows from knowing a little bit too much. Having previously worked for Soviet intelligence, Gabriel has used his contacts to set up his own detective agency and when an acquaintance from the past seeks his help he finds himself unable to say no. The consequences are immense as he investigates the seedy London underworld of art dealings where he learns power is money and death is inevitable when art changes dirty hands. As we follow his quest for the truth, the story focuses on the complex life of Gabriel himself, bringing together his past, his present and his intriguing relationship with his wife and the man 'who is Russia', Oleg. The prose is fluid and poetic . . . Likewise, there are a few gems in the storyline that throw up a great deal of mystery and intrigue. A seemingly cold and unfeeling novel, which perhaps isn't a million miles away from the life of a private investigator."

Angela Singh in the *Big Issue*

"A book of greys and muted colours. Reading it on the train I became infused with the gentle melancholy you get when reading a John Le Carré and it would be near perfect read for a wet Sunday with a bar of chocolate and the gas-fire on. Harking back to Cold War spy novels, with a lone hero, who used to work for the KGB and is now based in London with his invalid wife, *Gabriel's Bureau* is full of puzzles and enigmas, with an intriguingly labyrinthine plot, played out against the backdrop of a seedy underworld . . . an intricate and thought-ful book."

James Nash in *The Leeds Review*

£7.99   ISBN 978 1 87392 31 4   258p   B. Format

Music, in a Foreign Language – *Andrew Crumey*

"The strikingly inventive structure of this novel allows the author to explore the similarities between fictions and history. At any point, there are infinite possibilities for the way the story, a life, or the history of the world might progress. The whole work is enjoyably unpredictable, and poses profound questions about the issues of motivation, choice and morality."
The Sunday Times

"A writer more interested in inheriting the mantle of Perec and Kundera than Amis and Drabble. Like much of the most interesting British fiction around at the moment, *Music, in a Foreign Language* is being published in paperback by a small independent publishing house, giving hope that a tentative but long overdue counter-attack is being mounted on the indelible conservatism of the modern English novel. With this novel he has begun his own small stand against cultural mediocrity, and to set himself up, like his hero, as 'a refugee from drabness. From tinned peas, and rain.' "
Jonathan Coe in *The Guardian*

"*Music in a Foreign Language* used the brilliant conceit of a Britain just emerging from 40 years of polite Stalinism as a platform for some glittering intellectual fireworks."
Boyd Tonkin in *New Statesman & Society*

£7.99   ISBN 978 1 837982 11 2   243p   B. Format

Pfitz – *Andrew Crumey*

"Rreinnstadt is a place which exists nowhere – the concep-
tion of a 18th century prince who devotes his time, and that
of his subjects, to laying down on paper the architecture and
street-plans of this great, yet illusory city. Its inhabitants must
also be devised: artists and authors, their fictional lives and
works, all concocted by different departments. When
Schenck, a worker in the Cartography Office, discovers the
'existence' of Pfitz, a manservant visiting Rreinnstadt, he sets
about illicitly recreating Pfitz's life. Crumey is a daring writer:
using the stuff of fairy tales, he ponders the difference
between fact and fiction, weaving together philosophy and
fantasy to create a magical, witty novel."
The Sunday Times

"Built out of fantasy, Andrew Crumey's novel stands, like the
monumental museum at the centre of its imaginary city, as an
edifice of erudition."
Andrea Ashworth in *The Times Literary Supplement*

"*Pfitz* is a surprisingly warm and likeable book, a combination
of intellectual high-wire act and good traditional storytelling
with a population of lovers and madmen we do care about,
despite their advertised fictionality. Certainly Crumey's narrative gymnastics have not affected his ability to create strong,
fleshy characters, and none more fleshy, more fleshly, than
Frau Luppen, Schenck's middle-aged landlady, a great blown
rose of a woman who express her affection for her lodger by
feeding him bowls of inedible stew."
Andrew Miller in *The New York Times*

£7.99   ISBN 978 1 873982 81 5   164p   B. Format

The Arabian Nightmare – *Robert Irwin*

"Robert Irwin is indeed particularly brilliant. He takes the story-within-a-story technique of the Arab storyteller a stage further, so that a tangle of dreams and imaginings becomes part of the narrative fabric. The prose is discriminating and, beauty of all beauties, the book is constantly entertaining."

Hilary Bailey in *The Guardian*

"Robert Irwin writes beautifully and is dauntingly clever but the stunning thing about him is his originality. Robert Irwin's work, while rendered in the strictest, simplest and most elegant prose, defies definition. All that can be said is that it is a bit like a mingling of *The Thousand and One Nights* and *The Name of the Rose*. It is also magical, bizarre and frightening."

Ruth Rendell

". . . a classic orientalist fantasy tells the story of Balian of Norwich and his misadventures in a labyrinthine Cairo at the time of the Mamelukes. Steamy, exotic and ingenious, it is a boxes-within-boxes tale featuring such characters as Yoll, the Storyteller, Fatima the Deathly and the Father of Cats. It is a compelling meditation on reality and illusion, as well as on Arabian Nights-style storytelling. At its elusive centre lies the affliction of the Arabian Nightmare: a dream of infinite suffering that can never be remembered on waking, and might almost have happened to somebody else."

Phil Baker in *The Sunday Times*

£6.99   ISBN 978 1 873982 73 0   266p   B. Format

Box of Dreams – *David Madsen*

"An amnesiac man awakes on a train with a (but not the) Dr Freud, is forced into women's clothes, and is taken off to a gothic castle with mad counts and nymphomaniacs. Plot summary doesn't really help with Madsen's curious and at times ingenious novel. It's dreams within dreams within dreams; but they are so relentlessly extravagant and persistently onanistic that there's nary a 'pinch-me' moment."

SB Kelly in *Scotland on Sunday*

"On reaching the castle, the plots explodes into a carnivalesque mystery where we meet the delectably promiscuous Adelma and her madly patriachal father who are supported by all manner of grimy personnae. Madsen's whimsically grotesque characters are his strong point. As the layers of Hendryk's experience are peeled away under the smoggy baroque tone of the novel, an insanely off-key symphony is produced which, despite the characters repulsiveness, moves forward with charming ease."

CW in *The Crack*

"David Madsen first crawled into our consciousness with his magnificently unhygienic *Memoirs of a Gnostic Dwarf* set in Rome at the court of Leo X. This, his third novel, is altogether more sober in tone. But that's by Madsen standards. We still see a peculiarly British heartiness brought to esoteric themes and the result – in defiance to all erotic rules – is oddly arousing. This is a richly comic tale on the 'Walpurgisnacht' story, in which nothing goes right for the protagonist, and joy and fulfilment are forever just out of reach. Brisk, bracing and always funny."

Murrough O'Brien in *The Independent on Sunday*

£8.99   ISBN 1 903517 22 2   205p   B. Format

The Mystery of Algiers – *Robert Irwin*

In 1959 in Algiers, city of intrigue and disguises, the French settlers are making a last stand against the FLN liberation army. For Philippe, a desert intelligence officer, survival means knowing the mind of the enemy. But who is the enemy? How to find him?

"Robert Irwin's third novel confirms that, whatever his other main concerns may be, he has thoroughly mastered the art of telling a story. In a plot which snakes and twists, the reader cannot let his concentration drop for a moment... At times the death-defying narrow escapes are firmly in the tradition of James Bond... as well as being a rattling good yarn, this is a study of moral bankruptcy of those who pursue abstractions through violence.. very successful."
The Times Literary Supplement

"It is a gruesome black comedy, whose blackness is so intense as to be almost unreadable – if it weren't so well written."
Time Out

"What separates Irwin's story from the usual spy thrillers is not only his wit and satire but also his verbal pyrotechnics."
The Washington Post

£6.99   ISBN 978 1 873982 60 0   203p   B. Format